The Open
University

Science: a second level course

Astronomy
and
Planetary Science

Book 1

The Stars
and the
Interstellar Medium

Book Chair: Barrie Jones

*Prepared for the Course Team by Jocelyn Bell Burnell, Barrie Jones,
Bob Lambourne, John Zarnecki*

The Open University

S281 Course Team

Course Team Chair and General Editor Barrie Jones
Block 1 Chair Barrie Jones
Block 2 Chair Dave Rothery
Block 3 Chairs Barrie Jones and Bob Lambourne
Block 4 Chair Russell Stannard
Course Manager Cheryl Newport

Dave Adams *University of Leicester* (Author)
Jocelyn Bell Burnell (Author)
Cameron Balbirnie (BBC Producer)
Giles Clark (Publishing)
Alan Cooper (AV Production)
Sue Dobson (Graphic Artist)
Carol Forward (Course Secretary)
Peter Francis (Author)
John Greenwood (Library)
Charlie Harding (Author)
Karen Hill (Author)
Jonathan Hunt (Publishing)
Tony Jolly (BBC Series Producer)
Barrie Jones (Author)
Bob Lambourne (Author)
Jean McCloughry (Staff Tutor)
Elaine Moore (Author)
Lesley Passey (Designer)
Colin Pillinger (Author)
Ian Robson *University of Central Lancashire* (Author)
Dave Rothery (Author)
Dick Sharp (Editor)
Russell Stannard (Author)
Liz Swinbank (Consultant)
Margaret Swithenby (Editor)
Arnold Wolfendale *University of Durham* (Course Assessor)
Ian Wright (Author)
John Zarnecki *University of Kent* (Author)

Cover: The solar corona during a total solar eclipse. This eclipse, caused by the Moon passing between the Earth and the Sun, occurred on 16 February 1980. Image courtesy of Dr J. Dürst, Schönenberg, Switzerland.

The Open University, Walton Hall, Milton Keynes, MK7 6AA.

First published 1994

Edited, designed and typeset by The Open University.

Printed in the United Kingdom by Henry Ling Limited, The Dorset Press, Dorchester, DT1 1HD.

ISBN 0 7492 5125 5

This text forms part of an Open University Second Level Course. If you would like a copy of *Studying with The Open University*, please write to the Central Enquiry Service, PO Box 200, The Open University, Walton Hall, Milton Keynes, MK7 6YZ. If you have not enrolled on the Course and would like to buy this or other Open University material, please write to Open University Educational Enterprises Ltd, 12 Cofferidge Close, Stony Stratford, Milton Keynes, MK11 1BY, United Kingdom.

1.1

The stars and the interstellar medium

Contents

Introduction and study guide for Block 1

Block 1 of S281, *The stars and the interstellar medium*, deals with part of the traditional heartland of astronomy. Despite that, it contains many results that were unknown a few years ago. No subject provides a better illustration of the rapid advance of the joint fields of astronomy and planetary science, and no subject could form a more fitting start to a course concerning those topics. The main text of Block 1 is contained in this book, which consists of five chapters.

Chapter 1 deals with a subject that is close to home: the Sun, our own local star. Chapter 2 broadens the field of view by discussing the determination of stellar properties in general. In so doing, it provides a clear picture of the range of properties exhibited by the stars that surround us. Chapters 3 and 4 build on this snapshot of the stars 'as they are' by investigating the birth, evolution and death of stars. Some of the more exotic episodes described in these chapters, such as the discovery of neutron stars and the theoretical investigation of black holes, have been amongst the most exciting and attention-grabbing of recent scientific developments. Chapter 5, *The interstellar medium*, reports on one of the most rapidly advancing fields of research in astronomy and forms a link with the subsequent blocks on planets and galaxies.

Block 1 also includes three TV programmes and three video sequences. The first programme examines the way in which a variety of observational techniques have helped to clarify the nature of solar flares – a particularly violent form of activity taking place in the Sun's atmosphere. The second is devoted to the remarkable developments taking place in the design and operation of astronomical telescopes, and the third shows how the cycling of cosmic matter between the stars and the interstellar medium is studied. The video sequences deal respectively with solar activity, the early stages of star formation and the stability of stars. *It is important that you should read the associated notes before you watch the TV programme or video sequence.*

In parallel with Block 1 there is some project work: for further information you should consult the *Project file.* You will, of course, also need your copy of *Images of the Cosmos* while you are studying this Block.

The authors of Block 1 hope that you will find its contents academically challenging, intellectually stimulating and, ultimately, highly rewarding. If so, they will have succeeded in providing you with a fully appropriate introduction to the study of the stars and the interstellar medium.

Chapter 1
The Sun – our star

Prepared for the Course Team by Bob Lambourne

Contents

1.1   Introduction

For the most part, the stars seem cold and remote. Yet one star is so blindingly present in our lives that many people do not realize that it is a star at all. That star is the Sun, and it is the subject of this chapter.

As you read this chapter you should be aware that it has two main aims, which are roughly equal in importance:

- To develop your knowledge and understanding of many different aspects of the Sun – the star that we know most about;

- To provide you with some of the basic background science that you will need throughout the Course.

It would be quite possible to achieve these aims simply by giving you a list of facts and theories, but we have chosen to do it by addressing one fundamentally important question: 'How does the Sun shine?' Sections 1.2, 1.3 and 1.4 discuss the nature of the Sun's radiation in some detail, and Section 1.5 delves inside the Sun and seeks to reveal the ultimate source of the energy that we see as sunlight and feel as heat.

Video sequence 2, *The magnetic Sun*, contains material relating to the Sun's magnetic field that is essential to a full understanding of the chapter. You will need to watch this sequence at the end of Section 1.4. TV programme 1, *Our invisible Sun*, also contains important material relating to observations of the Sun. You may watch the programme at any stage during your study of the chapter.

1.2   Light and the photosphere: seeing the Sun's surface

1.2.1   Introducing the photosphere

Figure 1.1 is a photograph of the Sun. At first sight it looks like a pretty ordinary astronomical photograph – you might even mistake the Sun's image for that of some other body, a planet perhaps, or even a moon. But the Sun is neither a planet nor a moon; it is a star – our star – the only star that is sufficiently close for us to be able to examine its visible surface in great detail. For this reason a full discussion of Figure 1.1 is a good starting point for a block dealing with the stars.

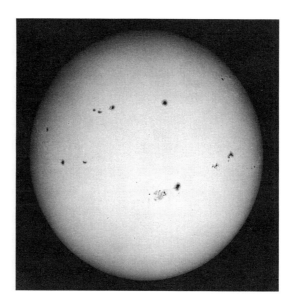

Figure 1.1   A photograph of the Sun.

There are a number of ways in which the Sun of Figure 1.1 differs from a planet or a moon. The most important of these differences is simply that the Sun is very much *brighter* than any planet or moon. The Sun produces an immense amount of energy, and that energy is crucial to our very existence. Energy emitted by the Sun provides us with warmth and light. Without it, life might never have arisen on the Earth, and life as we know it today could certainly not be sustained. The *rate* at which energy is radiated by the Sun (i.e. the total amount of energy radiated per second) is called the **solar luminosity**. It is denoted by the symbol $L_\odot$, and is about $3.84 \times 10^{26}\,\mathrm{J\,s^{-1}}$. (The $\odot$ symbol is an ancient astrological sign for the Sun. Despite the distaste with which most astronomers view astrology, the symbol is widely used to denote 'solar' quantities, i.e. quantities pertaining to the Sun.)

ITQ 1.1   What is the value of the solar luminosity, $L_\odot$, in terms of the SI unit of power – the watt (W)? Given that a typical large power station produces energy at the rate of $2\,500\,\mathrm{MW}$, work out the number of such power stations that would be required to match the energy output of the Sun.

Note that a table of often-used values is given on the back of the *Introduction and Guide*.

A second major difference between the Sun and the planets that orbit it concerns size. The visible disc portrayed in Figure 1.1 is actually about $1.4 \times 10^6\,\mathrm{km}$ in diameter. That's nearly ten times greater than the diameter of Jupiter, the largest planet, and about a hundred times greater than the diameter of the Earth. Clearly, the Sun is very much larger than any planet in the Solar System.

A third difference between a picture of the Sun and a picture of a body like the Earth or the Moon is that the visible surface of the Sun is not really a surface at all, but rather a thin, semi-transparent *shell* of gaseous material. Photographing the Sun is rather like photographing a cloud or a bank of fog; the light that makes up the photographic image comes from a range of depths and not from a single well-defined surface. In the case of Figure 1.1 almost all the light comes from a layer about 500 km thick called the **photosphere** (meaning 'the sphere of light'). Now, 500 km may sound pretty thick but, remember, the Sun is about 1.4 *million* kilometres across, so in comparison with the total solar diameter the photosphere really is a *thin* spherical shell, analogous to the tissue paper used to wrap an orange. When we photograph the Sun we see *into* the photosphere but not *through* it. Figure 1.2 gives a rough idea of the relative proportions of photospheric light coming from different parts of the photosphere.

In visual terms, the photosphere is the closest thing to a surface that the Sun has to offer, but in physical terms the photosphere is much more like an atmospheric layer. In fact, the air you are breathing right now is more than a thousand times denser than the material that makes up the photosphere. If a spaceprobe were sent into the photosphere the frictional resistance it encountered would be almost negligible. A far greater impediment to such a mission would be the temperature. The photosphere gives off light because it is hot. Typical temperatures range from about 9 000 K in the lowest parts of the photosphere to about 4 500 K at the top. (The kelvin (K) is the SI unit of temperature. If it is unfamiliar to you, consult *Preparatory science*, Subsection 2.4.1.) Most of the photospheric light comes from a region where the temperature is between 5 800 K and 6 000 K, so it is conventional to use values such as these to represent the 'surface temperature' of the Sun; however, the term is not really very meaningful and must be treated with some caution.

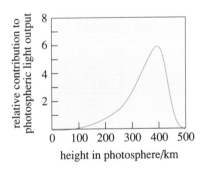

Figure 1.2   A graph indicating the relative amounts of photospheric light originating at various heights in the photosphere. Heights are measured from a precisely defined reference level that roughly corresponds to the greatest depth that can be 'seen'.

1.2.2   Large-scale features of the photosphere

Now that you are acquainted with the broad features of the photosphere (size, thickness, temperature, gaseousness) it makes sense to take a more detailed look at Figure 1.1. There are two main points to note. First, it should be fairly obvious that the edges of the photosphere are darker than the centre: there is a steady reduction in brightness as the distance from the centre of the image increases. Because the edge of the solar image is known as the **solar limb**, this gradual fall-off in brightness is called **limb darkening**. The second feature to note is that the photosphere is marked by dark blotches called **sunspots**. It turns out that both these features are important in understanding the Sun, so we shall discuss them in turn, starting with limb darkening.

Although limb darkening can be seen in Figure 1.1, it is more clearly demonstrated by using a graph to show the relative brightness of points along a line that crosses the solar disc, passing through the centre. Such a line is shown in Figure 1.3a and the corresponding graph in Figure 1.3b. As you can see from the graph, the brightness falls off very rapidly near the limb. This means that the solar limb is quite well defined, which is important because it makes it possible to use the location of the limb in various kinds of measurement.

Now, why should the limb of the Sun be darkened in the way indicated by Figure 1.3? In order to understand this, it is again necessary to recognize that the solar photosphere is something we look *into* rather than something we simply look *at*. Roughly speaking, the photospheric light that we see coming from each point on the Sun comes from a 500 km thick 'column' of photospheric material. However, the range of photospheric heights (that is, distances from the bottom of the photosphere) spanned by such a 500 km column will depend on which part of the solar disc we look at. Figure 1.4 shows this: if we look at the centre of the solar disc a 500 km column spans a 500 km range of heights, but close to the solar limb a 500 (or so) km column will span a much narrower range of heights, close to the top of the photosphere. Now, it was pointed out earlier that the temperature of the photosphere varies with height, the upper levels being cooler than those lower down. It follows that light coming from a region close to the solar limb will have mainly been emitted from a higher and cooler part of the photosphere than light observed at the centre of the solar disc, and this explains why the limb is darker. The cooler material seen close to the limb simply gives off less visible light than the hotter material seen at the centre. Thus the phenomenon of limb darkening provides direct evidence of the variation of photospheric temperature with height. Indeed, the photospheric temperatures quoted earlier may be determined, in part at least, by the requirement that they should agree with the implications of the observed limb darkening.

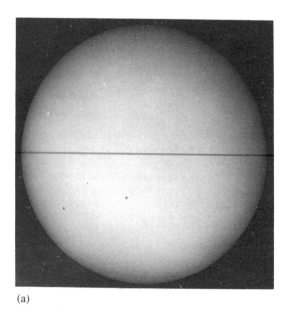

(a)

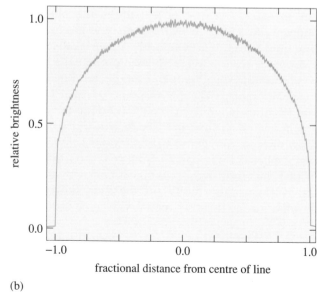

(b)

Figure 1.3 (a) Another photograph of the visible solar disc, this time crossed by a straight line. (b) A graph showing the relative brightness of the photosphere at various points along the straight line shown in (a).

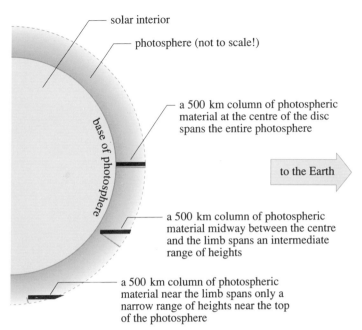

Figure 1.4 The range of photospheric heights spanned by a 500 km column of material (pointing towards the Earth) depends on how close the column is to the solar limb. (Photospheric height, as indicated by the coloured lines, is measured radially outwards from the base of the photosphere.)

Turning now to the sunspots seen in Figure 1.1, it's worth noting straightaway that their darkness is also a consequence of temperature. Sunspots are large, relatively cool regions of the photosphere; the temperature at the centre of a sunspot is typically 4 200 K, which is much less than the 6 000 K or so of the surrounding photosphere. Consequently, sunspots are seen as dark patches against the bright background of the photosphere.

ITQ 1.2 Using Figure 1.1, roughly estimate the diameter of a large sunspot. (*Caution*: some of the dark blotches seen in solar images are *groups* of sunspots; make sure you examine the spots *individually*.)

Sunspots have been observed since ancient times, but their serious study really began in 1610, or shortly thereafter, when telescopes were just beginning to be used for astronomical purposes. Early solar observers, such as Galileo Galilei (1564–1642), David Fabricius (1564–1617) and the appropriately named Christoph Scheiner (1575–1650), soon discovered that sunspots appeared to move across the face of the Sun. This was eventually accepted as clear evidence that *the Sun rotates*, carrying the sunspots with it as it turns on its axis.

Individual sunspots are transient phenomena, but their lives are sufficiently long – typically a few weeks – that it is often possible to observe them crossing the entire solar disc. Sometimes, particularly long-lived spots, or groups of spots, can even be seen re-emerging over the limb of the Sun after they have crossed the far side of the Sun. A sequence of photographs illustrating this effect is shown in Figure 1.5. In this particular case the spots were observed to take about 28 days to make a complete circuit (a value you can check from Figure 1.5). You might well think that this implies a 28 day rotational period for the Sun, or at least for the photosphere, but things are not quite so simple. In the first place, because the Earth orbits the Sun once a year (moving around the Sun in the same sense that the Sun rotates around its own axis), the rotational period observed from Earth is actually somewhat longer than the 'intrinsic' rotational period.

Warning: do not attempt to look directly at the Sun. Solar observations require special precautions and should only be undertaken in accordance with the guidance given in the *Project file*.

9

Figure 1.5 A sequence of
photographs showing the apparent
motion of sunspots across the face of
the Sun. Note that each photo is dated
and that the whole sequence covers a
period of about six weeks.

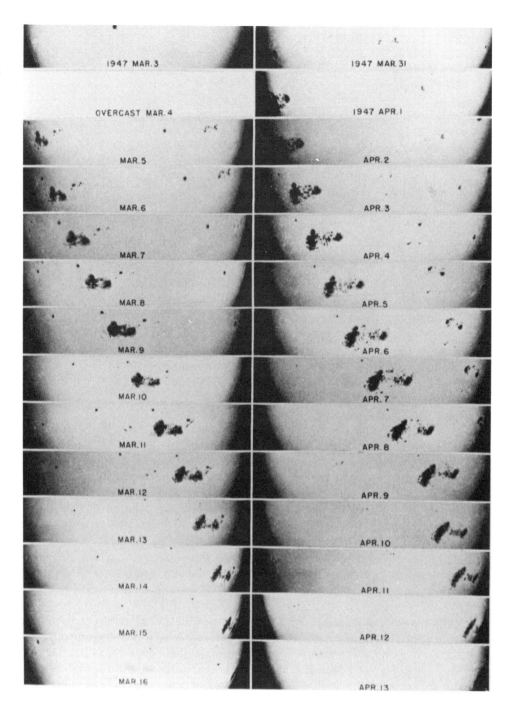

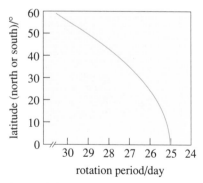

Figure 1.6 The intrinsic rotation
period (sidereal period) of the solar
photosphere at various latitudes.

Secondly, owing to the Sun's gaseousness, the nature of its rotation is very
different from the rotation of a solid body such as the Earth. On a solid body
everything 'rotates together', each part of the surface keeping in step with every
other part, but on a gaseous object it is quite possible for different parts to rotate
at different angular speeds, and this is just what happens on the Sun. Studies of
sunspots and other indicators of **solar rotation** show that points on the solar
equator have an intrinsic period of about 25 days whereas points farther north or
south have considerably longer periods: more than 26 days at a latitude of 30°,
and about 30 days at a latitude of 60°. It's actually very difficult to measure the
rotational period close to the poles, but it seems to be about 36 days. This rather
complicated state of affairs is described by saying that the Sun exhibits
differential rotation. More precise information about the varying rate of
photospheric rotation is given in Figure 1.6.

10

☐ The apparent period of about 28 days exhibited by the sunspots in Figure 1.5 corresponds to an intrinsic period of about 27 days. What is the approximate latitude of these sunspots?

■ From Figure 1.6, an intrinsic period of about 27 days corresponds to a latitude of about 35°.

Intrinsic rotational periods are dealt with in the *Project file* where they are given their formal name *sidereal periods*, that is periods measured with respect to the stars.

Apart from their role as tracers of rotation, sunspots are also good indicators of another large-scale phenomenon: **solar activity**. Data collected over many decades (see Figure 1.7) clearly show that the fraction of the solar disc covered by sunspots changes with time in a more or less regular way. A period of roughly 11 years separates each occurrence of maximum coverage, and hence of maximum solar activity, from its successor. Images of the Sun recorded at a time of maximum activity and at a time when activity is minimal differ markedly – as can be seen from Plate 1.3. Many other solar phenomena, some of which will be discussed later, also participate in the 11-year **solar activity cycle**, but none is as easy to observe as sunspots.

Remember, Plate 1.3, like all the other plates referred to in the Course, will be found in *Images of the Cosmos*.

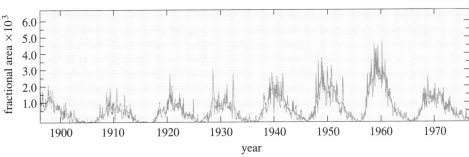

Figure 1.7 The 11-year variation of solar activity with time, as indicated by the fraction of the area of the Sun's visible disc covered by sunspots.

1.2.3 Small-scale features of the photosphere

Although the origin of the solar activity cycle remains one of the Sun's outstanding mysteries, a good deal is known about sunspots. For example, it is well established that sunspots have stronger magnetic fields and different patterns of motion from their surroundings. They are also known to correspond to shallow depressions in the photosphere. Knowledge of this kind partly results from the study of magnified views of localized regions of the photosphere rather than photographs of the full solar disc. A magnified view of just this kind, showing the detailed structure of a sunspot, is shown in Figure 1.8. Such views are of great importance; the Sun is the only star sufficiently close to allow such detailed imaging of its surface.

Another small-scale phenomenon that is thought to be common in stars, but which can actually be seen only in the Sun's photosphere, is shown in Figure 1.9. The figure provides an instantaneous snapshot of the **solar granulation** – a seething pattern of bright cell-like **granules** that covers the photosphere. Each granule is typically about 1 000 km across and lives for five to ten minutes. Detailed studies of the granules show that they are the tops of rising columns of hot material coming from deeper regions of the Sun where the temperatures are higher. The rising material travels upwards at a speed of $1 \, \text{km s}^{-1}$, or thereabouts, and then spreads out horizontally, radiating away its heat. The dark 'lanes' between granules are regions where the cooled material descends back into the solar interior. The significance of these motions will be more fully explored in Section 1.5.

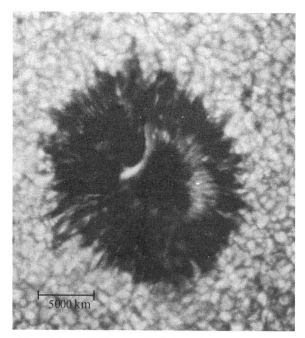

Figure 1.8 A highly magnified view of a sunspot.

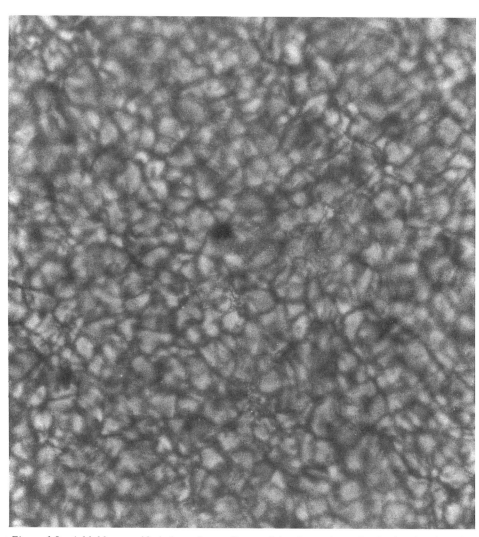

Figure 1.9 A highly magnified view of a small part of the photosphere clearly showing the solar granulation. The bright granules are typically about 1 000 km in diameter.

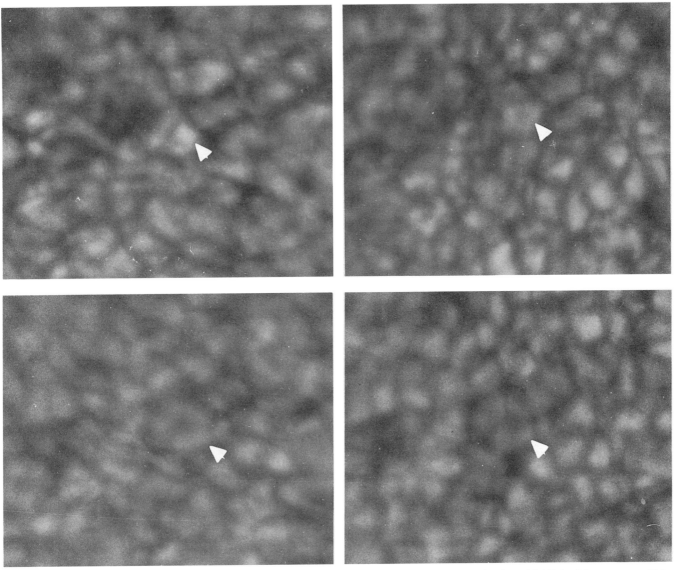

Figure 1.10 A sequence of photographs of the solar granulation. Note that one particular granule has been highlighted by an arrow. This granule grows and decays over the 12 minute period covered by the photographs.

The blurring effects of the Earth's atmosphere make it difficult to carry out detailed studies of the solar granulation. Nonetheless, it is sometimes possible to obtain sequences of photographs that clearly show the formation or disappearance of individual granules. Such a sequence is shown in Figure 1.10. The fate of the arrowed granule is particularly clear.

1.2.4 The nature of light

Although our discussion of the photosphere has concentrated on its visual appearance, it is important not to forget that the photosphere is the source of the light that illuminates the Earth and, through its heating effect, keeps us alive. From our human perspective, light is the main product of the photosphere and will be a major concern throughout the Course, so this is a good point at which to gather together a number of basic facts about the nature of light. Because these facts constitute 'essential scientific background' rather than a continuation of the astronomical storyline we have been developing so far, they will be separated

Note: throughout this chapter the term 'light' refers specifically to 'ordinary' visible light.

from the rest of the Section by enclosing them in a box. Such boxes will be used throughout the Course to enable you to identify items of background science wherever they arise.

The concept of a *field* was introduced in *Preparatory Science*, Subsection 1.4.1.

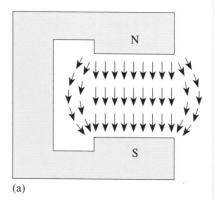
(a)

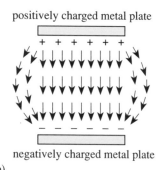

positively charged metal plate

negatively charged metal plate
(b)

Figure 1.11 (a) A magnetic field. (b) An electric field.

Box 1.1   *The nature of light*

The electromagnetic wave model of light

It is well known that a magnet is able to influence certain objects (e.g. other magnets) without touching them. This phenomenon is 'explained' by saying that the magnet produces a **magnetic field**, which occupies the space around the magnet and gives rise to the forces that act on the affected objects. To account for these forces, the magnetic field at any point must have both a strength and a direction. Consequently, the magnetic field at any point can be represented by an arrow, since an arrow has a length that can represent the strength of the field, and an orientation that can be made to correspond to the direction of the field. The use of arrows to represent a magnetic field is illustrated in Figure 1.11a. In a similar way, a suitable distribution of positive (+) and negative (−) electric charges will give rise to an **electric field**, which can also be represented, at any point, by an arrow of appropriate length and orientation, as in Figure 1.11b.

In the 1860s, while carrying out a mathematical investigation of electricity and magnetism, the Scottish physicist James Clerk Maxwell (1831–1879) showed that it was possible to create self-sustaining patterns of fluctuating electric and magnetic fields that could tumble together through space at a certain pre-determined speed. These fluctuating field patterns are called **electromagnetic waves**, and an instantaneous 'snapshot' of a small part of the simplest such wave is shown in Figure 1.12. The electric and magnetic fields that make up the wave are always at right angles to each other, and both fields are at right angles to the direction in which the wave is travelling. Remember, Figure 1.12 is only a snapshot, so you should imagine the whole pattern moving in the direction of travel rather like an ocean wave moving across open water. Maxwell found that the speed at which electromagnetic waves had to travel was very close to the best values then available for the speed of light, so he suggested that rays of light were nothing other than electromagnetic waves.

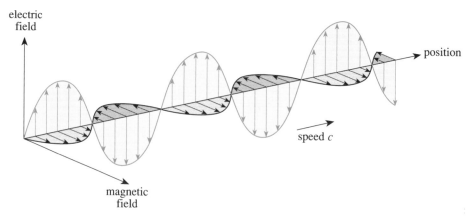

Figure 1.12   An electromagnetic wave.

An important characteristic of any electromagnetic wave is the distance between successive maxima of the electric or magnetic field (that is, the distance from one peak of the wave to the next). This distance is called the **wavelength** and is denoted by the Greek letter λ (pronounced 'lambda'). The wavelengths of all forms of visible light are very tiny, and different wavelengths correspond to different colours. Red light has a wavelength of about 700×10^{-9} m (= 700 nanometres, nm), and the wavelength of violet light is around 420×10^{-9} m (= 420 nm). White light, which is a mixture of all the possible colours, contains all the wavelengths between these rough limits. (You will find more on this subject in Box 1.2.)

Imagine yourself observing a wave like that in Figure 1.12 as it moves past some fixed point. If the speed of the wave is v and its wavelength is λ, then you should be able to convince yourself that the number of wavelengths that will pass the fixed point in a second is just v/λ. This quantity, the number of wavelengths passing a fixed point in one second, is called the **frequency** of the wave; it is measured in SI units called **hertz (Hz)** (equivalent to s^{-1}) and is denoted by the letter f. Thus, for any wave, $f = v/\lambda$. Or, more conventionally,

$$v = f\lambda \tag{1.1}$$

For electromagnetic waves the value of v depends on the medium (air, glass, water, etc.) through which they move. The maximum value of v occurs when the waves travel through a vacuum (that is, empty space). Under these conditions the speed of the waves is very nearly 3.00×10^8 m s^{-1} (the exact value is $2.997\,924\,58 \times 10^8$ m s^{-1}). This quantity is of such importance that it is given its own symbol, c, and is referred to as the **speed of light in a vacuum**. Thus, for electromagnetic waves travelling through a vacuum, we can write

$$c = f\lambda \tag{1.2}$$

The terms wavelength and frequency will be used freely throughout the rest of the Course and you will also be called on to use Equation 1.2. Make sure you understand these ideas before proceeding.

Note that when an electromagnetic wave travels from one medium to another, the *frequency* remains the same.

The identification of light with electromagnetic waves was a major development in the history of physics and was the source of much progress. However, scientists now recognize that the identification was not entirely correct. Electromagnetic waves can account for many of the properties of light, but not all of them. For this reason, rather than saying that light is electromagnetic waves, we prefer to say that electromagnetic waves provide a model of light. The **electromagnetic wave model of light** helps us to understand the behaviour of light but it is not the whole story. Other models are also useful.

The photon model of light

At present, the most complete scientific account of light involves a branch of physics called **quantum theory**. The full quantum theory of light is much too complicated to go into here, but during its development another simple model of light emerged that was quite different from the electromagnetic wave model yet, under the right circumstances, just as valuable. This alternative model is known as the **photon model of light**. According to the photon model, a ray of light of frequency f can be thought of as consisting of a stream of separate particles called **photons**. Each of these photons carries an identical amount of energy, denoted by the Greek letter epsilon, ε, that relates directly to the frequency of the ray, and is given by

$$\varepsilon = hf \tag{1.3}$$

The quantity h in this equation is one of the fundamental constants of physics; it is **Planck's constant** and it is given by $h = 6.6261 \times 10^{-34}\,\text{J s}$, though $6.63 \times 10^{-34}\,\text{J s}$ will do for us.

The photon model of light is of particular importance when considering the interaction of light with atoms. Individual atoms can absorb or emit only entire photons. Thus, when a cloud of atoms is illuminated by a beam of light there is no possibility of a single atom acquiring half a photon's worth of energy directly from the beam. This is a subject to which we shall return in Section 1.3.2, when we further develop the 'background science' of light.

It is important to realize that neither the electromagnetic wave model nor the photon model should be regarded as 'true'. Light is neither a wave nor a particle but, under the appropriate conditions, it may exhibit wave-like or particle-like behaviour; both possibilities are encompassed by the quantum theory.

Summary of Section 1.2 and SAQs

1   The Sun is the closest star to the Earth.

2   The solar luminosity ($3.84 \times 10^{26}\,\text{W}$) is the rate at which energy is radiated by the Sun.

3   The photosphere is the visible 'surface' of the Sun. It is a thin semitransparent shell of gaseous material about 500 km thick, 1.4×10^6 km in diameter and characterized by a temperature of about 6 000 K.

4   The photosphere exhibits limb darkening and differential rotation. The rotation can be traced by sunspots, which also indicate the level of solar activity.

5   The Sun is the only star sufficiently close to Earth to permit the detailed study of small-scale phenomena, such as sunspots and granulation.

6   Quantum theory provides the best available account of the nature of light, but simple models such as the electromagnetic wave model

$$v = f\lambda \tag{1.1}$$

and the photon model

$$\varepsilon = hf \tag{1.3}$$

are still of great value.

SAQ 1.1 (Objective 1.2)   The overall shape of the graph in Figure 1.3b clearly indicates the phenomenon of limb darkening. Additionally, the graph includes a good deal of small-scale structure: it is not smooth but contains many tiny peaks and troughs. How can you account for this on the basis of the information given in this Section?

SAQ 1.2 (Objective 1.3)   The electromagnetic waves used to model the various colours of visible light have wavelengths in a vacuum in the approximate range 400 nm to 750 nm. What is the corresponding range of frequencies?

SAQ 1.3 (Objective 1.3)   In terms of the photon model of light, what is the approximate range of photon energies corresponding to the range of wavelengths discussed in SAQ 1.2?

1.3 Spectroscopy and the chromosphere: seeing the Sun's inner atmosphere

1.3.1 Introducing the chromosphere

Although the majority of the Sun's light comes to us from the photosphere, we also receive small amounts of light from layers of hot, thin gaseous material that surround the photosphere. These outer layers of the Sun may be regarded as the Sun's 'atmosphere', though the term must be treated with the same degree of caution that we used when referring to the photosphere as the Sun's 'surface'.

In a **white light image** of the Sun, recorded using ordinary visible light (such as Figure 1.1), the feeble light from the Sun's atmosphere is normally drowned out by the overwhelming brilliance of the photosphere. Nonetheless, under the right circumstances, it is possible to see the Sun's atmosphere, as Plate 1.1 shows. The picture was taken during a **total eclipse of the Sun** – an infrequent but predictable event that occurs on average every eighteen months or so, when the Moon passes between the Earth and the Sun, and entirely blocks the light from the photosphere for a few minutes. (It is a remarkable coincidence that, although the Sun and Moon differ greatly in size and distance from the Earth, their diameters and distances are just right to allow such a very precise blockage to occur.)

The black circle in the middle of Plate 1.1 is the silhouette of the Moon. The bright halo that surrounds it is the solar atmosphere. As you can see, the atmosphere is very extensive. For the most part it is a pearly white, but very close to the photosphere there is a narrow region with a pink or reddish tinge: this can be clearly seen in Plate 1.2. The coloured layer, which is a few thousand kilometres thick, is called the **chromosphere** (meaning 'the sphere of colour'), and constitutes the inner (or lower) solar atmosphere. The chromosphere will be our main concern in this Section. The extensive outer (or upper) solar atmosphere is called the **corona**. This will be the subject of the next Section.

Although eclipse studies led to the initial identification of the chromosphere, and continue to play a role in its scientific investigation, they are not the only source of chromospheric information. Fortunately, much may be learnt from observations of the full solar disc, provided they are restricted to wavelengths where the chromosphere is more prominent than the photosphere. Just such a restricted wavelength view is shown in Figure 1.13. In this particular case the image was produced by red light in a narrow range of wavelengths centred around 656.3 nm. At these wavelengths, for reasons that will be explained shortly, hydrogen atoms throughout the chromosphere are highly effective absorbers and emitters of radiation. As a result, the chromosphere absorbs most of the 656.3 nm radiation coming from the photosphere, but its own emissions at that wavelength are quite prominent. It is these emissions that are mainly responsible for the reddish hue that gives the chromosphere its name. The particular kind of restricted wavelength view shown in Figure 1.13 is called an **Hα image** (pronounced 'aitch alpha'); the H indicates that the emitted light is coming from hydrogen atoms, and the α indicates that this is the first (longest) wavelength of visible light at which hydrogen atoms have this particular effectiveness as absorbers and emitters. The other, successively shorter, visible wavelengths at which hydrogen behaves in this way are 486.1 nm, 434.0 nm and 410.1 nm, which are respectively denoted by Hβ, Hγ and Hδ (respectively pronounced 'aitch beta', 'aitch gamma' and 'aitch delta'). Restricted wavelength images at other wavelengths, associated with other kinds of atom, are also of great value, particularly calcium H (396.8 nm) and calcium K (393.3 nm) images. (As their names imply, these kinds of image involve light emitted from calcium atoms. The letters H and K indicate the sequence of wavelengths and have nothing to do with the usual chemical symbols for hydrogen and potassium.)

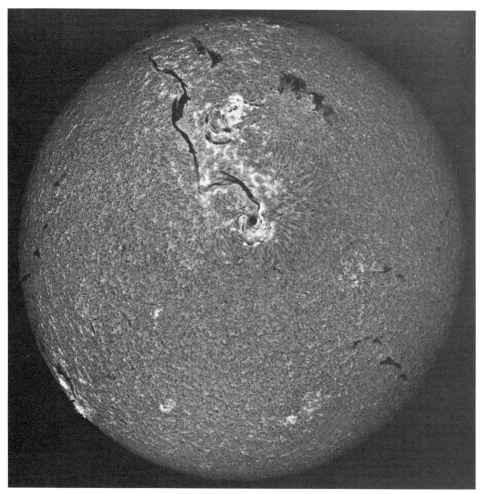

Figure 1.13 An Hα image of the Sun, produced by light from a narrow range of wavelengths centred on 656.3 nm. Such light comes mainly from hydrogen atoms in the chromosphere.

The chromospheric Hα image (Figure 1.13) is clearly very different from the photospheric white light image that we looked at earlier (Figure 1.1). In an Hα image the chromosphere is mottled with bright specks, some of which are gathered together into extensive bright regions called **plages** (rhymes with 'barges'). These are often seen in parts of the chromosphere that are directly above the active regions of the photosphere that contain sunspots. Also visible near the top of Figure 1.13 is a long, winding dark feature called a **filament**. Filaments are quite common in Hα images; they are caused by huge clouds of relatively cool gas held high above the chromosphere by magnetic forces. (These are the same clouds that account for the **prominences** seen above the limb of the Sun in video sequence 2 and in Plate 1.8.) Overall, the chromosphere is much less uniform than the photosphere. One solar physicist has even described the chromosphere as 'a layer of froth stirred up by the photosphere'.

To get a better understanding of the chromosphere, we really need to gain some insight into the processes that give rise to Hα images and to the other, similar, images obtained at different wavelengths. Only with the aid of such insight can the radiation emitted by the chromosphere be properly interpreted and used as a source of information about the physical conditions of the Sun, such as temperature, pressure and uniformity of structure. The starting point for this kind of investigation is really the study of *spectroscopy*. This is another of those items of essential background science with which you may already be familiar, so once again a box has been used to separate it from the rest of the text.

Box 1.2   Spectroscopy and sources of light

Sources of light may be divided into two broad categories: *thermal* and *non-thermal*. Not surprisingly, **thermal sources** emit light because of their temperature (basically, hot things glow), and **non-thermal sources** emit light for other reasons. The incandescent filament in a light bulb is a thermal source. The luminous hands of a wristwatch and the tail of a glow-worm are non-thermal sources. Many natural sources of light are partly thermal and partly non-thermal sources.

Most light sources, thermal or non-thermal, emit a whole range of wavelengths. Such a range is commonly called a **spectrum** (plural *spectra*). **Spectroscopy** concerns the production and study of spectra.

Continuous spectra

Light from many thermal sources is emitted over an unbroken range of wavelengths. Such sources are therefore said to have **continuous spectra**.

If a narrow rectangular beam of light passes through a glass prism, the beam will split up in such a way that different wavelengths travel in different directions. (This process is shown in Plate 1.4.) If the original beam contained just a few well separated wavelengths the result would be a set of quite separate and distinct images, each with its own characteristic colour (wavelength). However, if the beam came from a thermal source it would typically contain all visible wavelengths, and the result of passing it through the prism would be a continuous multicoloured band somewhat similar to a rainbow. The term 'continuous spectra' is also used to refer specifically to such unbroken bands of colour.

In days gone by, scientists engaged in spectroscopy spent a good deal of their time examining the kinds of multicoloured band described above. Nowadays things are different. It is now more common for spectral information to be given in the form of a graph. When spectra are presented in this way the horizontal axis of the graph usually shows wavelength or frequency (or sometimes photon energy). The vertical axis of the graph normally indicates the 'brightness' of the spectrum at any given wavelength. Unfortunately, the quantities used to measure spectral brightness have rather complicated definitions. In this chapter the vertical axes of some graphical spectra are labelled **spectral flux density**. At any given wavelength λ, the spectral flux density, F_λ, can be determined by the following procedure.

(a)   Using an appropriate detector of area 1 m^2, pointed directly towards the source, measure the rate at which energy from the source is delivered to the detector by electromagnetic waves with wavelengths in a fixed narrow range, $\Delta\lambda$, centred on λ.

(b)   Divide the measured rate of energy detection by the wavelength range $\Delta\lambda$ to obtain the detected power per square metre per unit wavelength range, typically measured in units of W m^{-2}μm^{-1}. This is the value of F_λ at wavelength λ.

In fact, most of the graphical spectra in this chapter will have vertical axes that show **relative spectral flux density**. In such cases, the spectral flux density at any wavelength is expressed as a *fraction* of some arbitrarily chosen reference value and there will be no SI units shown on the axis.

Figure 1.14 shows continuous spectra of a number of thermal sources at various different temperatures, but of the same size and at the same distance from the detector. These spectra are characteristic of a particularly important class of thermal sources, known as **ideal thermal sources**. (For mainly historical reasons these are also referred to as **black-body sources**, even though they may not be black at all.)

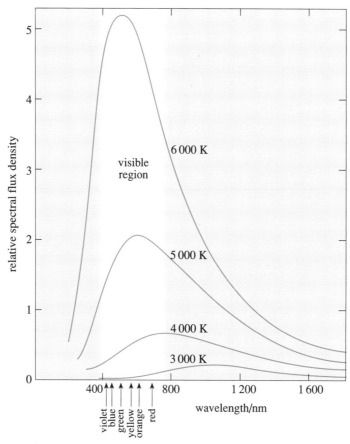

Figure 1.14 Graphical spectra for ideal thermal sources at temperatures between 3 000 K and 6 000 K. (Note that the spectra extend well beyond those wavelengths that correspond to the various colours of visible light. More will be said about these other emissions in the next Section.)

ITQ 1.3 Figure 1.14 clearly indicates that the observed spectral flux density from the hottest source is greater than that from the coolest. Is it necessarily the case that in a fixed wavelength range more energy will arrive per second from *any* ideal thermal source at 6 000 K than from *any* ideal thermal source at 3 000 K?

In any graph that shows how relative spectral flux density varies with wavelength for an ideal thermal source, the height of the graph will depend on factors such as the size and distance of the source, and the selected reference value. However, in all such graphs the overall *shape* of the curve is solely determined by the *temperature* of the source. This means, in particular, that the peak of each curve occurs at a wavelength, λ_{peak}, that characterizes the source's temperature, irrespective of the height of the peak. In fact, there is a simple law, called **Wien's displacement law**, that relates the value of λ_{peak} to the temperature, T, of the source:

$$\lambda_{\text{peak}} = \frac{2.90 \times 10^{-3}\,\text{m K}}{T} \tag{1.4}$$

With the aid of Wien's displacement law it is a simple matter to determine the temperature of any source of light, *provided it is an ideal thermal source*. Such sources are not common, but many real sources, including the Sun, are reasonable approximations to ideal thermal sources, so their temperatures may be estimated by this spectral technique.

ITQ 1.4 If you were to heat a metal ball, so that its temperature steadily increased, you would find that above a certain temperature the ball would start to emit a dull red glow. As the temperature increased further the ball would become brighter and the colour would change from red to orange-white to yellowish-white to white. How would you explain these changes in appearance?

The shapes of the curves that describe the spectra of ideal thermal sources are of great importance in science. Such curves are usually referred to as **thermal radiation curves** or **Planck curves** or **black-body radiation curves**. Non-ideal thermal sources and non-thermal sources may also produce continuous spectra, but, from the graphical point of view, those spectra will generally have a different shape from those of ideal thermal sources.

Line spectra: absorption and emission

If a beam of light from an ideal thermal source passes through a thin gas of atoms, the spectrum of the emerging beam will generally include a number of narrow *dark* lines. These lines are called **absorption lines** and correspond to narrow ranges of wavelength that have been wholly or partly absorbed by the gas. This situation is illustrated in Figure 1.15, which includes a graph of the so-called **absorption spectrum** that arises.

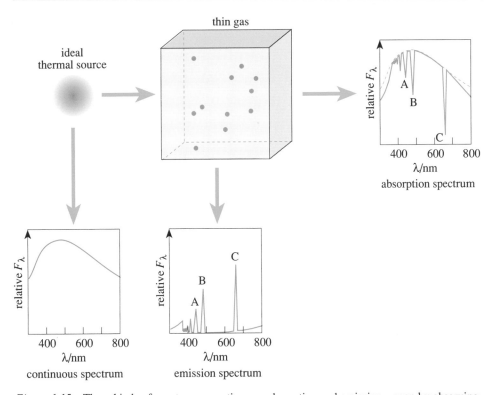

Figure 1.15 Three kinds of spectrum – continuous, absorption and emission – seen by observing an ideal thermal source and a thin gas of atoms from various different directions. The dashed line in the absorption spectrum shows the continuous spectrum that would have been observed in the absence of the gas.

If, instead of the emerging beam, the light emitted by the gas itself is examined, it will be found that its spectrum consists of a number of narrow *bright* lines. These lines are called **emission lines**, and a spectrum composed of them is called an **emission spectrum**. For many gases, the bright lines emitted cover the same narrow wavelength ranges as the dark lines in the absorption spectrum. The graph of such an emission spectrum is also included in Figure 1.15.

Emission spectra and absorption spectra are both examples of *line spectra*. Plate 1.5 shows the line spectra produced by a number of different gases. The occurrence of such spectra is a consequence of the fact that each of the gases is composed of a characteristic type of *atom* that has its own internal structure. (It is also relevant that the gas is sufficiently thin to ensure that the atoms do not significantly influence one another.)

Atoms were discussed in Section 2 of *Preparatory science*. As you saw there, a typical atom is about 2×10^{-10} m in diameter and consists of a tiny, dense, positively charged *nucleus* surrounded by one or more negatively charged electrons. According to quantum theory, each of the electrons belonging to a particular atom may be in any of a number of allowed states, each of which is associated with some fixed amount of energy. When an electron occupies a particular state in a particular atom, the atom has the energy associated with that state. Thus, changes in the pattern of occupied states within an atom entail changes in the total amount of energy possessed by the atom. A diagram showing the energy associated with each of the allowed states in a particular kind of atom is called an **energy-level diagram**. The simplest energy-level diagram, that of a hydrogen atom (which has just one electron), is shown in Figure 1.16.

To see how the behaviour of atoms can account for the existence of line spectra, consider an atom in which an electron initially occupies a state of energy E_i (the subscript i reminds us that this is the <u>i</u>nitial energy). Such an electron may make a transition to some other state of higher energy E_h (h for <u>h</u>igher), provided that the atom can acquire the necessary additional energy, $E_h - E_i$. If the atom is bathed in light from a thermal source, as in Figure 1.15, the requisite energy can be absorbed directly from the light. Now, you might think that energy absorption of this kind would involve a wide and continuous range of wavelengths, but that is not the case. The absorption of light by an atom is one of those processes that is best described by the photon model of light discussed in Box 1.1. The energy is acquired in one gulp, as it were, by the absorption of a *single* photon of just the right energy $\varepsilon_{hi} = E_h - E_i$. It follows from Equation 1.3 that such a photon corresponds to electromagnetic radiation of a specific frequency, namely

$$f_{hi} = \frac{1}{h}(E_h - E_i) \tag{1.5}$$

ITQ 1.5 Write down a formula for the corresponding wavelength, λ_{hi}, of the radiation that must be absorbed if a transition requiring an energy increase $E_h - E_i$ is to take place.

Applying the result of ITQ 1.5 to the gas of atoms shown in Figure 1.15, it should be clear that if a sufficient number of atoms in the gas increase their energy by $E_h - E_i$ every second, then a good deal of incoming radiation at the corresponding wavelength λ_{hi} will be absorbed, with the result that the spectrum of the emerging beam will have a dark absorption line at that wavelength. Since there are many possible values of E_i and E_h for any particular kind of atom, it follows that there are many possible values of $E_h -$

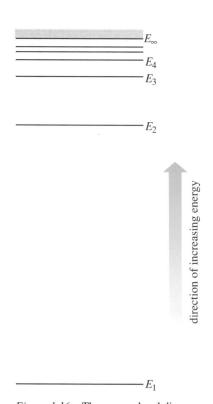

Figure 1.16 The energy-level diagram of a hydrogen atom. There are infinitely many energy levels but those of highest energy are too closely crowded together to be shown separately on a diagram of this kind.

Take care not to confuse the subscript h (for higher) with Planck's constant, h. The two are not connected.

E_i and hence many, quite distinct wavelengths at which absorption lines might occur. (Whether a particular line is seen or not depends on the *rate* at which the relevant transition is occurring in the gas.) Furthermore, since each kind of atom has its own characteristic energy-level diagram, different gases will produce different absorption spectra – just as you saw in Plate 1.5.

The above account of absorption spectra requires a large number of atoms to absorb energy every second, at many different wavelengths. What happens to all this absorbed energy? The answer is that most of it is very quickly emitted again, and it is this emission that accounts for the emission spectrum that an illuminated gas produces. Once an electron occupies a state associated with an energy E_h that is higher than the energy associated with one or more other states, it may be possible for the electron to make a spontaneous transition to one of those states of lower energy. In particular, if the electron originally came from a state of energy E_i, one of many possibilities is for it to return to that same state. Under these circumstances the atom would have to shed an amount of energy $\varepsilon_{hi} = E_h - E_i$. Once again, quantum theory demands that if the energy released in a transition of this kind is given off as light then it must take the form of a single photon corresponding to electromagnetic radiation of frequency

$$f_{hi} = \frac{1}{h}\,(E_h - E_i)$$

A gas is therefore capable of producing emission lines at exactly the same wavelengths that it produces absorption lines. However, and this is a crucial point, the emission is quite likely to occur in *any* direction. Thus, energy absorbed from the incoming beam in Figure 1.15 will not be entirely replaced by emitted energy; rather emitted energy will be given off in all directions, allowing the emission spectrum to be seen from many different angles, whereas the absorption spectrum can be seen only by looking along the beam.

1.3.3 Solar spectroscopy and the structure of the chromosphere

A good deal of what is known about the Sun has been learnt by studying its spectrum. A photo of the visible spectrum is given in Plate 1.6. As you can see it is essentially an absorption spectrum; the coloured bands are crossed by a large number of narrow absorption lines corresponding to various atomic transitions. In fact, something like 25 000 lines have been identified in the visible region; many originate in the photosphere, which is also responsible for nearly all the light between the lines, but some of the lines carry information about the chromosphere. Unfortunately, owing to the problems of reproducing colour images, not all of the features of Plate 1.6 are as clear as they could be, so a sharper black and white image of the Sun's spectrum is given in Figure 1.17. Some of the darkest lines in this image have been labelled and a wavelength scale (in nanometres) has been included to help you locate them. It is worth noting that even the darkest lines are not completely black; they are simply darker than their surroundings. Indeed, it is often the faint emissions found within the darkest lines that are most informative about the chromosphere. A particularly strong absorption line of this sort can be seen around 656.3 nm – the wavelength of the Hα image we looked at earlier. Not surprisingly, this is called the **Hα absorption line**. Another prominent absorption line due to hydrogen at 486.1 nm, and two lines due to calcium at 396.8 nm and 393.3 nm, were all mentioned earlier as important wavelengths for studies of the chromosphere.

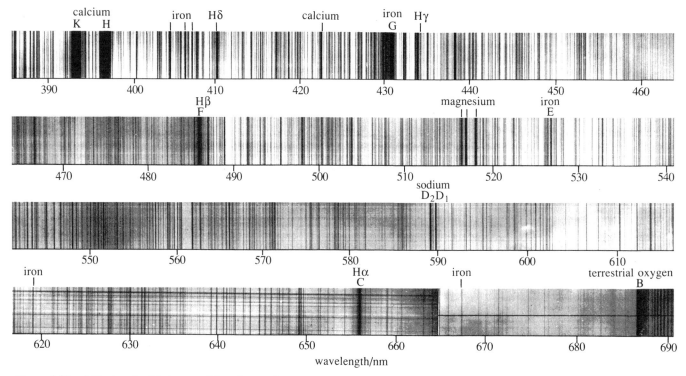

Figure 1.17 A black and white image of the solar spectrum.

ITQ 1.6   Why is it not surprising that studies of chromospheric emission lines often involve wavelengths that correspond to dark absorption lines in the solar spectrum?

Chromospheric emission lines can be observed in particular detail during total solar eclipses, when the light of the photosphere is blocked by the Moon. One of these emission lines, at 587.6 nm, has a particularly interesting history. When it was first observed, during the 18 August 1868 eclipse, its origin could not be explained in terms of any of the chemical elements then known. This led astrophysicist Norman Lockyer (1836–1920) to propose the existence of a new element, which he named *helium* after the Greek word for the Sun, *helios*. Lockyer's interpretation was correct, but confirmation did not come until 1895, when the British scientist William Ramsay (1852–1916) showed that helium exists on Earth.

By comparing absorption and emission lines of solar origin with lines observed in terrestrial laboratories, it is possible to determine which kinds of atom are present in the visible parts of the Sun. In this way the presence of more than 65 of the 100 or so known elements has been established. This is a notable achievement, but even more can be accomplished by examining the details of the lines – a task best done with the aid of the graphical spectra.

Figure 1.18 is a graphical representation of the solar spectrum. The dips corresponding to some of the more prominent absorption lines are easily seen. In order to explain the detailed appearance of this kind of graph it is not enough simply to identify which atoms are represented; the relative depths of the various lines must also be explained. Line depths depend on a number of factors, including the relative abundance of each kind of atom, the inherent likelihood of each atomic transition, and the proportion of atoms of a given kind that have an electron in the appropriate initial state to give rise to a particular line. This last factor will depend sensitively on temperature because, generally speaking, the higher the temperature the more likely it is that states corresponding to higher energies will be occupied. Thus, solar absorption lines provide information about

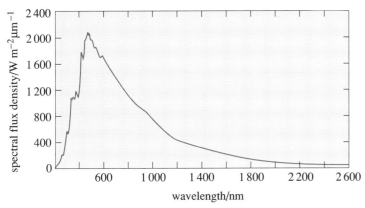

Figure 1.18 A graphical representation of the Sun's spectrum, above the Earth's atmosphere.

chemical abundance, temperature and related quantities such as density and pressure. Similar comments apply to the chromospheric emission lines; in fact, these lines provide some of the most direct information about the composition and structure of the chromosphere.

Information gained from spectral studies shows that the chromosphere is composed mainly of hydrogen and helium. The evidence indicates that there are from 40 to 100 helium atoms for every 1 000 hydrogen atoms. (Other kinds of study, to be discussed in Subsection 1.5.3, imply that the correct value is probably about 87, corresponding to about 25% of the mass.) In view of the prominence of the calcium lines, you might also expect that calcium atoms would be abundant, but this turns out not to be the case. The relative strength of the calcium lines results from the combination of two factors: chromospheric conditions are just right to ensure that a comparatively high proportion of calcium atoms have electrons in the correct initial states to produce those lines, and the relevant transitions have a relatively high likelihood of occurring, given electrons in the correct initial states. In fact, there are probably no more than three calcium atoms for every million hydrogen atoms.

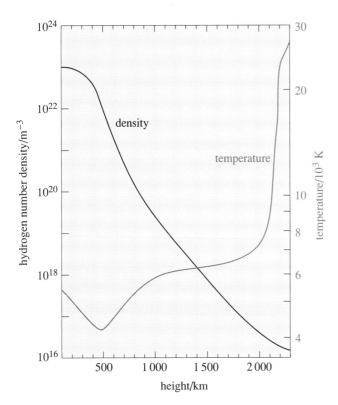

Figure 1.19 Variation of temperature and hydrogen number density (i.e. number of hydrogen atoms per cubic metre) with height throughout a 'quiet' part of the chromosphere. For comparison, at sea-level the Earth's atmosphere has on average a temperature of about 288 K, a number density (of oxygen and nitrogen molecules) of about 2×10^{25} m^{-3} and a pressure of about 10^5 N m^{-2} (that is 10^5 Pa). Note that this figure uses *logarithmic scales* on the vertical axes. If you are unfamiliar with this concept, you should consult the mathematical appendix in *Preparatory science*.

As far as temperature and density are concerned, it has already been emphasized that these quantities vary with height and from one region of the chromosphere to another. Nonetheless, typical values for a 'quiet' part of the chromosphere are shown in Figure 1.19. The rapid increase of temperature with height is very clear. Note that the height is measured from the usual reference level at the base of the photosphere (roughly, the greatest visible depth), so only data pertaining to heights greater than about 500 km are truly 'chromospheric'. It is thought that the chromosphere is heated mainly from below (by energy coming from the photosphere) so it is interesting, and not a little perplexing, that the temperature should rise with increasing height. Even more astonishing is the enormous rate at which the temperature rises, especially towards the top of the chromosphere. This surely indicates a very high temperature indeed for the Sun's outer atmosphere – the corona. The high temperature of the corona and upper chromosphere, its cause and its influence will be our major concern in the next Section.

Summary of Section 1.3 and SAQs

1 The Sun's chromosphere is a patchy layer of gaseous material, a few thousand kilometres thick, that overlies the photosphere. About 75% of the mass of the chromosphere is made up of hydrogen; helium accounts for most of the remainder.

2 An ideal thermal source of radiation (a black body) emits a characteristic continuous spectrum. The wavelength at which such a curve attains its maximum is determined solely by the temperature of the source, in accordance with Wien's displacement law:

$$\lambda_{peak} = \frac{2.90 \times 10^{-3}\,\text{m K}}{T} \tag{1.4}$$

3 The absorption and emission lines found in the spectra of many sources of radiation are caused by electrons making transitions between states of different energies within atoms.

4 Detailed studies of solar spectra provide information about the chemical composition of the chromosphere and its physical condition (temperature, number density, etc.). Such studies show that the temperature of the chromosphere increases rapidly with height, changing by about 20 000 K over 2 000 km.

5 Chromospheric spectra show a number of emission lines, notably an Hα line at 656.3 nm. Hα images of the Sun reveal details of the structure of the chromosphere and various signs of solar activity, such as plages and filaments.

SAQ 1.4 (Objectives 1.2 and 1.8)   Estimate the size of a plage.

SAQ 1.5 (Objective 1.3)   Using a certain detector it has been found that a particular source of electromagnetic waves produces the spectrum of an ideal thermal source with a temperature of 6 000 K. What is the ratio of the detector reading at 400 nm to that at 750 nm? What would the ratio have been if the spectrum had been that of a black body at 5 000 K?

SAQ 1.6 (Objectives 1.2 and 1.3)   Treating the Sun as a good approximation to a black body, estimate its temperature from the graphical spectrum of Figure 1.18.

SAQ 1.7 (Objective 1.4)   The energy levels of the hydrogen atom (labelled E_1, E_2, E_3, etc. in Figure 1.16) have energies that are well approximated by the formula

$$E_n = -\frac{2.18 \times 10^{-18} \text{ J}}{n^2}$$

Note that *all* the energies are given negative values; E_1 is the lowest (see *Preparatory science*, Subsection 2.2.2).

where n is the energy subscript, 1, 2, 3, etc.

(a)   Insofar as you can, confirm that the absorption occurring at the centre of the Hα line can be attributed to transitions from E_2 to E_3.

(b)   Which transition accounts for the Hβ absorption line? (Hint: attempt this by trial and error, with n no larger than 5. A useful skill to develop is that of bracketing an answer by guesswork and then homing in on it.)

(c)   Which transition would account for an emission line at the same wavelength as the Hβ absorption line?

(d)   Why is there no line corresponding to the transition from E_1 to E_2 in the spectrum of Figure 1.17?

1.4   The electromagnetic spectrum and the corona: seeing the Sun's outer atmosphere

1.4.1   Introducing the corona

As you saw at the end of the last Section, the temperature rises steeply in the upper parts of the chromosphere and the number of hydrogen atoms per cubic metre declines. These trends continue through a narrow and highly irregular **transition region** and on into the **corona** – the Sun's outer atmosphere. The corona is *very* extensive, *very* tenuous, and has a *very, very* high temperature.

The extent of the corona can be gauged from photographs taken during eclipses or from measurements made with a **coronagraph** – a special kind of telescope that uses an opaque disc to block the light from the photosphere and thus produce a sort of artificial eclipse. (Building a coronagraph that works is much harder than it sounds.) High quality images, such as that in Plate 1.1, show the corona stretching out to several times the radius of the photosphere. They also reveal detailed structures, often in the form of arches, rays, plumes or streamers. These features change with time, sometimes quite rapidly, and respond to the general level of (sunspot) activity visible on the photosphere. At times of low activity the corona is usually rather quiescent and elongated at the Sun's equator; at times of high activity it is much more lively, with streamers jutting out in all directions (Figure 1.20).

The total amount of light produced by the corona is small, about equal to that of the full Moon. Even the brightest parts of the corona are almost a million times less luminous at visible wavelengths than an equal area of the photosphere. So, at visible wavelengths, the corona is usually studied during total eclipses or with the aid of a coronagraph. Most of the observed coronal light is simply white photospheric light scattered by particles (mainly electrons) in the corona – that's why the light has a characteristic pearly white colour. In the outer parts of the corona, beyond about two solar radii from the centre of the Sun, it is even possible to see the photospheric and chromospheric absorption lines in the coronal spectrum. However, in addition to features attributable to the photosphere and chromosphere, the coronal spectrum also includes some emission lines that originate in the corona itself. The strongest of these is a green line at 530.3 nm, but there are also a prominent yellow line at 569.4 nm and a red line at 637.4 nm. A circular image of the corona in the light of the green 530.3 nm

Figure 1.20 The solar corona during an eclipse at a time of high photospheric activity (November 1966).

line can be seen on the emission spectrum in Figure 1.21; the incomplete arcs elsewhere in the spectrum are caused by the chromosphere.

When those coronal emission lines were discovered during the eclipse of 7 August 1869, their cause was unknown. It was suggested that they might be due to a previously undiscovered element, which was tentatively named *coronium*. But, in contrast to the story of helium, no other evidence was found to support this hypothesis, and the origin of the lines remained one of the most challenging problems in solar spectroscopy for over 70 years. It was finally solved in the early 1940s by the Swedish astrophysicist Bengt Edlén (1906–). In a series of experiments Edlén proved that an ionized iron atom that has lost half of its normal complement of 26 electrons has its energy levels altered in such a way that there is a transition capable of producing 530.3 nm radiation (no such transition exists in a neutral iron atom that retains all 26 electrons). Since neutral iron (chemical symbol, Fe) has 26 electrons in each of its atoms, it follows that iron atoms that have lost half their electrons will have a net positive charge that is equal in magnitude but opposite in sign to the charge of the 13 lost electrons. Such atoms, or, to be more precise, such *ions* are conventionally denoted by the symbol Fe^{13+}. Thus, Edlén had established that the green coronal emission was due to Fe^{13+}. The other coronal emission lines known at the time were also shown to be due to highly charged ions.

Figure 1.21 An emission spectrum recorded during an eclipse. The incomplete arcs are images of the chromosphere at various wavelengths. (The prominent arc on the left is due to Hβ emission.) The circular image on the right is caused by coronal emission at 530.3 nm.

The presence of ions in the Sun is not surprising. Temperatures throughout the Sun are so high that most of the atoms are ionized to some extent. Some of the effects due to the presence of these ions are already familiar to you: the prominent H and K lines due to calcium (chemical symbol, Ca) in the chromosphere come from Ca^+ ions, and much of the light from the photosphere is emitted when free electrons, liberated when atoms are ionized, combine temporarily with neutral hydrogen atoms to produce H^- ions. However, the discovery that a significant amount of Fe^{13+} exists in the corona, *was* a surprise. The presence of such highly ionized atoms implied that the temperature of the corona was very high indeed – at least 10^6 K. Previously it had been thought that temperatures decreased as distance from the photosphere increased; the discovery that this was not the case replaced the enigma of the emission lines by the mystery of the mechanism that could be responsible for such high temperatures.

Ions, ionization and electrical neutrality are discussed in *Preparatory science*, Section 2.2.

Why is the corona at such a high temperature? Even now, more than 50 years after Edlén's work, there is still no general agreement about the answer to this question. Some would even say that its solution is the greatest outstanding challenge in solar science – especially those who have devoted much of their life to it. One thing is certain, the corona cannot be heated simply by energy radiated by the photosphere or by heat conducted through the chromosphere; a basic law of physics (the **second law of thermodynamics**) prevents the transfer of energy from a cooler body to a hotter one by either of these methods. Nonetheless, there can be little doubt that the necessary energy does come from the lower regions of the Sun; the question is, how? Two main proposals have been under discussion for several years. According to one, the energy required to heat the corona is delivered by pressure waves originating in or below the photosphere and travelling out through the chromosphere. According to the other, coronal magnetic fields play an important role, though the precise mechanism is still elusive. The absence of a universally agreed solution to the problem of coronal heating is not due to a lack of ideas but is indicative of the extreme difficulty of producing detailed theoretical descriptions of such complex regions.

Like the chromosphere, the corona is highly non-uniform and conditions vary enormously from place to place within it. Nonetheless it is possible, using spectroscopic information and basic physical principles, to obtain a good idea of 'average' conditions in a quiet part of the corona. Figure 1.22 shows the variation of temperature and hydrogen number density with height under such quiet conditions in the chromosphere and the inner part of the corona. The graphs are essentially extensions into the corona of the chromospheric data shown in Figure 1.19. Note that the location of the transition region separating the chromosphere and the corona is defined by the very rapid temperature rise just below 2 500 km. The precise location depends on local conditions; it might well be as high as 8 000 km on some occasions. Also note that, at the greatest heights shown in the graph in Figure 1.22, the temperature of the corona is still increasing. Temperatures of 3 to 4×10^6 K are not uncommon, and even higher temperatures are sometimes attained over limited regions.

You might think that such enormous temperatures would make the corona a powerful source of thermal radiation, but this is not so. The density of the corona is very low, and such a relatively small amount of matter, even at a very high temperature, is a very poor emitter compared with the cooler but much denser photosphere. Nevertheless, the high temperature of the corona does have important implications for the electromagnetic radiation that is emitted.

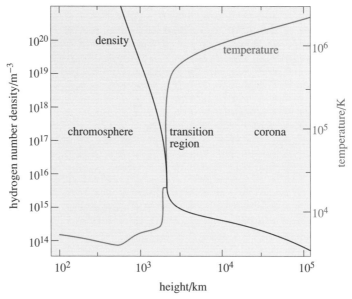

Figure 1.22 Variation of temperature (coloured line) and hydrogen number density (black line) with height above the base of the photosphere. Note that all the scales are logarithmic.

ITQ 1.7 The corona as a whole is far from being an ideal thermal source of radiation. However, by treating it as such and taking 2×10^6 K as its temperature, work out the wavelength at which its Planck curve (black-body radiation curve) would have its maximum.

The wavelength at which the Planck curve of a 2×10^6 K source has its maximum is more than a hundred times less than the shortest visible wavelengths. Does electromagnetic radiation with such a tiny wavelength exist? If so, what is it? Once again, it's time for a box.

1.4.2 The electromagnetic spectrum

Box 1.3 The electromagnetic spectrum

In terms of the electromagnetic wave model, introduced in Box 1.1, visible light spans a range of wavelengths from approximately 400 nm to approximately 750 nm. Electromagnetic waves with wavelengths outside this range cannot, by definition, represent visible light of any colour. However, such waves do provide a useful model of many well known phenomena that are more or less similar to light. For example, everyone is familiar with radio waves; we all rely on them to deliver radio and TV programmes. Radio waves are known to have wavelengths of about 3 cm or more; their well established properties include the ability to be reflected by smooth metal surfaces and to travel through a vacuum at the same speed as light. Both of these properties, and many others that could have been quoted, are also exhibited by electromagnetic waves of the same wavelengths. Thus we can say that radio waves can be 'well modelled' by electromagnetic waves with wavelengths greater than about 3 cm. Indeed, because the relatively long wavelength of radio waves makes their wave-like nature so obvious, it is really rather pedantic to talk about an electromagnetic wave *model* of radio waves at all. Most people would happily accept the statement that radio waves *are* electromagnetic waves.

The wide range of phenomena that can be modelled by electromagnetic waves is illustrated in Figure 1.23. As you can see, the full **electromagnetic spectrum**, as it is called, ranges from long wavelength **radio waves**, through **microwaves** and **infrared radiation**, across the various colours of **visible light** and on to such short wavelength phenomena as **ultraviolet radiation, X-rays** and **γ-rays** (pronounced 'gamma-rays'). These various kinds of **electromagnetic radiation** arise in a wide range of contexts (as illustrated) but fundamentally they differ from one another only in the wavelength (or frequency) of the electromagnetic waves used to model them.

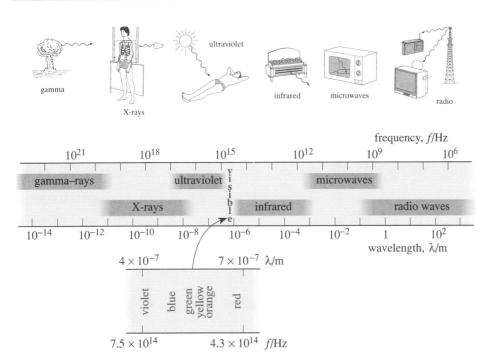

Figure 1.23   The electromagnetic spectrum. Note that the frequency and wavelength scales are logarithmic. Note also that the ultraviolet (meaning 'beyond the violet') adjoins the visible violet, and the infrared (meaning 'below the red') adjoins the visible red. The boundaries of the various regions are deliberately vague; scientists and technologists often draw the divisions somewhat loosely.

The photon model that was introduced in Box 1.1 can also be applied throughout the electromagnetic spectrum. In fact, when it comes to γ-rays, their very short wavelengths make it quite difficult to demonstrate their wave-like properties, and it is much more conventional to speak of them as though they were particles.

Of course, the true situation is that all forms of electromagnetic radiation are, at the present time, most accurately described by the quantum theory mentioned in Box 1.1. No part of the electromagnetic spectrum 'really' consists of waves *or* particles but any part may, under the appropriate conditions, exhibit wave-like or particle-like behaviour; both possibilities are encompassed by the quantum theory.

Many of the ideas in Box 1.2 concerning spectroscopy and sources of light are also applicable to the entire electromagnetic spectrum. Every kind of electromagnetic radiation may come from thermal or non-thermal sources, and the continuous spectrum produced by an ideal thermal source always extends beyond the wavelength range of visible light. (This last point is already implicit in Figure 1.14, which shows the Planck curves stretching into the ultraviolet and the infrared.) Similarly, Wien's displacement law applies throughout the electromagnetic spectrum. Also spectral lines may arise at any wavelength provided transitions of the appropriate energy exist to cause them. Such transitions are not necessarily confined to atoms; they may involve nuclei, molecules or many other systems.

ITQ 1.8 Complete Table 1.1.

Table 1.1 The electromagnetic spectrum

Wavelength, λ/m	3×10^{-14}	6×10^{-10}			5×10^{-3}	10
Corresponding frequency f/Hz	1×10^{22}	5×10^{17}			6×10^{10}	3×10^{7}
Corresponding photon energy, ε/J			6×10^{-19}			
Temperature, T/K, of black body that has a peak in its spectrum at this value of λ				300		
Corresponding part of the electromagnetic spectrum						radio wave

1.4.3 The Sun's electromagnetic spectrum and the corona

Figure 1.24 shows the electromagnetic spectrum of the entire Sun across a range of wavelengths from 10^{-13} m to 10 m, or at least it attempts to do so. The central region of the graph, roughly from 10^{-7} m to 10^{-4} m, which accounts for most of the emitted power (note the logarithmic scales), is not difficult to interpret. Emission in this region is dominated by the photosphere and, apart from some absorption lines that do not really show up on this scale, the solar spectrum is well approximated by the Planck curve of an ideal thermal source at 6 000 K. Provided the Sun is in a quiet state with relatively little activity taking place, the emission of microwaves and short wavelength (i.e. less than 10 m) radio waves will also be predominantly thermal. However, at longer radio wavelengths the emissions come predominantly from the hotter regions higher in the Sun's atmosphere. One consequence of this is that the observed diameter of the Sun increases as the wavelength of observation increases, another is that the 6 000 K Planck curve provides a progressively less satisfactory approximation to the observed spectrum. Moreover, if there is a significant amount of activity on the Sun, as is often the case, the related bursts of radio emission may well dominate the spectrum over a broad range of wavelengths. This is especially true of explosive events such as **solar flares**, one of the most energetic kinds of solar activity. The existence of these bursts makes the radio spectrum highly variable and difficult to represent on a simple graph.

Flares are a major topic in TV programme 1 and are the subject of Plate 1.11.

Similar problems exist in the X-ray and γ-ray parts of the spectrum. The thermal emissions from the photosphere fall off very rapidly with decreasing wavelength and are essentially negligible below a wavelength of about 10^{-8} m. Solar radiation is seen at shorter wavelengths, but it comes mainly from the hot coronal material and especially from the active regions where the temperatures are greatest. At the very shortest wavelengths (below 10^{-10} m) the individual X-ray and γ-ray photons each carry a relatively high energy, and it is quite normal to see spectra presented as 'counts' of the numbers of photons observed in various narrow wavelength (or energy) ranges in a given time. There is still relatively little information available at these very short wavelengths, but it is clear that the emission is related to coronal activity and is largely non-thermal.

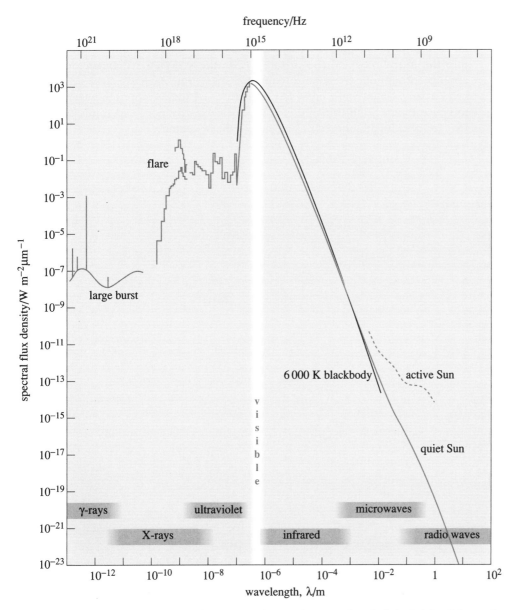

Figure 1.24 The solar electromagnetic spectrum. At any given wavelength λ, the height of the graph represents the amount of energy that would be received in 1 s by a detector, of area 1 m^2, pointed directly towards the Sun, in a range of wavelengths of width 1 µm centred on λ, *provided* the detector was above the Earth's atmosphere. The shape of the graph is discussed in the text. The black line is the Planck curve of a black body at 6 000 K.

The reason for the relative lack of information at certain wavelengths is both interesting and important. The simple fact is that the Earth's atmosphere is a very effective absorber of certain wavelengths of electromagnetic radiation, with the consequence that Earth-based solar observations are impossible across wide ranges of wavelength. Figure 1.25 provides a clear indication of the effectiveness of the Earth's atmosphere as a barrier to solar radiation. The atmosphere is largely transparent to visible light and to certain longer wavelengths, particularly to narrow bands in the infrared and to radio waves, but everything else is effectively stopped. In order to overcome this barrier, many observations have to be made from high-altitude rockets and balloons, or satellites and space probes. Such ventures are complicated and costly, but they have been responsible for many of the most important recent advances in solar science (and in many other fields).

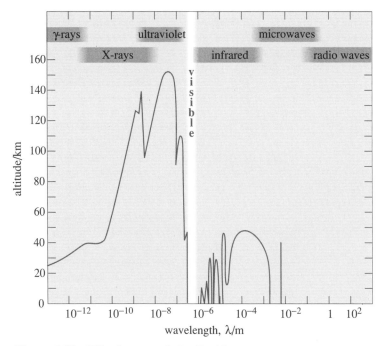

Figure 1.25 Effectiveness of the Earth's atmosphere as a barrier to incoming solar radiation. For a given wavelength λ, the graph shows the altitude at which the spectral flux density (F_λ) due to the Sun is reduced to 50% of its value at the top of the atmosphere.

Five solar images, representing different parts of the electromagnetic spectrum, are shown in Plate 1.7. It should be clear from the above discussion of the solar spectrum that the images formed at very long and very short wavelengths will have been produced largely by radiation from the corona. The X-ray image (Plate 1.7a) is essentially confined to temperatures above $1.6 \times 10^6\,\mathrm{K}$ and is particularly informative about coronal structure. Bright regions associated with solar activity are easy to see, but more intensive study reveals that the corona is generally composed of 'loops' of various sizes. These loops are magnetic in origin; they are known to result from the interplay of the highly ionized coronal gases and the Sun's magnetic field.

Another feature commonly seen in X-ray images is known as a **coronal hole**. Some idea of its behaviour can be obtained from Figure 1.26, which shows a sequence of X-ray images taken at intervals of 27 days from the orbiting Skylab space station in 1973. The rotation of the coronal hole – the dark boot-shaped object stretching from the pole to the equator – with the Sun is quite clear. The hole's shape and size change with time, and sometimes it seems to fragment and then merge together again. Coronal holes are devoid of the large loops seen elsewhere in the corona: they are regions where the solar magnetic field opens outwards to interplanetary space rather than looping back on to the Sun. The existence of such regions is of great importance, since they are thought to be a major source of the **solar wind** – a gusty stream of high-speed particles that spreads out from the Sun, carrying traces of the Sun's magnetic field with it. Amongst other things, the solar wind is thought to be instrumental in creating the aurora, shown in Plate 1.10.

☐ Why were the Skylab images in Figure 1.26 taken 27 days apart?

■ The Sun rotates; 27 days were required for the coronal hole to return to the centre of the field of view of the Skylab detector.

Although a great deal has been said in this Section about images of the Sun from various parts of the electromagnetic spectrum, almost nothing has been said

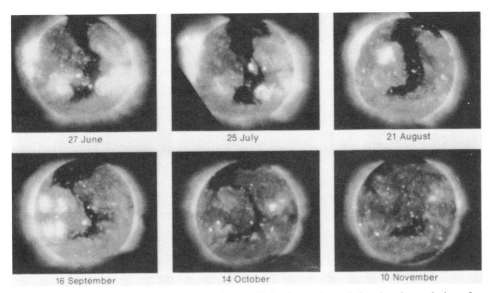

Figure 1.26 X-ray images of the corona taken at 27 day intervals, and showing the evolution of a coronal hole. Such images must be obtained from space because the Earth's atmosphere absorbs electromagnetic radiation in this wavelength range.

about how such images are obtained. This is clearly a topic of vital importance and the focus of much effort at the time of writing. Some of the issues relating to it are explored in TV programme 1. If you already have this on video, now would be an excellent time to watch it. You should now also watch video sequence 2 The magnetic Sun. *Don't forget to read the associated notes first.*

Summary of Section 1.4 and SAQs

1   The outer atmosphere of the Sun is called the corona. It is tenuous and extensive, and separated from the chromosphere by the narrow, irregular transition region.

2   The structure of the corona is highly variable and responds to the level of solar activity.

3   Spectral signatures of highly ionized atoms reveal that temperatures of several million degrees are common in the corona. Accounting for these high temperatures is still a major challenge for solar scientists.

4   The electromagnetic spectrum encompasses such diverse phenomena as radio waves, microwaves, infrared radiation, visible light, ultraviolet radiation, X-rays and γ-rays. All these forms of electromagnetic radiation can be modelled by electromagnetic waves of decreasing wavelength or by photons of increasing energy, under the appropriate circumstances.

5   The Sun emits radiation across the entire electromagnetic spectrum, from radio waves to γ-rays. The central wavelength range (10^{-7} m to 10^{-4} m), which accounts for nearly all the radiated power, is approximately described by a 6 000 K black-body curve, and is dominated by photospheric emissions. The extreme wavelengths are more strongly related to solar activity and are often dominated by coronal emissions.

6   X-ray images of the Sun reveal coronal holes, which are believed to be a source of the solar wind.

SAQ 1.8 (Objectives 1.2 and 1.4)   In addition to the green emission line due to ionized iron, the corona produces two other prominent emission lines in the visible part of the spectrum: a yellow line at 569.4 nm due to calcium atoms that have lost 14 electrons, and a red line at 637.4 nm due to iron atoms that have lost 9 electrons.

(a)   How can the ions responsible for the yellow and red lines be represented symbolically?

(b)   Calculate the difference in energy between the relevant energy levels in the ions responsible for the yellow and red lines.

SAQ 1.9 (Objective 1.3)   Treating the transition region as an ideal thermal source of electromagnetic radiation with a temperature of 100 000 K (which it isn't), work out the wavelength at which you would expect its Planck curve to have a peak. In which part of the electromagnetic spectrum would this peak be located?

SAQ 1.10 (Objectives 1.2 and 1.3)   At visible wavelengths, images of the Sun exhibit the phenomenon of limb darkening, as described earlier. At radio wavelengths the opposite effect, limb brightening, is seen. Explain the origin of limb brightening. (Hint: recall that temperatures in the solar atmosphere increase with height.)

1.5   Inside the Sun

1.5.1   Introducing the solar interior

We have now examined in some detail the outer parts of the Sun and the radiation they emit. In particular, we have seen that most of the energy received from the Sun is carried by radiation from the photosphere. There are three factors that account for the photosphere's effectiveness as a source of energy. First, the atmospheric layers above the photosphere are, for the most part, transparent at the visible wavelengths, which dominate photospheric emission. Secondly, the photosphere itself is opaque. Thirdly, the photosphere is sufficiently large and at a sufficiently high temperature, around 6 000 K, to be a powerful thermal source of radiation.

In our quest to understand the nature and origin of the Sun's radiation, the task that now confronts us is that of explaining why the photosphere has such a temperature and how that temperature is maintained despite the prodigious rate at which solar energy is radiated into space. You may already be familiar with the broad answers to these questions: the photosphere is heated from below by energy coming from deeper and hotter regions of the **solar interior**; this state of affairs persists because the **core** of the Sun – roughly the central 2 or 3% of the Sun's volume – is a steady and long-lived energy source powered by nuclear processes. The rest of this chapter will be devoted to expanding these answers and giving you some feel for the nature of the solar interior.

1.5.2   The internal structure of the Sun

Discussions of the solar interior are bound to be largely theoretical because the whole region is currently inaccessible, and is hidden from view by the photosphere. Most of what we know (or think we know) about the interior is based on a number of theoretical **solar models** that have gained wide acceptance amongst solar scientists. The various models in use at present differ in matters of detail but agree about general principles and give broadly similar results.

Each solar model is based on a few fundamental physical principles and some plausible assumptions about the interior. The *physical principles* include the requirement that the rate at which the Sun radiates energy should equal the rate at which nuclear processes produce energy in the interior, and the need for the solar material at a given depth to be able to support the weight of the matter that sits on top of it. The *plausible assumptions* relate to many issues, including the importance of internal magnetic fields and the rate at which the internal layers of the Sun rotate about the Sun's axis.

Given certain items of information about the Sun, such as the radius ($R_\odot$), total mass ($M_\odot$), luminosity ($L_\odot$) and chemical composition, solar models provide numerical values for the temperature, pressure and density at any given distance from the centre of the Sun. This latter quantity is usually expressed as a fraction of the Sun's radius and is often denoted $R/R_\odot$, where $R_\odot$ is the radius of the photosphere. It is called the **fractional radius**. Representative results from a particular solar model are displayed graphically in Figure 1.27. More will be said about the route that leads to such results in the next subsection.

The overall rise of temperature, pressure and density with increasing depth indicated by Figure 1.27 is not surprising. The pressure should be expected to increase with depth, owing to the growing weight of overlying material, and the temperature to rise, because of the increasing proximity to the central energy source. Nevertheless, the details, which emerge from a very lengthy computer-based calculation, are surprising. Temperature, pressure and density all change very rapidly near the photosphere, but it's not until a fractional radius of about 0.5 that the density is equal to that of water on Earth ($1.0 \times 10^3 \, \text{kg m}^{-3}$). Even at the centre of the Sun, where the temperature is about $15 \times 10^6 \, \text{K}$, the density is predicted to be only fourteen times that of lead, though the pressure is more than 10^{10} times that of the Earth's atmosphere at sea-level.

1.5.3 The internal composition of the Sun

When dealing with the composition of the solar interior, it is traditional to divide the constituents into just three categories: hydrogen, helium and everything else. In this context, all those materials that fall into the 'everything else' category will be referred to as **heavy elements**, irrespective of precisely how heavy they are compared with hydrogen and helium. Thus elements such as boron, oxygen and carbon will be called heavy elements, along with iron, copper and gold. Accepting this convention, at least for the moment, the composition of a sample of material at any depth within the Sun can be defined by assigning numerical values to three simple parameters:

The **hydrogen mass fraction** (X):

$$X = \frac{\text{mass of hydrogen in sample}}{\text{mass of sample}}$$

The **helium mass fraction** (Y):

$$Y = \frac{\text{mass of helium in sample}}{\text{mass of sample}}$$

The **metallicity** (Z):

$$Z = \frac{\text{mass of heavy elements in sample}}{\text{mass of sample}}$$

ITQ 1.9 What can you say about the value of $X + Y + Z$ at any depth within the Sun?

As you saw earlier, spectroscopic studies of the outer parts of the Sun can provide detailed information about the relative abundance of the various chemical elements found there. However, such information is unlikely to be a reliable guide to the constitution of the solar interior. Instead, determinations of X, Y and Z in the interior, like structural determinations, are usually based on calculations that involve a solar model.

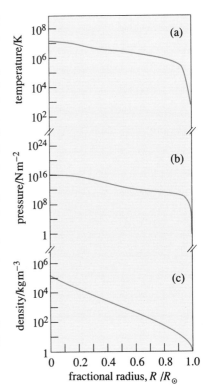

Figure 1.27 Variation with fractional solar radius of (a) temperature, (b) pressure and (c) density in the solar interior. Note that the vertical axis is logarithmic in each case.

It is universally accepted that the nuclear processes that power the Sun convert hydrogen into helium. Thus, the values of the hydrogen and helium mass fractions (X and Y) change with time. Now, any solar model that provides a reasonably full account of energy production must take into account these changes, and the changes they produce in temperature, pressure and density. Consequently, a detailed solar model is capable of simulating the evolution of the Sun – including the evolution of its composition. By adjusting the initial values of X, Y and Z, until the simulated evolutionary process results in a structure that agrees with our knowledge of the present-day Sun, it is possible to obtain estimates for the current values of X, Y and Z at any depth.

The results of one such calculation of the Sun's present internal composition are shown in Figure 1.28. In this particular case, the value of Z was initially set at 0.017 and was assumed to be independent of depth and constant in time. The value of X, which was initially set at 0.735, is now expected to vary from 0.341 at the core, where a good deal of hydrogen has been converted into helium, to 0.735 at the surface, where there has been no conversion. Since $X + Y + Z = 1$, the present day helium mass fraction, at any depth, is given by $Y = 1 - 0.017 - X$. It follows that, throughout the upper parts of the interior, where $X = 0.735$, Y retains its initial value, 0.248. This sort of result is common to many solar models and is generally taken to provide a precise determination of solar helium abundance.

To summarize, throughout most of its interior the Sun is approximately 73% hydrogen, 25% helium and 2% everything else (by mass). However, in the central 30% or so of its radius the percentage of hydrogen is increasingly depleted (and helium compensatingly increased), with about half the hydrogen initially present in the core of the Sun having been converted into helium.

Before leaving the subject of the Sun's composition, one point, mentioned earlier, deserves special emphasis. Most of the atoms in the Sun are *ionized*. This is particularly true in the hot, dense interior, where essentially all the hydrogen and helium atoms are completely ionized. Such a highly ionized gas is called a **plasma**. So, although it is quite common to see the Sun referred to as a gaseous body, it is actually more correct to say that it is made of plasma. In this case, the plasma consists mainly of hydrogen and helium ions, together with the electrons that were liberated when those ions were produced.

ITQ 1.10   Assuming that solar material pretty much stays in one place during the life of the Sun (that is, there is no significant internal mixing of solar constituents), what can you deduce so far about the location of the nuclear processes that convert hydrogen into helium?

Indeed, the location of the nuclear processes in a central core is a *direct* and continuing consequence of the increase of temperature with depth in the models: the rates of nuclear reactions rise very rapidly as the temperature increases.

1.5.4   The energy source of the Sun

In this subsection, we assume that you are reasonably familiar with some of the basic concepts of nuclear physics, such as atomic number, mass number *and* nuclide. *If you don't think you are, you should consult Section 2.2 of* Preparatory science *before you continue.*

The subsection addresses two questions:

• What are the main energy-releasing nuclear processes that take place in the core of the Sun?

• At what rate do those nuclear processes occur?

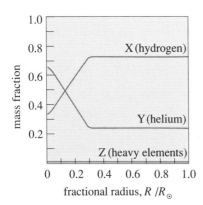

Figure 1.28 Variation of the mass fractions X, Y and Z with the fractional radius, $R/R_\odot$, for the Sun.

The answers to these questions provide the ultimate solution to our search for the true origin of the Sun's electromagnetic radiation. But, as you will see, they also raise other questions.

What are the energy-releasing nuclear processes?

The basic energy-releasing process taking place in the Sun is *nuclear fusion*. This was described in *Preparatory science* as a process in which nuclei of relatively low mass are fused together to form nuclei of somewhat greater mass. The fusion is brought about by a sequence of nuclear reactions in which colliding nuclei combine and fragment, to produce new nuclei together with other particles that were not in any sense 'within' the colliding nuclei that triggered the reaction. No energy is actually generated in these reactions: it is simply that energy is liberated from the *reactants* and is redistributed amongst the *products* in such a way that some of it replaces the energy radiated by the Sun. This replacement of lost energy maintains the high temperature of the core, thus sustaining the nuclear reaction rates.

A full account of the nuclear processes taking place in the Sun would be very complicated indeed. Our discussion will be limited to the one process that is thought to be responsible for the bulk of the Sun's radiant energy – the so-called **ppI chain**. (The name indicates that it is the first of several different chains of reactions that start with colliding protons – p is the symbol for the proton, as is $^1_1$H, the proton being the nucleus of the common nuclide of hydrogen.) The nuclei involved in the ppI chain are the hydrogen nuclides $^1_1$H and $^2_1$H and the helium nuclides $^3_2$He and $^4_2$He. The other particles that are involved are of three types:

A nuclide is a nucleus with a particular atomic number, Z, and mass number, A.

Gamma rays (denoted by γ). These are just energetic photons of electromagnetic radiation, a concept that should already be familiar from the discussions in Boxes 1.1 and 1.3.

Positrons (denoted by e^+). These are particles similar in many ways to electrons (denoted by e^-); they have the same mass for instance. However, some of their properties are radically different. For example, positrons have positive charge (hence their name) whereas electrons have negative charge. Positrons are sometimes called *anti-electrons*.

Neutrinos (denoted by ν, pronounced 'new'). These are electrically neutral particles (hence the name) with a mass so tiny that no one has yet succeeded in measuring it – if it is anything at all. Neutrinos travel at essentially the speed of light and interact with other particles so weakly that they are able to travel through ordinary matter with great ease. Day and night, enormous numbers of neutrinos stream through the Earth with hardly any impediment. While you are reading this sentence, more than a million million neutrinos will pass through your own head.

The various steps in the ppI chain are shown in Figure 1.29. Pruned of its details, the overall effect of the chain is the following:

$$4\,^1_1\text{H} \longrightarrow \,^4_2\text{He} + e^+ + 2\nu + 2\gamma$$

Thus, four protons are consumed and a helium nucleus containing two protons and two neutrons is produced along with two positrons, two neutrinos and two gamma rays. Each occurrence of the ppI chain is accompanied by a number of supplementary reactions that result, amongst other things, in the annihilation of the two positrons (along with two of the Sun's many electrons – this reaction does, of course, conserve charge), and the release of yet more gamma rays. So, apart from the production of helium nuclei and neutrinos, the final outcome of the ppI chain is the release of gamma rays. It is these gamma rays that are the ultimate source of most of the Sun's electromagnetic radiation.

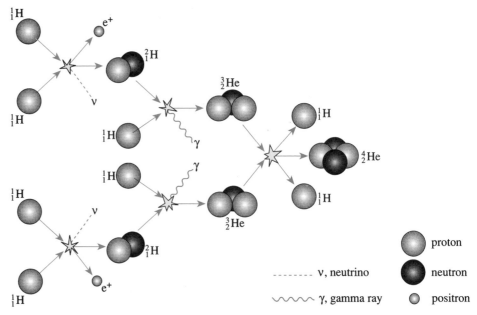

Figure 1.29 The ppI chain of nuclear reactions predominantly responsible for the conversion of hydrogen into helium in the Sun. Note that *six* hydrogen nuclei are required to initiate the chain but *two* are released again at the end.

At what rate do the nuclear processes occur?

We have now identified the process that is mainly responsible for the Sun's radiant energy. How common is this process? In order to get a rough idea of the answer to this question all we have to do is to divide the Sun's luminosity (the energy radiated per second) by the radiant energy liberated by each occurrence of the ppI chain. Making that estimate is our next goal. To start with, we need to know the energy released per occurrence.

☐ Why does the above procedure provide only a rough idea of the rate at which the process occurs?

■ Because we are neglecting all the other nuclear reaction chains, apart from the ppI chain, that also contribute to the generation of energy in the Sun.

As explained in Section 2.2 of *Preparatory science*, nuclear reactions are constrained by a number of regulating principles called *conservation laws*. These dictate which reactions are possible and determine how much energy the various particles may carry away from a reaction. You can remind yourself about conservation laws by answering the following ITQ.

ITQ 1.11   The individual nuclear reactions that make up the ppI chain are shown in Figure 1.29. There are three distinct kinds of nuclear reaction in the figure.

(a) Write out each of the reactions symbolically using the notation introduced in the discussion of the overall effect of the ppI chain.

(b) For each of the three reactions you have written down, work out the total amount of electric charge (expressed as a multiple of the proton's charge, e) entering and leaving the reaction, and confirm that these reactions obey the principle of *conservation of electric charge*.

(c) Given that the baryon number of each proton and each neutron is +1, and that positrons, neutrinos and gamma rays have no baryon number at all, work out the total baryon number entering and leaving each reaction, and confirm that these reactions obey the principle of *conservation of baryon number*.

Just as nuclear reactions conserve electric charge and baryon number, so they must also obey another principle, mentioned in Section 1.5 of *Preparatory science*, that of *conservation of energy*. The total energy emerging from a reaction must be equal to the total energy that entered the reaction. In applying this principle to nuclear reactions, it is important to include any **kinetic energy** (i.e. energy by virtue of motion) that the particles may have, but it is also important to remember Einstein's famous discovery that even particles at rest have a certain amount of energy, called the **rest energy**. The rest energy of a particle of mass m is given by

$$E = mc^2 \tag{1.6}$$

By using this formula, together with the principle of conservation of energy, it is possible to estimate the amount of radiant energy ultimately released (as gamma rays) by each occurrence of the ppI chain. In order to make the estimate we shall assume that, once all the supplementary reactions are taken into account, there is no significant change in the kinetic energy of the particles present before and after each occurrence of the ppI chain. We shall also assume that the energy associated with the two neutrinos is negligible (even though it's actually about 2% of the total). With these assumptions, we have to consider only the rest energies involved in the ppI chain – though we must remember to add the contribution arising from the annihilation of the two positrons with two of the Sun's electrons to produce yet more radiant energy. Thus,

radiant energy eventually resulting from each occurrence of the ppI chain $= [(4 \times$ rest energy of $^1_1$H$) - ($rest energy of $^4_2$He $+ 2e^+)] + ($rest energy of $2e^+ + 2e^-)$

Having got this far, there is no reason why you shouldn't do the rest of the work for yourself, so here's your chance.

ITQ 1.12 The mass of the helium nucleus, $^4_2$He, is 6.645×10^{-27} kg. That of the hydrogen nucleus, $^1_1$H, is 1.673×10^{-27} kg, and that of each electron or positron is 9.110×10^{-31} kg.

(a) Use this information to find the radiant energy eventually resulting from each occurrence of the ppI chain, under the assumptions given above.

(b) Use your answer to part (a), together with the value of the solar luminosity of 3.84×10^{26} J s^{-1}, to estimate the rate at which the ppI chain occurs.

(c) Just for fun, use your answer to (b) to estimate the mass of hydrogen consumed per year by the ppI chain.

The Sun is such a massive body – 1.99×10^{30} kg – that, despite the consumption of an enormous amount of hydrogen every year, it has been able to shine fairly steadily for about 4.5×10^9 years and will probably continue for do so for another 4 or 5×10^9 years.

The above discussion should have given you a clear general picture of the main processes leading to the release of energetic gamma rays in the hot, dense conditions of the Sun's core, and hence of the origin of solar radiation. However, you should also be aware that there are some major questions that still need to be answered. A fairly obvious one that arises whenever conditions in an inaccessible region are described is 'how do you know it's really like that?' This will be addressed shortly in the subsection entitled 'Testing theories of the solar interior'. But an even more pressing question is this: 'How does the energy liberated in the core of the Sun (mainly carried by gamma rays) account for the visible light that emerges from the Sun's surface?' This issue, which relates directly to our concern about how the Sun shines, is the subject of the next subsection.

1.5.5 How energy reaches the surface

The core of the Sun is a hot dense plasma – more than ten times denser than metals in our everyday world. Photons are not likely to travel very far through this material before they encounter an electron or an ion. So the gamma rays produced by the ppI chain and other solar nuclear reactions are quite unable to travel directly to the Sun's surface and onward into space. Instead, there must be some mechanism, or set of mechanisms, whereby energy is *transported* from the core of the Sun to its surface. There are three fundamentally different methods of transferring energy from place to place that might, in principle, be involved – *radiation*, *conduction* and *convection*. Before explaining which are important in the Sun, we shall examine the basic principles of all three as a piece of background science in Box 1.4.

Box 1.4 Methods of energy transfer: radiation, conduction and convection

Radiation

In the case of **radiation**, the energy is carried from place to place by waves, rays or streams of particles that are emitted and absorbed. We usually think of *radiative energy transport* in terms of electromagnetic radiation, as in the case of the infrared radiation from an electric fire, or the light from the Sun. However, radiative energy transport is not really quite so limited. In some circumstances, for instance, streams of neutrinos can transfer substantial amounts of energy. A characteristic of radiation is that it may operate across a vacuum, though it does not necessarily have to do so.

Conduction

In contrast to radiation, **conduction** can transfer energy only between places that are physically linked by a material medium. In *conductive energy transport* the basic mechanism is that moving particles collide and redistribute their energy, and a common characteristic is the existence of a temperature gradient between the source of the energy and its destination. A common example of conduction is the heating of a metal spoon used to stir hot soup. The soup heats the end of the spoon with which it is in contact, causing the atoms in the metal to vibrate rapidly. The energy of these vibrations is gradually passed (mainly by electrons) to more slowly moving neighbouring atoms in cooler parts of the spoon. In this way the cooler parts are heated and some of the energy initially contained in the soup is eventually transferred to the handle of the spoon.

Convection

Convection, like conduction, requires a medium. Moreover, in the case of convection, the medium must be a fluid (a gas, a liquid or a plasma) and it must be in a gravitational field. *Convective energy transport* can also be exemplified by a common culinary experience, that of heating a saucepan of water. When a saucepan is placed on a gas ring or an electric hob the water at the bottom of the pan is heated and expands. This reduces the density of the water at the bottom of the pan, so, under the influence of the Earth's gravitational field, it starts to rise, displacing the cooler denser water above. When the heated water reaches the surface it radiates away some of its energy and cools down while the water at the bottom of the pan is warmed by more energy coming (by conduction) from below. Thus, the cycle is able to repeat itself and a pattern of **convection currents** is established within the saucepan – as indicated in Figure 1.30.

---

energy lost to surroundings by radiation (and by convection in air)

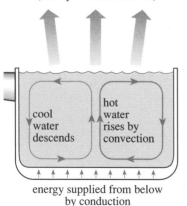

cool water descends

hot water rises by convection

energy supplied from below by conduction

Figure 1.30 Radiation, convection and conduction in and around a heated saucepan of water.

Given the high density of the deep solar interior, you might expect that conduction would be important there, but this turns out not to be the case. The main mechanism of energy transport throughout the central 70% or so of the Sun's radius is actually radiation involving photons. Of course, the radiative energy transfer that takes place there is not the sort with which we are familiar. Because of the conditions there, the photons have to make their way through the solar material via a lengthy sequence of encounters with other particles, in which they are either scattered, or absorbed and re-emitted. The photons emerging from each of these encounters have an almost equal chance of travelling in any direction, so their progress up to the photosphere takes the form of a **random walk**, as indicated schematically in Figure 1.31. A typical step in the random walk is only a few centimetres long (even less in the core), so the outward spread of energy from the core is a gradual 'diffusive' process.

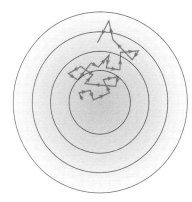

Figure 1.31 Radiant energy emerging from the solar core initially makes its way outwards via a series of radiative processes along a random walk. The contours represent increasing distance from the Sun's centre.

The gradual nature of the outward transport of energy is responsible for the fact that the photons emerging from the surface of the Sun mainly correspond to visible light rather than the γ-ray photons produced in the core. As we have seen, basic physical principles, the principles that provide the foundation for a solar model, lead to the conclusion that the interior temperature of the Sun decreases as the distance from the centre increases. This decrease in temperature is reflected in the distribution of speeds found amongst electrons or ions of a given type at various distances from the Sun's centre. On the whole, the lower the temperature in any given region, the lower the average speed of particles (of a given type) in that region (this point was discussed briefly in Subsection 2.4.1 of *Preparatory science*). As photons diffuse outwards they are influenced by the particles that scatter and absorb them, with the result that the energy of the average photon is gradually reduced. No energy is lost in this process; it is simply redistributed and shared amongst increasing numbers of photons. This sharing and redistribution of energy is so effective that the local electrons and ions may be regarded as the immediate source of the radiation. This state of affairs is described by saying that the radiation is in **local thermodynamic equilibrium** with the material through which it passes. It follows that, in a region where the temperature is T, the spectrum of the electromagnetic radiation will take very nearly the form of the thermal radiation curve that characterizes emissions from an ideal thermal source at temperature T. This applies right up to the photosphere.

☐ Would you expect the same to be true of sunlight passing through the Earth's lower atmosphere?

■ No. The solar spectrum roughly approximates that of a 6 000 K black body, whereas the temperature of the Earth's lower atmosphere is about 300 K. This is possible because the Earth's atmosphere is largely *transparent* to sunlight. There are so few interactions between the incoming sunlight and the air in the lower atmosphere that there is no opportunity to establish local thermodynamic equilibrium.

Detailed calculations show that, under the conditions of temperature and density found in the solar interior, convection is the main mechanism responsible for energy transport throughout the outer quarter or so of the Sun's radius. In the solar context, it is very strongly suspected that the convection currents are divided into a number of **convection cells**. The uppermost cells are quite small, typically 1 000 km across, but quite deep. They account for the ever-changing solar granulation seen in the photosphere. (This was described in Subsection 1.2.3 and shown in TV programme 1.) A deeper layer of larger cells, typically 30 000 km across, is thought to account for a similar but less obvious phenomenon called **supergranulation**. Supergranules are not seen as light and dark patches on the photosphere, but their presence can be deduced from detailed observations of the movement of photospheric material or from various magnetic field measurements. It has also been suggested that there might be an underlying layer of giant convection cells, but there is no strong evidence in favour of this proposal.

Figure 1.32 shows a cross-section of a sector of the Sun and is designed to emphasize energy transport (see also Plate 1.12). As you can see, beyond the core (where the nuclear reactions take place), it is conventional to call the region in which energy is still mainly transported by radiation the **radiative zone**, and the outer region in which convection dominates the **convective zone**. The top of the convective zone roughly corresponds to the photosphere, where radiation once again becomes the dominant mechanism for energy transport.

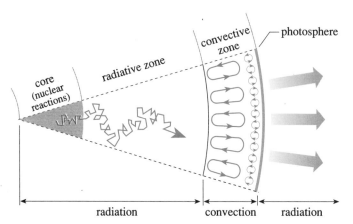

Figure 1.32   Energy transport in the Sun.

Light takes about 8.3 minutes to travel from the photosphere to the Earth. If the Sun were entirely transparent it would only take radiation about 2.3 seconds to make the journey to the photosphere from the core. However, the Sun is *not* transparent and the journey actually takes a lot longer. It has been estimated that energy being released in the core right now will take about a million years to reach the surface. Fortunately, as you will learn in the next subsection, there is evidence that energy is still being released in the Sun's core.

1.5.6   Testing theories of the solar interior

Are our ideas about the Sun's interior right? Of course, theories are constantly under review; theorists are engaged in an unending search for inconsistencies or unseen implications within existing ideas, while at the same time looking for possible applications of new ideas. There is also a constant interplay of theory and experiment as new laboratory measurements of quantities such as nuclear reaction rates permit improved calculational precision. But, at the end of the day, theories must be tested against observation. It is just such observational tests that are the subject of this subsection.

In the case of the solar interior, current ideas can be subjected to a number of observational tests, though some are less conclusive than others. For example, attempts have been made to use the Earth's climatic history as an indicator of the constancy of solar luminosity. Such work is very interesting, but its interpretation is fraught with difficulty, making it hard to obtain definite results concerning the Sun. More success has been achieved by those who attempt to explain the observed properties of Sun-like stars on the basis of modified solar models (more on this subject in Chapter 3), but observations of other stars inevitably lack the detail and precision that are easily obtained in solar observations. Important information about the solar interior has been obtained from observations of the Sun's overall shape and surface composition, but even these data fail to provide much insight into the properties of the deep interior. Despite this catalogue of woes, recent years have witnessed two major observational developments that have already had an enormous influence on theorists, and which appear to have the potential for even greater impact in the future. These two developments will now be described.

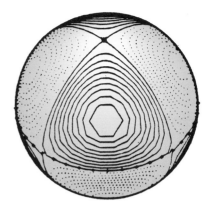

Observations of solar oscillations

It has been known since the early 1960s that the Sun oscillates – its surface moves up and down, at speeds of up to 1 km s^{-1}. The observed motions are not, at first sight, particularly orderly – localized regions of the photosphere rise and fall, somewhat irregularly, through distances of many kilometres in characteristic time periods of five minutes or so. Despite the lack of apparent coherence it was established in the mid-1970s that the observed movements partly result from the combined effect of many simple **global oscillations** that individually are very orderly indeed. Contour plots of a few of these global oscillations are illustrated in Figure 1.33. Each involves a coherent movement of the entire solar surface, and each has its own characteristic time period. Some of the low-frequency global oscillations actually penetrate deep into the solar interior, as indicated in Plate 1.11a. In view of this, it is not surprising that conditions in the Sun's interior influence the relative significance of the various global oscillations and thus the detailed surface movements they jointly produce.

Thanks to the existence of these deep-rooted global oscillations it is possible to learn about the Sun's interior by observing its surface. Because this is similar to the way that terrestrial seismologists learn about the Earth's interior by studying the vibrations initiated by earthquakes, the subject has come to be called **helioseismology**. This is a relatively new subject and is still the focus of intensive research. However, results to date are broadly consistent with standard solar models and have been used to dismiss at least one unorthodox theory of the solar interior. The outcome of one particular study of internal solar rotation is shown in Plate 1.11b.

Figure 1.33 Contour plots of some global oscillations. The solid lines represent zones of temporary expansion, the dotted lines show zones of temporary contraction.

Observations of solar neutrinos

Although electromagnetic radiation has a hard time escaping from the Sun's core, the neutrinos produced there have no such difficulty. Observations of **solar neutrinos** potentially provide a very direct test of our ideas about solar nuclear reactions but, unfortunately, the low interaction rate that allows the neutrinos to escape from the Sun also makes them very hard to detect when they reach (and pass through) the Earth. Nonetheless, one experiment has been observing solar neutrinos since 1970. The experiment is located in the Homestake Goldmine in South Dakota. (The underground location has no influence on the neutrinos, but it does cut out various other particles that might otherwise lead to spurious results.) The neutrino detector (Figure 1.34) is rather unusual; it consists of a large tank containing 610 tonnes of perchlorethylene (tetrachloroethene, C_2Cl_4) – a liquid used in the cleaning business. As neutrinos flood through the tank, one occasionally interacts with a chlorine nucleus to produce a $_{18}^{37}Ar$ nucleus. At the end of a typical 80 day run the tank is emptied, its contents are analysed, and the $_{18}^{37}Ar$ nuclei are counted. This is no mean feat, because usually only about 50 argon nuclei are found amongst the roughly 10^{30} nuclei in the tank.

The results of the Homestake mine experiment have been a source of controversy for many years. The small number of observed neutrinos implies a rate of neutrino production that is only about one third of that expected. Naturally, many attempts have been made to explain this deficit. One possible explanation is that existing solar theories need adjustment. If so, it is probably the assumed lack of mixing in the solar core that is in error. However, many other explanations are possible and, in the view of some experts, more likely. According to one currently popular explanation, it is the nature of the neutrino that is causing the problem. Physicists know of three kinds of neutrino, respectively referred to as 'electron-type', 'muon-type' and 'tauon-type'. The

Figure 1.34   The tank of C_2Cl_4 used to trap solar neutrinos at the Homestake Goldmine in South Dakota.

neutrinos created in the Sun's core should all be 'electron-type' and this is the only sort of neutrino that can be detected in the tank of C_2Cl_4. It has been suggested that a particular kind of interaction, between the neutrinos leaving the core and the solar material through which they must pass, causes the neutrinos to change type – with the consequence that only about a third of the neutrinos emerging from the Sun are still of 'electron-type'. If this proposal were correct it would neatly explain the observations without requiring any change to our existing views about the Sun.

A major shortcoming of the C_2Cl_4 experiment is that it is really sensitive to only the most energetic solar neutrinos, and those come from a relatively rare process involving the decay of boron (^8_4B) nuclei. Clearly, investigators would prefer to have direct evidence concerning the far more numerous neutrinos from the ppI chain itself. This is just starting to become available, thanks to a number of exciting new experiments. Such neutrinos have certainly been observed but their rate of arrival is not yet clear. Keep your eye on the *Yearbook* for news of the latest developments in this important field of research. The fate of the theory is very much in the balance.

1   The temperature and density of the Sun increase as the distance from the centre (fractional radius) decreases. The core temperature is thought to be about 15×10^6 K.

2   Theoretical models of the solar interior provide detailed structural information and favour a composition that is (by mass) roughly 73% hydrogen, 25% helium and 2% heavy elements, except in the central core, where the high temperatures promote chains of nuclear reactions that convert hydrogen nuclei into helium nuclei.

3   The Sun's electromagnetic radiation originates in the central core, where it is released by the nuclear reactions that convert hydrogen nuclei into helium nuclei. In addition to high-energy gamma rays, these reactions also produce neutrinos.

4   Energy released in the core makes its way to the surface by radiation and convection. Radiative energy transport in the solar interior is a gradual diffusive process in which the radiation is in local thermodynamic equilibrium with the material through which it passes.

5   The broad features of theories of the solar interior are not currently in dispute. However, observational tests involving solar neutrinos, solar oscillations and other sources of data may require some alteration in the details of those theories.

SAQ 1.11 (Objective 1.5)   Estimate the numbers of hydrogen and helium nuclei contained in the Sun.

SAQ 1.12 (Objective 1.6)   Use the result of ITQ 1.12c to estimate the total amount of time for which the solar luminosity can be sustained at its current value by the conversion of hydrogen into helium.

SAQ 1.13 (Objective 1.6)   Why are the following nuclear reactions impossible?

(a) $^1_1H + ^4_2He \longrightarrow ^5_3He$

(b) $^7_4Be + ^1_1H \longrightarrow 2\,^4_2He + e^+ + \gamma + 2\nu$

(c) $^3_2He + ^4_2He \longrightarrow ^7_3Li + \gamma$

SAQ 1.14 (Objective 1.5)   If the Sun's luminosity is entirely due to the loss of rest energy from the solar core, how much mass does the Sun lose each year?

SAQ 1.15 (Objective 1.6)   Estimate the number of solar neutrinos per second passing through a $0.01\,m^2$ detector located on the Earth and pointed directly towards the Sun. You may assume that the distance from the Sun to the Earth is 1.50×10^{11} m, and you will find it useful to know that the surface area of a sphere of radius r is $4\pi r^2$. Take care to write down any other assumptions you make in obtaining your estimate.

After studying Chapter 1 (and any associated audio, video or TV material), you should be able to:

1.1 Give brief definitions of the terms, concepts and principles listed at the end of the Objectives.

1.2 Describe the general features of the photosphere, the chromosphere and the corona.

1.3 Define the basic characteristics of electromagnetic radiation, list the fundamental ideas of the wave and photon models, and explain the significance of the Planck curve. In addition, you should be able to write down and use the equations

$$v = f\lambda \tag{1.1}$$

$$\varepsilon = hf \tag{1.3}$$

$$\lambda_{\text{peak}} = \frac{2.90 \times 10^{-3}\,\text{m K}}{T} \tag{1.4}$$

1.4 Explain the origin and nature of spectral lines.

1.5 Describe the chemical and physical composition of the Sun, and comment on the structural and physical significance of the core, the radiative zone and the convective zone.

1.6 Recognize the reactions of the ppI chain, check that given reactions purporting to be part of this chain are consistent with fundamental physical principles, and summarize the detailed reactions in terms of a simple overall reaction in which hydrogen is converted into helium with the release of energy and the emission of neutrinos.

1.7 Explain the role of solar neutrinos and solar oscillations in providing insight into the nature of the Sun's interior.

1.8 Describe various kinds of solar magnetic activity (including sunspots, flares and prominences) and outline the major features of the solar activity cycle. (Relates mainly to TV programme 1 and video sequence 2.)

List of scientific terms, concepts and principles used in Chapter 1

Term	Page	Term	Page	Term	Page
absorption lines	21	Hα image	17	relative spectral flux density	19
absorption spectrum	21	heavy elements	37	rest energy	41
black-body radiation curves	21	helioseismology	45	second law of thermodynamics	29
black-body sources	20	helium mass fraction	37	solar activity	11
chromosphere	17	hertz (Hz)	15	solar activity cycle	11
conduction	41	hydrogen mass fraction	37	solar flares	32
continuous spectra	19	ideal thermal sources	20	solar granulation	11
convection	41	infrared radiation	31	solar interior	36
convection cells	43	kinetic energy	41	solar limb	8
convection currents	41	limb darkening	8	solar luminosity	7
convective zone	44	local thermodynamic equilibrium	43	solar models	36
core	36	magnetic field	14	solar neutrinos	45
corona	17, 27	metallicity	37	solar rotation	10
coronagraph	27	microwaves	31	solar wind	34
coronal hole	34	neutrinos	39	spectral flux density	19
differential rotation	10	non-thermal sources	19	spectroscopy	19
electric field	14	photon model of light	15	spectrum	19
electromagnetic radiation	31	photons	15	speed of light in a vacuum	15
electromagnetic spectrum	31	photosphere	7	sunspots	8
electromagnetic wave model of light	15	plages	18	supergranulation	43
electromagnetic waves	14	Planck curves	21	thermal radiation curves	21
emission lines	22	Planck's constant	16	thermal sources	19
emission spectrum	22	plasma	38	total eclipse of the Sun	17
energy level diagram	22	positrons	39	transition region	27
filament	18	ppI chain	39	ultraviolet radiation	31
fractional radius	37	prominences	18	visible light	31
frequency	15	quantum theory	15	wavelength	15
gamma (γ) rays	31	radiation	42	white light image	17
global oscillations	45	radiative zone	44	Wien's displacement law	20
granules	11	radio waves	31	X-rays	31
Hα absorption line	23	random walk	43		

Chapter 2
Measuring the stars

Prepared for the Course Team by Barrie W. Jones

Contents

2.1 Introduction

The Sun, we have asserted, is a star. But all of the other stars are so far away that they appear as mere points of light in the sky, seemingly unchanging. And yet there have always been clues that the starry heavens are not as changeless as they appear to be. On rare occasions a new star will flare up in the sky, perhaps becoming visible in daylight, before fading in a few months back into invisibility. Such bright new stars are rare, and before the advent of the telescope in 1609, only ten or so had been recorded. Of particular importance was the one observed by the Danish astronomer Tycho Brahe ('Tie-co Bra-hay') (1546–1601) in 1572. Using the method of trigonometric parallax, which you will meet shortly, he was able to show that the new star lay beyond the Moon, thus overthrowing the then prevailing view that transient phenomena were confined to the volume of space closer to us than our satellite. So here was the first observational evidence that all regions of the cosmos are subject to change.

We now know that Tycho's new star was a **supernova,** which, as you will see in Chapter 4, is a star ending its life in a gigantic explosion. This has been established through painstaking studies, since Tycho's time, of the radiation from those points of light in the sky – we have catalogued the observable properties of the stars, and have thus deduced how stars of different mass evolve.

Massive stars are rare, and evolve quickly, particularly at the supernova stage. Earlier stages of their evolution, and the evolution of less massive stars, are usually too slow to be observed directly. We thus have to piece the evolution story together from observations of many stars of each particular type, at as many stages in each type's evolution as we can observe.

The observable properties are, however, almost entirely of *external* appearances and *external* events, and can take us only so far in revealing the evolution of the stars. To go further we must understand their interiors, and in Chapters 3 and 4 we shall be particularly concerned with how this understanding has been developed, and where it leads us in our understanding of stellar evolution. In this chapter, we shall be concerned with the essential preliminary step, namely measuring the observable properties of the stars, and the stellar menagerie that those measured properties reveal.

But before we look at the stars as bodies, what about the stars in space: how much farther away are the stars other than the Sun, and are the constellations really fixed?

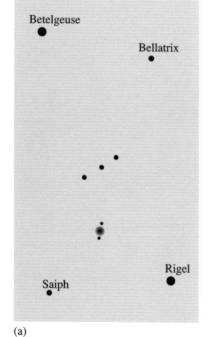

(a)

(b)

Figure 2.1 The patterns of the brighter stars in (a) Orion and (b) The Plough; the latter is part of a larger constellation called The Great Bear (Ursa Major, in Latin).

2.2 Stars in space

2.2.1 Are the stars fixed in space?

For thousands of years, and perhaps ever since the human species emerged on this planet, we have identified patterns in the stars – the constellations – and given them names. Today, we still use constellations that originated in antiquity, from the Romans and earlier, and Figure 2.1 shows the relative positions of the brighter stars in two of the better known: the constellation representing the mythological hunter Orion (see also Plate 1.15a) and, perhaps the best known of all, The Plough. How fixed are these patterns? Let's take The Plough as an example.

Figure 2.2a shows The Plough as it appeared to our ancestors 100 000 years ago, during the Old Stone Age. It certainly looks different. However, over a human lifespan the change is negligible. Thus, Figure 2.2b shows The Plough about 70 lifespans, or 5 000 years into the past, at the beginning of written history.

☐ Compare this with The Plough today, in Figure 2.1b. Do you think that, to the unaided eye, it would have been noticeably different 5 000 years ago?

■ Not to my eyes, though it would have been easier to find 5 000 years ago, when light pollution was a lot less!

Not surprisingly, it was a long time before such stellar motions were discovered, in 1718 by the British astronomer Edmond Halley (1656–1742). The motions continue, and Figure 2.2c shows The Plough as it will appear 100 000 years in the future.

The motion of a star across the sky is called its **proper motion**. It is usually expressed in seconds of arc per year, arcsec yr^{-1} (3 600 arcsec = 1 degree).

☐ What further information would need to be added to Figure 2.2 to enable you to calculate the proper motions?

■ A fixed reference point is needed, with zero proper motion. (In fact, *all* the stars shown happen to have non-zero proper motions, and all the values happen to lie within the rather narrow range of 0.087 arcsec yr^{-1} to 0.138 arcsec yr^{-1}, but in different directions across the sky.)

Currently, the proper motion record is held by Barnard's Star, a faint star with a proper motion of 10.3 arcsec yr^{-1}. By contrast, the bright star Albireo, in the constellation Cygnus, has a miniscule proper motion of only 0.002 arcsec yr^{-1}.

The proper motion of a star arises from its motion relative to us, in particular the component of its motion in a direction transverse to our line of sight to the star, as shown in Figure 2.3. This is called the **transverse velocity**. The magnitude of the transverse velocity, the transverse speed v_t, is given by

$$v_t = (p/\text{radians}) \times d \tag{2.1}$$

where p is the proper motion, d is the distance to the star, and where we have used the small angle approximation discussed in the mathematical appendix of *Preparatory science*. Thus, a small proper motion at a large distance can give a larger transverse speed than a large proper motion at a small distance. We shall discuss the measurement of stellar distances later, but v_t varies enormously, from under 1 km s^{-1} to well over 100 km s^{-1}. (For Barnard's star and Albireo, the values are 89 km s^{-1} and 1.1 km s^{-1}, respectively.)*

The remaining component of the star's motion relative to us is called its **radial velocity**. In Figure 2.3 it is directed away from the Earth, but it could equally well have been directed towards us. Unlike the transverse velocity, the radial velocity can be obtained without knowing the distance to the star. The method relies on the Doppler effect, which has many applications in astronomy. The Doppler effect is described in Box 2.1, which you should now read.

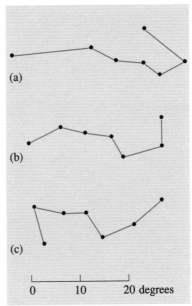

Figure 2.2 The Plough (a) 100 000 years ago, (b) 5 000 years ago, and (c) 100 000 years in the future.

---

* In the preceding paragraph we gave p in arcsec yr^{-1}, and now, via Equation 2.1, we have v_t in km s^{-1}. Let's follow this through. With p in arcsec yr^{-1} and d in km, Equation 2.1 gives v_t in (arcsec yr^{-1}/radians) km, or (arcsec/radians) km/yr. This is the same as (arcsec/radians)(s/yr) km s^{-1}. Because (arcsec/radians) and (s/yr) are both pure numbers, we get v_t in units of km s^{-1}. Note that (arcsec/radians) is the number of radians in a second of arc (1/206 265) and (s/yr) is the number of years in a second (1/(3.16 × 10^7)).

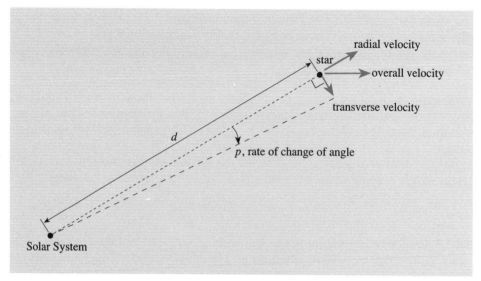

Figure 2.3 A star's motion through space, relative to the Sun.

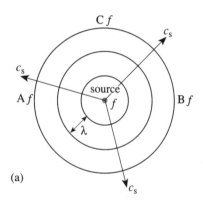

(a)

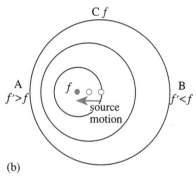

(b)

Figure 2.4 The Doppler effect with a car horn. (a) The car is stationary. (b) The car is in motion: an observer at A hears the horn at a higher pitch than the car driver; an observer at B hears it at a lower pitch than the driver; and an observer at C hears the it at the same pitch as the driver.

Box 2.1 The Doppler effect

The **Doppler effect** is named after the Austrian physicist Johann Christian Doppler (1803–1853). It is the name given to the observed change in frequency of the waves emitted by a source when it is moving with respect to the observer. It is familiar in the change in pitch of the sound received from a car horn as the car sweeps past. As the car approaches the pitch is higher – the frequency is higher; as the car recedes the pitch is lower – the frequency is lower.

Figure 2.4 shows how the Doppler effect arises. In Figure 2.4a the car is stationary with respect to the observers at A, B, and C. Its horn emits sound at a frequency f, and the sound waves spread out at the speed of sound, c_s, in the air. The circles are separated by one wavelength, λ, of the sound, given by

$$\lambda = c_s/f \qquad (2.2)$$

The observers at A, B, and C all hear the same frequency, f, as that emitted by the horn. There is no Doppler effect.

In Figure 2.4b the car is moving with respect to the observers, and again it emits sound at a frequency f. Once the sound is emitted it still travels away from the car through the air at the speed c_s, which is unchanged by the car's motion. Thus the motion of the car causes the waves to pile up ahead of it, giving rise to a decrease in wavelength at A, and hence (Equation 2.2) to an increase in frequency. Behind the car the waves are spread apart, giving rise to an increase in wavelength at B, and hence to a decrease in frequency. When the motion is perpendicular to the line from the car to the observer then there is no change in frequency: the observer at C hears the emitted frequency. The change in frequency thus requires that the velocity of the car has a component along the direction from the car to the observer, that is it requires a radial velocity: a transverse velocity produces no Doppler effect. It can be shown that the magnitude of the radial velocity is given by

$$v_r = c_s \times |f - f'|/f' \qquad (2.3)$$

where f' is the observed frequency. Thus, the Doppler effect provides us with a way to measure radial velocities. (The modulus sign, | |, ensures that v_r is positive, as must be the case for the magnitude of a vector – see Subsection 1.4.2 of *Preparatory science*.)

If a star behaves in any way like a car horn, then we can use the Doppler effect to obtain the radial velocity. A star does indeed have the equivalent of a horn – in the radiation that it emits. In Chapter 1 you learned that the solar spectrum exhibits many spectral lines. This is also the case for any stellar spectrum. A spectral line is like a car horn in that it corresponds to an emission or an absorption at a specific frequency. Moreover, we can identify the atomic transition giving rise to a spectral line, and thus we know the emitted frequency ('emitted' here covers absorption lines as well as emission lines). Therefore, if the frequency we observe differs from the emitted frequency, then from the size of the difference we can use Equation 2.3 (with the speed of light, c, in place of c_s) to obtain the radial speed, and from the sign of the difference we can tell whether the star is moving towards or away from us: we can thus obtain the radial velocity.*

In the case of stars, it is more usual to work in wavelengths rather than frequencies, using $\lambda = c/f$.

☐ If the observed wavelength is longer than the emitted wavelength, in which direction is the star moving?

■ It is moving away from us.

Increases in wavelength are called **red shifts**, from the days when observations at visible wavelengths dominated astronomy: at visible wavelengths an increase in wavelength takes us towards the red end of the spectrum. Likewise, decreases in wavelength are called **blue shifts**. These shifts are collectively called **Doppler shifts**.

Radial velocities are roughly of the same order as transverse velocities. The two velocities together specify the overall motion of the star through space with respect to us. These overall motions are not entirely random, but are partly systemized by the large-scale motions in our galaxy, which you will meet in Block 3, and by the grouping of many stars in clusters, which you will meet later in this Block. Indeed, whether a star belongs to a cluster can be decided by comparing its motion through space with that of the cluster members.

2.2.2 How far are the stars?

Throughout history, humanity has been fascinated by the question of how far away are the stars. What gulf of space separates the stars from the Sun? Are all the stars at the same distance? The stars are so remote that the measurements that provided definitive answers to these questions began to emerge only in the first half of the 19th century. In addition to helping us to establish cosmic architecture, we also need to know stellar distances in order to investigate the stars as individual bodies. For example, until their distances were known, no progress could be made on determining either the size of the stars, or how much energy they radiated. Thus, one star could appear to us to be much brighter than another simply because it is far closer.

So, how do we measure the distances to the stars? Of the several methods available, the one we shall describe was the first to yield a stellar distance, is still the most accurate for the nearer stars, and provides us with an important unit of distance widely used in astronomy.

Figure 2.5 illustrates the principle of the method. When the Earth is at point A in its orbit, the relatively nearby star appears as shown against the background of far more distant stars. Six months later, from point B, the position of the star against the distant background appears to have shifted. You can easily demonstrate this kind of shift to yourself by holding up a finger at arm's length in front of you, and viewing it against a distant background alternately with one eye and then the other. Try it now.

---

* For light (or any other form of electromagnetic radiation), Equation 2.3 is an approximation requiring $v \ll c$, a condition met by stellar radial speeds.

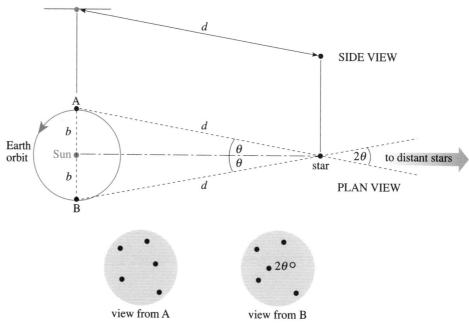

Figure 2.5 Trigonometric parallax.

Returning to the stars, from the apparent shift in position of the nearby star, the angle 2θ in Figure 2.5 is measured by an Earth-based observer, and the distance d to the star is then given by

$$d = b/(\theta/\text{radian})$$

where b is the distance from the Earth to the Sun, and where we have again used the small angle approximation, θ always being very small. Thus, if we know b then we can obtain d. The distance b can be obtained in a variety of ways, nowadays by measuring the times it takes radar pulses, which travel at the well-known speed of light, to return to the transmitter after being reflected off various bodies in the Solar System. The details will not concern us: the important point is that b is known, and therefore the distance d to the nearby star can be obtained. This method of obtaining stellar distances is called **trigonometric parallax**, this being the change in direction to an object as a result of a change in the position of the observer. In everyday parlance it is just called parallax.

So far, we have referred to *the* distance from the Earth to the Sun. In fact this distance varies slightly from point to point in the Earth's orbit. The average distance is called the **astronomical unit** (AU), and it has the value 1.50×10^{11} metres. The angle 2θ can easily be scaled to the value it would have had, had the distance between A and B in Figure 2.5 been 2AU rather than a slightly different value. This angle is written 2ϕ, where ϕ is the **stellar parallax** (often abbreviated to parallax), and it is related to θ by $\phi = \theta /(b/\text{AU})$. Thus, the above equation becomes

$$d = b/(\phi(b/\text{AU})/\text{radian})$$

and so

$$d/\text{AU} = 1/(\phi/\text{radian}) \tag{2.4}$$

The important unit of distance referred to earlier is the **parsec** (pc), defined as the distance d corresponding to a stellar parallax of 1 arcsec, as shown in Figure 2.6. Thus, by definition,

$$d/\text{pc} = 1/(\phi/\text{arcsec}) \tag{2.5}$$

With 206 265 arcsec in a radian, it is not too difficult to show, from Equations 2.4 and 2.5, that 1 pc = 206 265 AU.

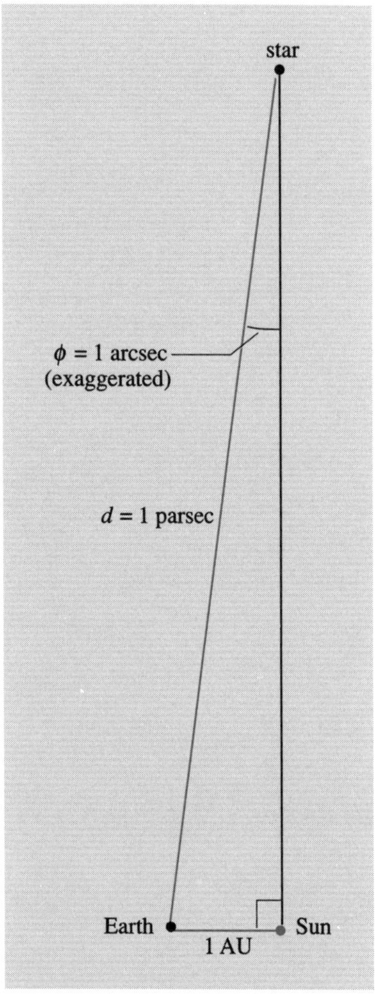

Figure 2.6 The definition of the parsec.

□ Is 'parsec' a reasonable name for this new unit?

■ Given that it is made up from *par*allax and arc*sec*, it *is* a reasonable name.

Stellar parallaxes are all very small. The first measurement was by the German scientist Friedrich Wilhelm Bessel (1784–1846) in 1838. He found the parallax of the star 61 Cygni ('sig-nee') to be (0.314 ± 0.020) arcsec*. This is a very small angle, 6 000 times smaller than the angular diameter of the Moon. It is therefore not surprising that science had to wait so long for this first parallax measurement. It gave us the first measurement of a distance to a star (other than the Sun).

ITQ 2.1 Calculate the distance to 61 Cygni, expressing your answer in parsecs, AU, and metres. How much farther away from us is 61 Cygni than the Sun?

The largest parallax is for the star Proxima Centauri, which is therefore the nearest star, though with a parallax of only 0.772 arcsec it is 1.295 pc away, which is nearly 270 000 times farther from us than the Sun. Clearly, a large gulf of space separates us from the stars. It's not that we are particularly isolated: the distances between the stars, at least in our part of the Milky Way, are generally of the same order as the distance to Proxima Centauri.

Table 2.1 lists the ten nearest stars after the Sun. From Earth-based observatories we can currently measure parallaxes for 30 or so stars with an uncertainty of about 0.002 arcsec, and for a few hundred stars with an uncertainty of not much better than about 0.01 arcsec. We thus obtain distances with useful accuracy for a few hundred stars, mostly within a range of about 100 pc. We can do far better from space, above the troublesome effects of the Earth's atmosphere. For example, the Hipparcos satellite, launched by the European Space Agency in 1989, is dedicated to the measurement of stellar positions with an accuracy not achievable on Earth. From these positions, the parallaxes of a large number of stars will be obtained, giving distances with reasonable accuracy out to about 500 pc. Moreover, ground-based developments are underway to counter atmospheric turbulence that should enable us to get to even greater distances. At present, the distances to nearly all stars beyond about 100 pc are obtained by other methods, one of which you will meet later in this chapter.

Table 2.1   The ten nearest stars after the Sun

Name	Parallax/arcsec	Distance		Comment[a]
		In parsecs	In light years	
Proxima Centauri	0.772	1.30	4.22	
α Centauri A	0.750	1.33	4.35	triple
α Centauri B	0.750	1.33	4.35	system
Barnard's Star	0.545	1.83	5.98	
Wolf 359	0.421	2.38	7.75	
BD + 36°2147	0.397	2.52	8.22	
L-726-8A	0.387	2.58	8.43	binary
L-726-8B	0.387	2.58	8.43	system
Sirius A	0.377	2.65	8.65	binary
Sirius B	0.377	2.65	8.65	system

[a] In a binary system, two stars are in orbit around each other. In a triple system there are three such stars.

* Some of the various conventions for naming stars are outlined in the *Project file*.

Finally, note that the parsec is not used solely to express the distances to the stars: it is commonly used to express *any* distance greater than the size of the Solar System. Another unit commonly used for such distances is the **light year** (ly), which is the distance that electromagnetic radiation would travel in a vacuum in a year, and is 0.307 pc. A table on the back cover of the *Introduction and Guide* gives the conversions between the various units of distance that you have now met.

Summary of Section 2.2 and SAQs

1   Stars move through space with velocities that we split into transverse and radial components. The magnitude of the transverse velocity is given by

$$v_t = (p/\text{radians}) \times d \tag{2.1}$$

where p is the proper motion. The magnitude of the radial velocity is given by

$$v_r = c \times |f - f'|/f'$$

The speeds with respect to the Sun range up to the order of hundreds of kilometres per second. The stars are so remote that transverse velocities produce changes to the familiar constellations that would be noticeable to the unaided eye only over periods of thousands of years.

2   Stellar distances were first measured using trigonometric parallax. The distance d is given by

$$d/\text{pc} = 1/(\phi/\text{arcsec}) \tag{2.5}$$

where ϕ is the stellar parallax. In this equation pc stands for parsec, an important unit of distance in astronomy.

3   The distances between the stars are of the order of a million times greater than the distance from the Earth to the Sun. The average distance from the Earth to the Sun is called the astronomical unit (AU).

4   Trigonometric parallax has yielded stellar distances with useful accuracy for a few hundred stars, mostly within a range of about 100 pc, but is now being extended to many more stars, out to 500 pc and beyond.

SAQ 2.1 (Objectives 2.2 and 2.3)   The bright star Procyon A ('pro-sigh-on') has a proper motion of 1.25 arcsec yr^{-1}, and a stellar parallax of 0.285 arcsec. Its spectral lines are blue-shifted.

(a)   Calculate how many years this star will take to travel an angular distance across the sky equal to the angular diameter of the Moon (0.5°).

(b)   Calculate its transverse speed, expressing your answer in km s^{-1}.

(c)   Is its radial velocity directed towards us, or away from us?

(d)   Why should the large proper motion of this star suggest that it should have a readily measurable parallax?

2.3   *The stars as bodies*

We come now to those measurable properties of the stars that enable us to investigate their interiors, and learn about their life cycles. By studying other stars we also learn a lot about the Sun's life cycle. Of the many properties that are measured, we shall be concerned in this Section only with size, temperature, brightness and composition. These alone are sufficient to reveal much about the stars. In a later Section we shall be concerned with measurements of stellar mass.

2.3.1 How big are the stars?

The Sun, you have seen, is a spherical body with a radius about 110 times that of the Earth. The volume ratio is a more impressive million or so. What of the other stars? Is there a great range of sizes? Is the Sun typical, or exceptionally small, or particularly large? Of one thing we can be certain: with a few readily identified exceptions, the stars are spherical, just as we expect for massive bodies dominated by their own gravity. Thus we can characterize size by radius.

For a star of known distance d, the most direct way to get the radius is to measure the angular diameter α. Then, as Figure 2.7 shows, the star's radius is given by

$$R = [(\alpha/2)/\text{radians}] \times d \qquad (2.6)$$

provided that α is small, which it certainly always is!

If we have a telescope that can show a star as a disc then we can measure α. Alas! this is possible for only those stars with particularly large values of α. This is because a telescope, even when looking at an object of *negligible* angular size, will produce an image that is not a point but a blur of finite size. Thus, a star has to have a sufficiently large angular diameter to produce an image with a size that considerably exceeds that of the point blur. This blur arises partly from turbulence in the Earth's atmosphere, and partly from fundamental optical limits that are more severe the smaller the main mirror or lens in the telescope. Modern techniques can overcome turbulence blur, and telescopes can be combined to make, in effect, a single large telescope. Using such techniques, the angular diameters of a few hundred stars have been measured, from the star with the largest angular diameter, namely Betelgeuse ('betel-jers'), prominent in Orion (Figure 2.1a and Plate 1.15a), with $\alpha = 0.050$ arcsec, down to as little as 0.0004 arcsec for ζ Puppis (Greek zeta) – equivalent to the width of a human hair at a distance of a few kilometres! (The value for Betelgeuse is so large that surface details have been imaged – see Plate 1.24.)

These measured values of α, multiplied by d as in Equation 2.6, have yielded stellar radii ranging from rather less than that of the Sun, to about 1 000 times greater. Thus there is a great range of stellar radii, and the Sun is a rather small star.

A few hundred stars are rather a small sample. However, there are other ways of obtaining stellar radii, and we shall meet one of these later in this chapter.

ITQ 2.2   Betelgeuse is about 160 pc away. Calculate its radius, in metres, and in solar radii.

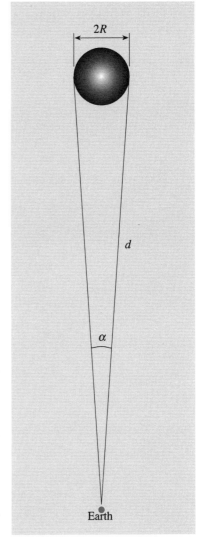

Figure 2.7   A star's angular diameter and radius.

Remember always to make appropriate use of the data on the back cover of the *Introduction and Guide*.

2.3.2 How hot are the stars?

You have seen in Chapter 1 that the radiation that we observe from the Sun originates largely from the photosphere, and that its distribution over wavelength – its spectrum – is close to that of a black body. If the distribution were *exactly* that of a black body then there would be a single temperature for the emitting region. Figure 2.8 shows some black-body spectra at different temperatures T in kelvin. The Sun's spectrum is not exactly that of a black body, and so we cannot give the photosphere a unique temperature. However, the spectrum at 5 770 K in Figure 2.8 is a good fit to the solar spectrum, which means that the temperature of the source of the photospheric radiation is nowhere enormously different from 5 770 K. Thus the radiation from the Sun comes largely from a region with a temperature around 5 770 K. This is the Sun's 'surface' temperature.

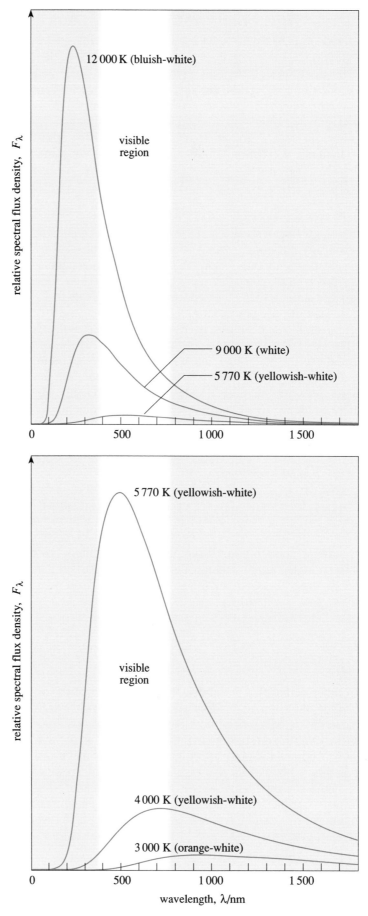

Figure 2.8 Black-body spectra at different temperatures. Each source is of the same size, and at the same distance from the detector that measures the flux density. Note that the vertical scale for the upper set of spectra is greatly elongated compared with that for the lower set.

60

The other stars, too, have spectra that are not very different from black-body spectra. Therefore we can obtain meaningful photospheric temperatures from well-fitting black-body spectra. A crude way of doing this is from the star colour that we perceive: from Figure 2.8 we see that white and bluish-white stars are hotter than the yellowish-white Sun, and orange-white stars are cooler than the Sun. A better way is to compare the radiation that the star emits at two different wavelengths, as you saw for the Sun in SAQ 1.5, or over two different wavelength *ranges*, as illustrated in Figure 2.9. From such a comparison, we can obtain the temperature of the photosphere. This is the basis of the **photometric method** of temperature determination. Note that we do not need to measure the complete spectrum: one ratio suffices.

However, for many individual stars, more accurate values of photospheric temperatures are obtained by the **spectrometric method**, which is based on examination of the spectral absorption lines in starlight. The lines of interest are those formed, as in the Sun, by absorption in the star's upper photosphere and in the region just above it. For example, consider the hydrogen **Balmer absorption lines**. This is the name of the group of lines that you met in Chapter 1, with the individual labels Hα, Hβ, Hγ, and so on. They correspond to the electron transitions in the hydrogen atom shown in Figure 2.10. For all the Balmer lines the lower energy level is that for which $n = 2$. If the temperature is very low, then nearly all the electrons are in the $n = 1$ level, and the Balmer lines are very weak. If, on the other hand, the temperature is very high, then nearly all the hydrogen atoms are ionized, and the lines are again weak. The variation of line strength with temperature is shown schematically in Figure 2.11.

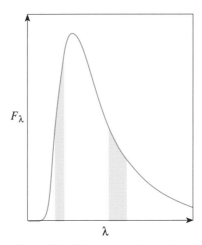

Figure 2.9 The photometric method of obtaining photospheric temperatures.

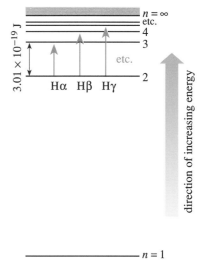

Figure 2.10 Electron transitions for the hydrogen Balmer absorption lines.

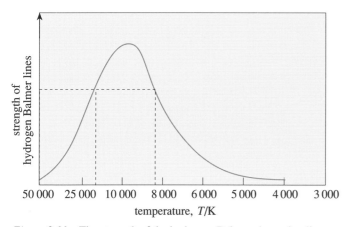

Figure 2.11 The strength of the hydrogen Balmer absorption lines versus photospheric temperature.

Clearly there is a basis here for measuring temperature. However, there are two difficulties. Figure 2.11 indicates one of them.

☐ What is this first difficulty?

■ A given line strength corresponds to two temperatures.

Thus, a very hot and a very cool star will have Balmer lines of similar weakness. We overcome this difficulty by observing other absorption lines that, like the hydrogen Balmer lines, are also particularly sensitive to temperature, but which have a different variation of strength with temperature from that of the hydrogen Balmer lines. Figure 2.12 shows schematically a collection of such line strengths.

☐ On the basis of Figure 2.12, what is the temperature of a star for which the hydrogen Balmer and (unspecified) helium lines have equal strength?

■ About 20 000 K.

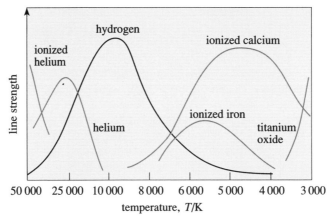

Figure 2.12 The strengths of various absorption lines versus photospheric temperature.

The second difficulty is that the strengths of the various lines are also sensitive to the elemental abundances. Clearly, we are not going to get any calcium lines at *any* temperature if there is no calcium present. We overcome this difficulty from spectral studies that reveal the composition of the region from which the absorption lines originate (Subsection 2.3.5). The elements chosen for temperature measurements are those that do not exhibit large variations in abundance from star to star.

With these and other difficulties overcome, the spectrometric method of obtaining photospheric temperatures was well established by the 1920s, mainly through the efforts of the US astronomer Annie Jump Cannon (1863–1941) at Harvard University. On the basis of the strengths of their spectral lines, stellar spectra were classified by letter in a scheme called the **Harvard Spectral Classification**. Originally, spectra were sorted into groups labelled A to Q. Later, some of the groups were dropped, some were merged with others, and the remainder were ordered according to temperature, to give the scheme widely used today. In order of descending temperature the spectral classes are labelled O B A F G K M, which you should remember: a useful mnemonic is '*O*h *B*other, *A*n *F* *G*rade *K*ills *M*e!'. The classes B to M are subdivided 0, 1......9, with 0 at the hotter end. For example, F9 and G0 are spectral classes of stars that are not very different in temperature. Class O is (perversely) subdivided 5, 6, 7, 8, 9, 9.5(!), with 5 at the hotter end. Table 2.2 gives the temperatures around the *middle* of each class.

☐ On the basis of the strengths of its spectral lines, the Sun is placed in spectral class G2. Is the corresponding temperature consistent with the value given earlier?

■ From Table 2.2, G2 corresponds to a temperature of about 6 000 K, which is consistent with the value of 5 770 K given earlier.

You should have seen these star colours in the project *In and around Orion*

Stars are found across the full range of spectral classes in Table 2.2, and so the Sun is not a particularly hot star. Far hotter is the bluish-white star Rigel A ('rye-jel' A), in the constellation Orion, which has a spectral class B8. (Rigel B and C are faint companion stars.) Somewhat cooler than the Sun is Betelgeuse, which has a spectral class M2, and looks orange-white.

Table 2.2 Temperatures of stars around the middle of each spectral class

Spectral class	O	B	A	F	G	K	M
Temperature/K	40 000	17 000	9 000	7 000	5 500	4 500	3 000

☐ Make a rough estimate of the temperatures of Rigel A and Betelgeuse.

■ The approximate values are 13 000 K for Rigel A and 3 500 K for Betelgeuse.

Figure 2.13 shows a few stellar absorption spectra belonging to various spectral classes, in the form of graphs of relative spectral flux density (Subsection 1.3.2) versus wavelength: these are the sort of quantitative spectra now used to establish spectral class, and hence temperature. If we can establish a star's subclass, then we can determine its average photospheric temperature with an uncertainty of only about 5%.

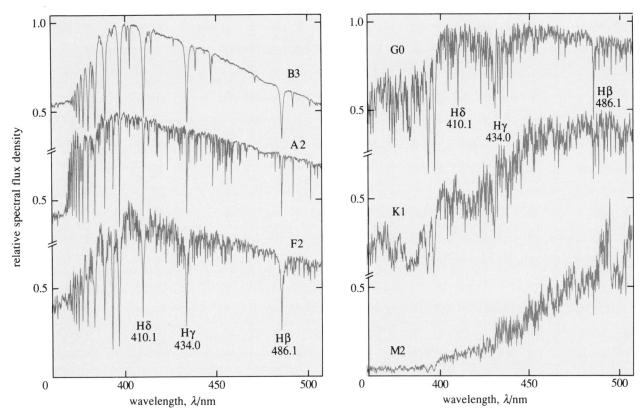

Figure 2.13 Graphs of stellar absorption spectra for different spectral classes.

ITQ 2.3 From Figure 2.12 and Table 2.2, which spectral classes have weak hydrogen Balmer lines, and what are the corresponding temperatures?

2.3.3 How bright are the stars?

By stellar brightness we mean the total amount of power a star radiates into space, over all wavelengths. This is called the **luminosity**, L, which in SI units is measured in watts. In Chapter 1 you saw that the Sun's luminosity is 3.84×10^{26} W, enormous by terrestrial standards, but how does it compare with the other stars?

The luminosity of a star depends on two of its properties that we have already met.

☐ What do you think these properties are?

■ The two properties are radius and temperature.

On the basis of everyday experience this is reasonable: as a ball of steel goes from red-hot to yellow-hot to white-hot it glows more brightly, and a pinhead of hot steel would radiate less power than a cannon ball of steel at the same temperature. We can readily develop a quantitative relationship between luminosity, radius, and temperature, because, just like the Sun (Chapter 1), any star radiates rather like a black body.

The power l radiated by unit area of a black body at an absolute temperature T (such as the kelvin scale) can be shown to be given by the simple equation $l = \sigma T^4$, where σ is called **Stefan's constant**: in SI units, σ has the value $5.67 \times 10^{-8}\,\mathrm{W\,m^{-2}\,K^{-4}}$. For a star, we have the approximation $l \simeq \sigma T^4$, where T is the average photospheric temperature. We can take a star to be spherical, and therefore its surface area is $4\pi R^2$, where R is the radius of the star. Thus the power emitted by the whole surface – the luminosity – is given by

$$L \simeq 4\pi R^2 \sigma T^4 \tag{2.7}$$

Therefore, if we know a star's radius and temperature then we can obtain its luminosity.

☐ Can you see any problem with this approach?

■ In Subsection 2.3.1 you saw that only a few hundred stars have had their radii measured. Therefore, this approach can yield the luminosities of only a few stars.

Fortunately, stellar spectrometry rides to the rescue! In the early years of this century, astronomers compared the spectra of stars with similar temperatures but different luminosities, the luminosities having been obtained non-spectrometrically. They found that, *at a given temperature,* the more luminous the star the narrower its spectral absorption lines, and the stronger the absorption lines due to certain ionized atoms. Figure 2.14a illustrates the difference between the strength and the narrowness of an absorption line. First, recall from Chapter 1 that an absorption line is not infinitely thin, but covers a narrow range of wavelengths. A line thus has an area, as indicated in Figure 2.14a, and this area is a measure of the strength of the line: the greater the area, the greater the strength. By contrast, the narrowness of a spectral line is simply a measure of the range of wavelengths that it covers: the smaller the range the narrower the line, and the greater the range the wider the line. In Figure 2.14a the two lines have the same strengths (areas), but different widths. Figure 2.14b shows a real example.

The reasons for these effects of luminosity on linewidth, and on the strengths of certain ion lines, are understood, but the important point for us here is that as soon as astronomers had correlated luminosity with such spectral features, then for stars of unknown luminosity these spectral features could be used to determine their luminosity.

Using this spectrometric method, many stellar luminosities have been measured, and they cover an *enormous* range, from less than 10^{-4} times that of the Sun, to over 10^6 times the solar value. Thus, the Sun is a comparatively dim star. Most of the stars that we see with the unaided eye are more luminous than the Sun: for example, Rigel A and Betelgeuse are over 10^5 times as luminous.

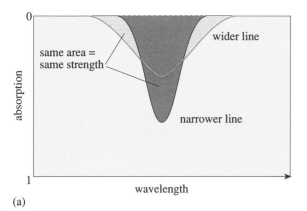

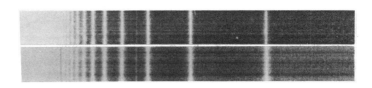

Figure 2.14 The effect of stellar luminosity on spectral linewidth: (a) graphical representation; (b) a real example, where the upper spectrum is for a giant star and the lower for a main sequence star at the same temperature; note that these are *negatives* of photographs, so that the absorption lines appear bright on a dark background.

This is not because bright stars are common – in fact they are not – but because if dim stars, such as the Sun, are beyond about 20 pc, they are visible only through a telescope!

Note that the effect of luminosity on the strength of lines due to certain ionized atoms means that spectral classification can be influenced by luminosity as well as temperature: remember that spectral classification depends on the strengths of various spectral lines, including lines from ionized atoms. Fortunately, over a wide range of luminosities, the effect of luminosity is a good deal less than the effect of temperature. Moreover, the effect of luminosity on spectral class can be allowed for. Thus the evaluation of temperature on the basis of spectral line strengths is not undermined by the effect of luminosity.

ITQ 2.4 You have seen that the temperature and luminosity of a star can both be obtained spectrometrically. This gives us a new way of obtaining stellar radius. Explain what this new way is, and apply it to obtain the radius of Aldebaran B, the faint companion of Aldebaran A. For Aldebaran B, $T = 3\,400$ K and $L = 0.06L_\odot$, where $L_\odot$ is the solar luminosity. Express your answer in solar radii.

Not only do we now have a new way of obtaining radius, we also have a new, and very important way of obtaining distance. This is the subject of the next subsection.

2.3.4 Distance, again

You will know that if you want to read a book at night, then the closer you hold the book to the source of light the greater the illumination. In more scientific terms, for a source of given luminosity, the closer the source to a surface facing it, the greater the flux density on the surface. **Flux density**, F, is the rate at which energy from a source crosses unit area facing the source.

☐ How does it differ from spectral flux density, defined in Chapter 1?

■ Spectral flux density is the rate within a narrow wavelength range, divided by the width of the range.

The physical units of flux density are power per unit area, which in SI units is watts per square metre.

By measuring the flux density received from a star of known luminosity L, we can obtain a value for the distance d from the star to the Earth. Moreover, the

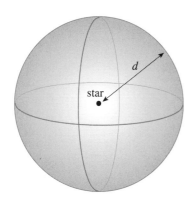

Figure 2.15 A spherical surface, radius *d*, centred on a star.

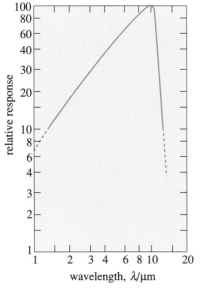

Figure 2.16 The spectral response of an infrared detector.

method works for distances that extend well beyond the limit for trigonometric parallax. The method is as follows.

At a distance *d* from the star, its luminosity *L* is spread over a sphere of area $4\pi d^2$, as in Figure 2.15. For all practical purposes a star can be considered to radiate uniformly in all directions. Thus, at any point on the sphere the flux density is given by

$$F = L/(4\pi d^2) \qquad (2.8)$$

We have assumed that the effects of interstellar matter between the star and the point where *F* is measured are negligible. Thus, if we measure *F* and *L*, then we can obtain *d* from a straightforward rearrangement of Equation 2.8, namely

$$d = [L/(4\pi F)]^{1/2} \qquad (2.9)$$

If we obtain *L* spectrometrically, then this is called the method of **spectroscopic parallax** for obtaining stellar distances, a perverse name, given that it has nothing to do with the method of trigonometric parallax outlined earlier!

In practice, it is very difficult to measure *F*. One reason for this is the limited spectral range over which any one flux detector will respond. For example, the response of the infrared detector shown in Figure 2.16 is useful only over the approximate wavelength range (waveband) from 1 μm to 13 μm. We therefore require a great range of detectors, coupled to suitable telescopes, to measure *F* over the full wavelength range. There is a further difficulty in measuring *F* if we make measurements from the Earth's surface: the Earth's atmosphere is not perfectly transparent to any wavelengths, and is opaque to many, as you saw in Figure 1.25. The best we can do is to make measurements over the more transparent wavebands, and apply corrections to obtain the flux density values that we would have obtained at the top of the atmosphere.

ITQ 2.5 List the more transparent wavebands in the Earth's atmosphere.

We can avoid these difficulties if we can make do with flux density measurements over limited wavelength ranges. We can indeed do so: moreover, a single waveband suffices. Let's illustrate the approach by selecting one often-used waveband – the V band (or V channel). Any V-band detector has the well-defined spectral response shown in Figure 2.17: it approximates the spectral response of human vision, hence the label 'V', for visual. All stars emit a significant fraction of their luminosity in the V band, and the Earth's atmosphere can be very transparent at these wavelengths. Thus we can readily obtain the flux density F_V, where the subscript V indicates that the flux density has been measured with a detector that has the spectral response of the V band.

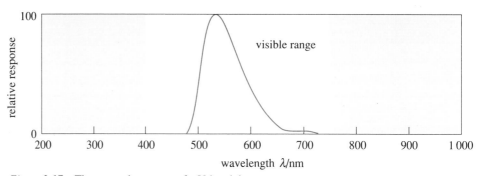

Figure 2.17 The spectral response of a V-band detector.

To obtain the distance we make use of Equation 2.9, which applies not only to the whole output of a star, but also to any part of it. In the particular case of the V band, Equation 2.9 becomes

$$d = [L_V/(4\pi F_V)]^{1/2} \qquad (2.10)$$

If we measure F_V, then to obtain the star's distance d we only further need to know L_V. If we know a star's surface temperature and luminosity, L, then L_V is readily obtained from L: we apply the spectral response in Figure 2.17 to the spectrum of a black body at the star's temperature. For the Sun, $L_V = 4.44 \times 10^{25}$ W: you can check that this is reasonable by comparing Figure 2.17 with the 5 770 K curve in Figure 2.8, remembering that $L_\odot = 3.84 \times 10^{26}$ W.

This illustrates the general idea of the method of spectroscopic parallax for obtaining stellar distances. The method is subject to error, in that F_V can be reduced by interstellar matter. Even in the absence of such a reduction, or if a correction is applied for it, the distance is rather uncertain, because the luminosity obtained from spectral lines is itself uncertain. However, the method can provide reasonable estimates of the distances to very bright stars well beyond those that we can obtain at present from trigonometric parallax, and it is therefore an important method of distance determination.

ITQ 2.6 The star ι^1 (Greek iota) Scorpio has $F_V = 4.4 \times 10^{-10}$ W m^{-2} (after correction for reduction by interstellar matter) and $L_V = 6.1 \times 10^{30}$ W. Calculate the distance to this star, expressing your answer in parsecs. To the eye, ι^1 Scorpio does not seem very bright. Given that its apparent brightness is not much reduced by interstellar matter, is it in fact a bright star at a large distance?

Magnitudes

If you were to look up a table of stellar properties, you would not find F_V and L_V, but closely related quantities called, respectively, apparent and absolute visual magnitudes. Figure 2.18 shows the relationship between F_V and the **apparent visual magnitude**, V. Note that as F_V increases V decreases, and that F_V is on a logarithmic scale. Why should astronomers not simply use F_V? It is part of the burden of history, dating back to antiquity, and particularly to the Greek astronomer Hipparchus (before 160 BC to after 127 BC). He classified the stars according to their visual brightness, the brightest stars being of first magnitude, the faintest of sixth magnitude, the ones between being placed according to their brightness into an appropriate intermediate magnitude. European astronomers used and refined this system right through to the appearance in the nineteenth century of detectors that could measure F_V. Subsequently, instead of abandoning V, astronomers have set up the precise relationship in Figure 2.18, and quote V rather than F_V. Of course, for exploring the sky visually, V is a most appropriate measure of stellar brightness.

The value of F_V, and therefore of V, is not an intrinsic property of a star, but depends on the distance to the star, and on the effects of any intervening interstellar material. By contrast, L_V *is* an intrinsic property. Likewise, the **absolute visual magnitude**, M_V, is also an intrinsic property: it is the value of V that would be obtained at the standard distance of 10 pc from a star, in the absence of any interstellar matter. In this Course we shall make little use of magnitudes, preferring instead luminosities and flux densities.

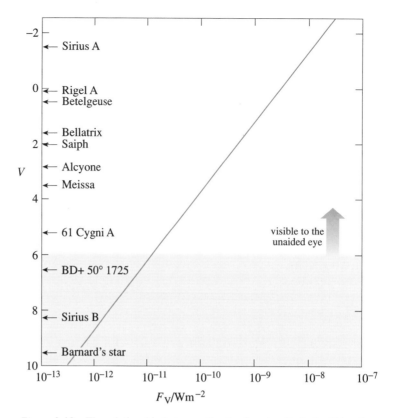

Figure 2.18 The relationship between F_V, the flux density in the V band, and apparent visual magnitude V. Approximate values of V are indicated for a number of stars.

2.3.5 What are the stars made of?

We come now to the final property of individual stars that we shall consider before we start on a comparison of the stars with each other. This is their chemical composition, by which we mean the relative abundances of the chemical elements that make up a star.

The familiar world around us is dominated by certain chemical elements. Thus, the atmosphere consists mainly of oxygen and nitrogen, rocks and soil consist mainly of compounds of silicon and oxygen with metals such as calcium, aluminium, magnesium and iron, and the oceans consist almost entirely of water, a compound of two atoms of hydrogen with one atom of oxygen. The Earth as a whole is made up largely of the elements iron, silicon, oxygen and magnesium, all but iron being present mostly in compounds.

When we turn to the stars, we are looking at a much larger sample of the cosmos than that provided by the Earth, and we find that the stars are very different from the Earth in their composition. Though they do contain the sort of elements that dominate the Earth, stellar compositions are dominated by two elements that are but *minor* constituents of our planet, namely hydrogen and helium. Before we look more closely at stellar composition, let's consider briefly how it is measured.

Stellar compositions are obtained from studies of the spectral absorption lines in stellar atmospheres. If we can see the lines of a certain element then we can conclude that the element is present. But how much of it is there? The strength of a single absorption line is *not* a good guide.

☐ Why not?

■ Line strength is sensitive to temperature – see Subsection 2.3.2.

However, we can obtain the amount of an element present by comparing the absorption line strengths of different lines from the element, and it helps if lines are observed not only from the neutral element, but also from the ionized element. The great range of wavelengths covered by the various elements, particularly when we include their ionized forms, led to an enormous flood of data in the second half of the twentieth century with the advent of infrared and ultraviolet astronomy. Thus, today we have very extensive knowlege of the compositions of the atmospheres of many stars.

ITQ 2.7 Use is made of more than one absorption line in obtaining *temperature*. In what way does this procedure differ from the one to obtain *composition*, where more than one line is again used?

We shall not go into further details of how stellar compositions are obtained, except to note that today spectrometry is used to obtain composition, temperature and luminosity in not quite such a separate manner as implied above. Instead, a model is constructed of a stellar atmosphere, and the composition, temperature and luminosity in the model are adjusted simultaneously until the model reproduces the great range of observed line strengths and line shapes of all the various elements.

Turning to the results, we find that stellar atmospheres are largely made up of hydrogen, with remarkably small variations from star to star. For a star of average composition, like the Sun, 73% of the mass of the atmosphere consists of hydrogen. This is the lightest element, and so its dominance is even more impressive when expressed in terms of the percentage of nuclei, rather than of mass: 92% of the nuclei are hydrogen. Next comes helium, the next lightest element, at 25% by mass and 7.8% by number. If you add the hydrogen and helium figures together you will see that there is not a whole lot left for the 90 or so heavy elements (atomic number more than 2) – only about 2% by mass and 0.2% by number!

It is important to realize that these measurements are for stellar atmospheres, and so the question arises of whether they are typical for whole stars. Here we have to appeal to stellar modelling, where the model has to reproduce the observed properties: the modelling procedure is similar to that for the Sun, outlined in Subsection 1.5.2. We find that, except for the cores of stars where considerable nuclear fusion has presumably occurred, stellar interiors are indeed dominated by hydrogen and helium, the above values being typical for most stars. Among the heavy elements considerable variations do occur, though among many stars there are still remarkable similarities.

A standard stellar composition has been defined, based on the Sun outside its core and on the composition of a particular class of meteorites – small bodies that reach the Earth's surface from interplanetary space. The class in question is thought to have changed little since the origin of the Solar System, and is the carbonaceous chondrites, to be discussed in Block 2. The standard composition is thus that of the material from which the Solar System formed, and it is called, rather grandly, the **cosmic relative abundances of the elements**. Figure 2.19 shows the broad features, and the full details are given in the Appendix (p.90).

ITQ 2.8 From the Appendix, what are the ten most abundant elements by number of nuclei, and by mass?

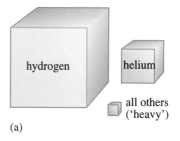
(a)

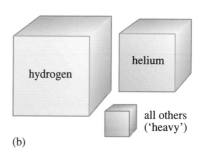
(b)

Figure 2.19 The cosmic relative abundances of the elements (a) by relative numbers of atomic nuclei and (b) by relative mass.

Stellar radius

1   The stars with the greatest angular diameters as seen from the Earth can have their angular diameters α directly measured. The stellar radius is then given by

$$R = [(\alpha/2)/\text{radians}] \times d \qquad (2.6)$$

where d is the distance to the star.

2   If, for a star, we know its luminosity L, and its photospheric temperature T, then the radius is given by

$$R \simeq [L/(4\pi\sigma T^4)]^{1/2} \qquad (\text{ITQ } 2.4)$$

The approximation sign arises because a star's spectrum is not quite that of a black body.

Photospheric temperature

Photospheric temperature can be obtained by comparing the flux density that we receive from a star in two different wavebands – this is the basis of the photometric method. However, for most stars a better method is to use the strengths of various absorption lines produced by different elements in, and just above, the photosphere. From these lines, a star is assigned to one of the spectral classes O, B, A, F, G, K, and M, and then to one of the subclasses. The average photospheric temperature is then obtained from the relationship between subclass and temperature. This is the spectrometric method.

Stellar luminosity

1   If we know the radius and temperature of a star, then its luminosity can be obtained from

$$L \simeq 4\pi R^2 \sigma T^4 \qquad (2.7)$$

2   The luminosity of a star can be estimated from the width of its absorption lines, and from the strength of the absorption lines of certain ions. To apply this spectrometric method, we do not need to know the star's radius, but we do need to know its temperature.

Stellar distance

From L and T we can obtain the luminosity L_V in the V (visual) waveband. We can readily measure the flux density F_V that we receive from the star in this band, and therefore the distance is given by

$$d = [L_V/(4\pi F_V)]^{1/2} \qquad (2.10)$$

Sometimes it is necessary to correct F_V for the effects of interstellar matter before applying Equation 2.10.

Stellar composition

1   The great majority of stars, apart from those in which considerable nuclear fusion has occurred, consist mainly of the two lightest elements, hydrogen and helium. The Sun is fairly typical, with the following composition outside its core:

hydrogen: 73% by mass, 92% by number of nuclei

helium: 25% by mass, 7.8% by number of nuclei

2 The composition of the Sun, excluding its core, and that of a class of meteorites called carbonaceous chondrites, define a standard composition called the cosmic relative abundances of the elements. These are given in the Appendix.

SAQ 2.2 (Objectives 2.3–2.6) This question is about the star Rigel A, the prominent bluish-white star in the constellation Orion.

(a) From its spectral class, B8, Rigel A is given a photospheric temperature of 13 000 K. Is this reasonable? How strong are the hydrogen Balmer lines compared with the helium lines, and with the lines of ionized helium and ionized calcium?

(b) Spectroscopic studies lead to an estimate of $1.4 \times 10^5 L_\odot$ for its luminosity. How do its spectral lines differ from those of a far less luminous star of the same temperature?

(c) Calculate its radius, expressing your answer in solar radii.

(d) From its luminosity and photospheric temperature, use Figures 2.8 and 2.17 to make a *rough* estimate of its luminosity, L_V, in the V waveband. Hence estimate its distance, given that $F_V = 3.0 \times 10^{-9}\,\mathrm{W\,m^{-2}}$.

(e) Would it have been feasible to obtain its radius from its angular diameter, as measured from the Earth?

SAQ 2.3 (Objective 2.7) From the Appendix, plot a graph of cosmic relative abundance by mass, versus atomic number Z, for the heavy elements as far as Z = 30, using a linear scale on the abundance axis extending from 0 to a suitable upper limit. (Some of the abundances will be too small to show.) Hence describe briefly the relationship between cosmic relative abundance and Z.

2.4 Comparing stars: the Hertzsprung–Russell diagram

So far, we have been largely concerned with the individual properties of individual stars, in particular photospheric temperature, luminosity, radius and composition. We learn a lot more about the stars if we compare them, but what should be the basis of our comparison? We certainly want to use *intrinsic* properties, such as luminosity, and not properties that depend on the distance to the star, such as the flux density received on Earth. Also, as an initial step, we want to avoid properties that are well removed from what we actually observe. Three properties admirably suitable for our comparison are temperature, luminosity and radius. However, we don't need all three.

☐ Why not?

■ They are related, via Equation 2.7. Thus, if we know any two, we can obtain the third.

Temperature and luminosity are more directly measurable for a far greater number of stars than radius, and so it is these two properties that are used, as shown in Figure 2.20. Each point displays the temperature and luminosity of a particular star: you should check that the values given for the Sun are in accord with the values given earlier. *Note the logarithmic scales on both axes, and that temperature increases to the left.*

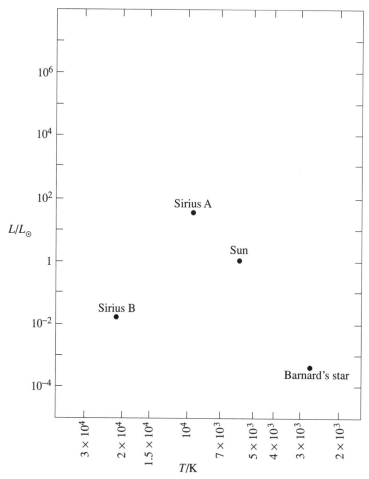

Figure 2.20   The Hertzsprung–Russell diagram for the Sun and a few nearby stars.

Such a diagram is called a **Hertzsprung–Russell diagram**, or H–R diagram, after the Danish astronomer Ejnar Hertzsprung (1873–1967), and the US astronomer Henry Norris Russell (1877–1957). *The H–R diagram is the most important diagram in stellar astronomy.*

ITQ 2.9   Where, in the H–R diagram, do the following types of star appear: hot, high luminosity stars; hot, low luminosity stars; cool, low luminosity stars; cool, high luminosity stars?

The H–R diagram in Figure 2.20 contains too few stars to give us an overall picture. Before we examine a diagram containing many more stars we can speculate on what we might find. Will we find that the stars are fairly uniformly peppered over the diagram, with, for example, as many hot, high luminosity stars as any other kind? Or will we find that certain combinations of luminosity and temperature are more common than others? Emphatically the latter case, as Figure 2.21 shows. The shaded regions show where stars tend to concentrate: the darker the shading, the greater the concentration. The concentrations are really quite striking, and are something that our theories of stellar evolution in Chapters 3 and 4 have to account for. Each concentration defines a particular class of stars, and we shall shortly examine each main class in more detail, but first let's add stellar radius to Figure 2.21.

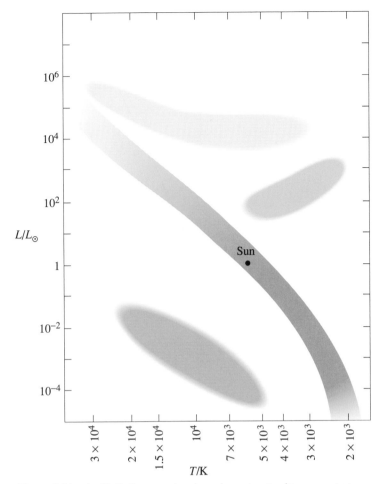

Figure 2.21　An H–R diagram, showing where stars tend to concentrate.

From the relationship between radius, temperature and luminosity in Equation 2.7, we see that at each point in the H–R diagram there is a unique stellar radius, given by $R = [L/(4\pi\sigma T^4)]^{1/2}$. Let's now add to the diagram lines of constant radius. For example, consider stars with a radius equal to that of the Sun, $R_\odot$. From Equation 2.7 we see that any other star with the same radius will have its luminosity and temperature related by

$$L \simeq (4\pi R_\odot^2 \sigma)T^4 \qquad (2.11)$$

Thus, as T increases, L also increases: for a given radius, the hotter the star the more power it radiates. With T increasing to the left in the H–R diagram, this gives a line sloping upwards from lower right to upper left, as in Figure 2.22.

The line is actually straight! This is a consequence of the log scales used, though here we are interested only in the result, and not in the details of how the straightness comes about. Figure 2.23 is the H–R diagram in Figure 2.21 with several lines of constant radius added, and you can see that there are some classes of stars that are considerably smaller and some that are considerably larger than the Sun. These relative sizes are reflected in the names given to many of the classes, as shown in Figure 2.23, names with a fairy-tale quality, like white dwarfs, red giants, supergiants. As you might expect, white dwarfs are small, red giants are large, and supergiants even larger. Some relative stellar sizes are illustrated in Plate 1.23.

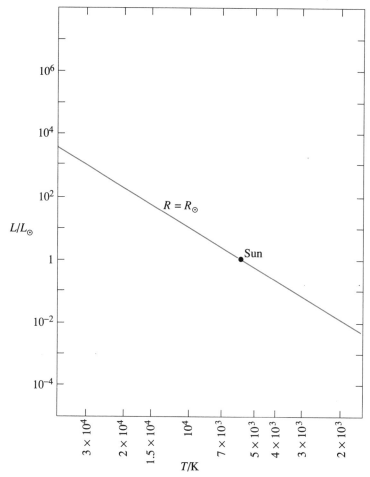

Figure 2.22 An H–R diagram showing where stars of solar radius lie.

ITQ 2.10 In terms of the Earth's radius, and the Earth's distance from the Sun, how large are white dwarfs and red giants?

The class names are descriptive in ways other than size.

☐ Why *white* dwarfs, *red* giants?

■ White dwarfs have temperatures that are centred on white, extending from yellowish-white to bluish-white. Red giants have tints towards the red end of the visible spectrum, embracing orange-white and yellowish-white.

We have added to Figure 2.23 an indication of the colour associated with each temperature. However, to the unaided eye, star colours are in many cases not very striking. This is partly because too little light is being received for our colour vision to be strongly excited, and partly because the colours are, in any case, rather weak. However, star colours can be emphasized photographically, as in Plate 1.14.

Let's now look at the main classes of stars in more detail.

2.4.1 The main classes of stars

The main classes of stars are shown in Figure 2.23.

The **main sequence** is 'main' in the sense that about 90% of stars fall into this class, and 'sequence' in the sense that it is a long, thin region that trails across the H–R diagram, covering a very wide range of temperatures and luminosities. The Sun is a main sequence star, of very modest temperature and luminosity, and correspondingly modest radius (Figure 2.23). It is yellowish-white. Sirius A is a main sequence star rather hotter than the Sun, and appears bluish-white to the eye. In the sky it is south east of Orion, and has the greatest apparent visual brightness of any star in the sky. This is not because it is very luminous, but because it is both fairly luminous and rather close, at 2.65 pc the ninth closest star after the Sun (Table 2.1).

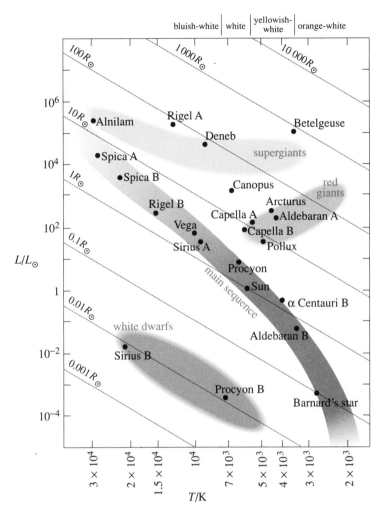

Figure 2.23 The H–R diagram in Figure 2.21, with the addition of stellar radii, and other information.

Above the lower part of the main sequence we come first to the **red giants**. These stars are cool, hence their orange tinge, and are of order 10 to 100 times larger in radius than main sequence stars of comparable temperatures. Thus were our Sun a large red giant, it would extend a considerable distance towards the Earth (ITQ 2.10)!

☐ If you knew that a red giant was larger than a main sequence star of comparable temperature, what could you say about its luminosity?

■ From Equation 2.7 we could say that its luminosity is greater than that of the main sequence star. (This conclusion is borne out by Figure 2.23.)

The star Dubhe ('doob-ay') in The Plough (Figure 2.1b) is a red giant. (It's actually two stars close together, but the red giant is dominant.)

Above and to the left of the red giants we come to the **supergiants**. These are larger, and thus more luminous than red giants of comparable temperature, but they also extend to higher temperatures, where they are larger and more luminous than main sequence stars of comparable temperature. Rigel A is a hot supergiant, which, as you might have seen in the project work, appears bluish-white to the eye. Betelgeuse is a cooler supergiant, and you might have seen that it appears distinctly orange-white.

Though we have not delineated it on Figure 2.23, there is a class of stars that comprises the red giants plus the stars to their left that lie between the main sequence and the supergiants. These are the **giants**. In later chapters we shall often refer to this class, which is broader than that of *red* giants alone.

You can see from Figure 2.23 that **white dwarfs** are, as their name implies, hot, and, as their name also implies, small, only about the size of the Earth (ITQ 2.10). Consequently their luminosities are low. Indeed, there are no white dwarfs sufficiently close to us to be visible to the unaided eye. The closest is Sirius B, the faint companion to Sirius A, but its visual magnitude is only 8.3, well outside the limit of about 6 for very good, unaided human eyes, in the very best observing conditions (Figure 2.18). Even if it were a bit brighter, its light would be swamped by Sirius A, and we would still be unable to see it.

The tendency for stars to concentrate into certain regions of the H–R diagram is clearly meaningful. But what does it mean?

2.4.2 How can we explain the distribution of stars on the H–R diagram?

Here is a possible explanation for the concentration of stars into certain regions on the H–R diagram. It is based on the reasonable assumptions that

- Any particular star is luminous for only a finite time;
- There are distinct stages between the star's cradle and grave, each stage being characterized by some range of temperature and luminosity; the star thus moves around the H–R diagram as it evolves;
- The stars today are not all at the same stage.

From these reasonable assumptions it follows that if we observe a large population of stars today, then the longer a particular stage lasts the greater will be the number of stars that are observed in that stage. Conversely, we will catch very few stars going through a short-lived stage.

We can thus explain the concentrations on the H–R diagram as those regions where the stars spend a comparatively large fraction of their lives. On this basis a star must spend most of its life on the main sequence, because this is where about 90% of the stars lie. Where it lies before it joins the main sequence, and where it goes afterwards, we cannot tell without further information, but the red giant, supergiant and white dwarf regions are where, on our assumptions, we might expect some stars to dwell for a while.

There are two other factors that influence the concentrations of stars on the H–R diagram. First, the concentration depends not only on how quickly a star passes through a region, but also on what fraction of stars pass through the region at all. Second, some regions of the H–R diagram might be bereft of stars simply because they correspond to stages in stellar lifetime when stars tend to be shrouded in cooler material.

We clearly need more observational data to make further progress. Observations of individual stars actually evolving would be of enormous value. By making observations over a period of time can we see such evolution?

Unfortunately, with very few exceptions, we can't. This is because stars evolve extremely slowly: we have good evidence (Chapter 1) that the Sun is about 4.5×10^9 years old, and that it will be about as long again before it runs out of hydrogen fuel in its core. Only two types of change in individual stars have been commonly observed.

◻ Which one have you already met in this chapter?

■ A rare but spectacular stellar explosion called a supernova – Section 2.1.

There are several types of supernova, but the observational evidence, as you will see in Chapter 4, indicates that one of them, the **Type II supernovae**, marks the end of supergiant stars. Thus, Betelgeuse and Rigel A seem fated to disappear after a final blaze of glory, their luminosity rising 10^8 times in a few days, followed by a few months of decline into oblivion, when they will vanish from the sky and from the H–R diagram.

The second type of change is far more modest, and is exhibited by what are called **variable stars**. There are two broad classes, regular and irregular.

As their name implies, **irregular variables** exhibit variations that are irregular in time. The most spectacular are the novae, a name that means 'new stars'. A **nova** is a star that brightens by about 1000 times in a few days, followed by a slower decline to about its original luminosity – the star is not destroyed. For some novae, only one outburst has been observed. Other novae are known to repeat the performance, though irregularly, with the average interval between outbursts varying from star to star from tens of days to tens of years. All types of nova are in **binary systems**, that is, a system of two stars close enough to be in orbit around each other. In a minority of binary systems the two stars are so close together that they interfere with each other's evolution (Plate 1.25). In some cases, this will lead to one of the two undergoing a nova outburst. Observations of novae thus help us to understand disturbances to the normal course of stellar evolution, and this also helps us to understand the normal course itself.

There are *many* other types of irregular variable, but one type that is of particular importance to stellar evolution is the **T Tauri stars** ('tory'), named after one star of this kind. These stars exhibit variations in luminosity by factors of two or three over intervals of the order of a few days. In the H–R diagram (Figure 2.24) they lie just above the main sequence in a zone that covers a wide range of temperatures, including that of the Sun, and they lie among traces of the sort of interstellar material from which stars are thought to form. These observations suggest strongly that they are very young stars, about to settle on to the main sequence. Indeed, some T Tauri stars probably have been seen to do just this. Therefore, the early phase of stellar evolution can be elucidated by the study of these stars. Chapter 3 discusses T Tauri stars in more detail.

Regular variables exhibit variations that are regular in time, and so the variations have fairly well defined periods. Like the irregular variables, there is a very large number of types. Here we shall mention only the **Cepheids** ('sefeeds'), named after δ Cephei (Greek delta), the first to be discovered, in 1786, by the deaf and dumb English astronomer John Goodricke (1764–1786). Cepheids are giant or supergiant stars (Figure 2.24), and Figure 2.25 shows a typical luminosity variation, where the period can be anything from about a day to about 100 days, and the luminosity change can be up to a factor of 10. The pole star, Polaris, is a Cepheid, with a period of 3.969 6 days, but with only a few percent change in luminosity. Cepheids help us to understand some of the processes that drive evolution at certain stages in a star's life, as you will see in Chapter 3*.

Have we now exhausted the main sources of observational data that help us to build models of the stars and of their evolution? No, we have not. There is one further property of enormous importance that we can measure, and this is a star's mass. So, how do we measure stellar masses, and what is the outcome of these measurements? These questions are answered in the next Section.

---

* In Block 3, you will see that Cepheids provide us with yet another way to measure distance.

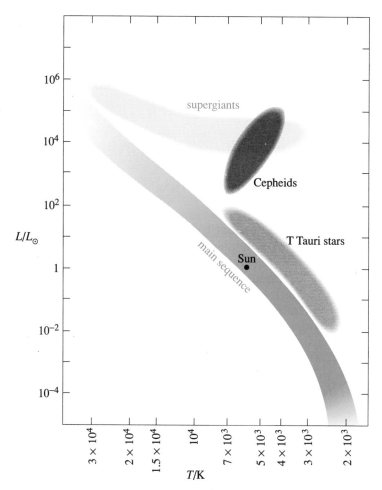

Figure 2.24 An H–R diagram, showing where the T Tauri stars and Cepheids lie.

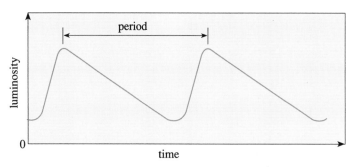

Figure 2.25 A typical luminosity variation for a Cepheid.

ITQ 2.11 If most stars were to end their lives quietly, by gradually cooling at roughly constant radius, what sort of tracks would they make across the H–R diagram?

Summary of Section 2.4 and SAQs

1 The Hertzsprung–Russell (H–R) diagram displays the photospheric temperatures and luminosities of the stars. The corresponding radii are obtained from Equation 2.7. The H–R diagram is a very useful aid to our understanding of the stars and their evolution.

2   The stars tend to concentrate into certain regions of the H–R diagram, and so some combinations of temperature and luminosity occur far more commonly than others. These concentrations define various classes of stars, the main classes being main sequence stars (about 90% of observed stars), red giants, supergiants, and white dwarfs.

3   We can explain the concentrations on the H–R diagram as places where stars spend comparatively large fractions of their lives, the main sequence phase accounting for the largest fraction.

4   Some stars evolve sufficiently rapidly through certain phases of their lives for us to be able to see the changes, and this aids our understanding of stellar evolution. Thus, it seems that the supergiant phase ends in a Type II supernova – a huge explosion that destroys the star. Also, the T Tauri stars (one type of irregular variable) seem to be on the threshold of joining the main sequence, approaching it from above.

5   Regular variables, such as the Cepheids, give us clues about some of the processes that are of importance in stellar evolution.

6   The novae (another type of irregular variable) help us to understand disturbances to the normal course of evolution that occur in binary systems, and this aids our understanding of the normal course itself.

SAQ 2.4 (Objective 2.10)   In what ways, if any, does the distance to a star influence its position on an H–R diagram?

SAQ 2.5 (Objectives 2.9 and 2.10)   Here are the photospheric temperatures and luminosities of five stars that are visually fairly bright in the sky.

Star	T/K	L/W
Alkaid (in The Plough)	17 000	6.1×10^{29}
Alcyone (in The Pleiades)	12 000	3.2×10^{29}
ε Eridani	4 700	1.4×10^{26}
Propus	3 000	4.2×10^{29}
Suhail	2 600	1.8×10^{30}

(a) Plot these stars on an H–R diagram (such as Figure 2.23), and hence try to assign each star to one of the main stellar classes described in Subsection 2.4.1.

(b) Suppose that we were to compare stars by preparing an H–R diagram that includes only the stars with the greatest apparent visual brightness. Discuss why such a diagram would be unrepresentative of stars as a whole.

SAQ 2.6 (Objective 2.10)   In terms of photospheric temperature, luminosity and radius, compare the Sun with other main sequence stars.

SAQ 2.7 (Objectives 2.10 and 2.11)   Given that T Tauri stars become main sequence stars with little change in photospheric temperature, discuss whether this transition is accompanied by a change in stellar radius.

2.5 How massive are the stars?

2.5.1 Measuring stellar masses

That stellar masses *can* be measured probably comes as no surprise to you in the light of all the measured stellar properties that you have already met. So, how is it done? The basis of the method is to observe how a star moves when a force is applied to it: this is a direct application of Newton's second law of motion (*Preparatory science*, Subsection 1.3.1), which states that the force applied to a body is equal to its mass times its acceleration. Therefore we must observe a star being accelerated.

Any star is accelerated by any other mass in the Universe through gravitational attraction, but measurably big accelerations occur only when the other mass is large, and relatively close to the star. Of particular importance are systems in which just two stars are sufficiently close together to be in orbit around each other – these binary systems were briefly referred to in Subsection 2.4.2. Over half the known 'stars' are, in fact, binary systems, and so such systems account for over two thirds of single stars. (Note that the word 'star' applies to an apparently single point of light in the sky, as well as to truly individual stars. A binary system is often called a binary star, and so a binary star actually contains two stars!)

Stellar masses are most readily obtained from those binary systems in which both stars can be seen as distinct points of light, if necessary with the aid of a large telescope. These are called **visual binary systems**, though nowadays the observations are made by electronic or photographic imaging, and not by the eye at the telescope eyepiece. One of the most famous visual binaries is Sirius, introduced in Subsection 2.4.1. In a large telescope we can see two stars, the main sequence star Sirius A, and the much fainter white dwarf Sirius B, first seen by the US telescope maker Alvan G. Clark (1832–1897) in 1862, while he was testing a new telescope lens. The orbital period of each with respect to the other is 50 years, and their angular separation on the plane of the sky has a maximum of 11.5 arcsec. Another example of a visual binary is shown in Figure 2.26, in the form of the orbit of one star with respect to the other (the small irregularities arise from uncertainties in the observations – the orbit is really quite smooth).

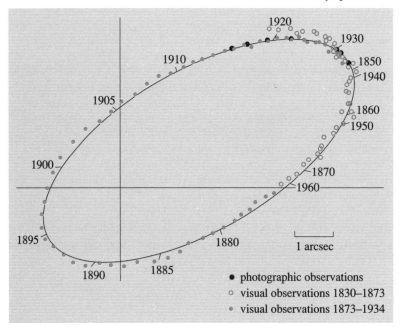

Figure 2.26   The orbit in the sky of one star relative to another in the visual binary system 70 Ophiuchi ('ophee-ookey'). The orbital period is 88 years.

The procedure of obtaining stellar masses from visual binaries is of wide applicability: for example, it can be used to obtain planetary and satellite masses in the Solar System. Therefore, we want to present the procedure to you in the manner of background science, and so it is described in a box, Box 2.2, which you should now read.

Box 2.2   Obtaining masses from orbital motions

It is assumed that you are familiar with Section 1.3 and Subsection 1.4.1 of *Preparatory science*.

Suppose that two stars are in circular orbits around each other, as in Figure 2.27a. This is a view from a point of observation that is not accelerating. One special point in the system itself is also not accelerating, and it lies on the straight line joining the two stars. This is called the **centre of mass** of the system, labelled P in Figure 2.27a. It lies at the centre of each of the circular orbits of the two stars, and thus the orbits shown are with respect to this centre of mass. The stars, however, *are* accelerating: their speeds are constant, but their directions of motion are constantly changing. Therefore, there must be a force acting on each of them.

☐   What are these forces?

■   The force on the star of mass m is the gravitational force exerted on it by the star of mass M, and vice versa. (The *speeds* are constant because the force on each star is always perpendicular to its direction of motion.)

Suppose now that, by some extraordinary feat, we were to sit on M and observe m. It would appear to move around M in an orbit that is called the orbit of m relative to M. If, as here, the orbits with respect to the centre of mass are circular (Figure 2.27a), then this relative orbit is also circular, as shown in Figure 2.27b, with m moving around its relative orbit at constant speed. Furthermore, the orbital periods are also the same from both points of view.

The relative orbit is important because its radius appears in the gravitational force between the two stars. This force has a magnitude, F, given by Newton's law of gravitation

$$F = GMm/r^2 \qquad (2.12)$$

where G is the gravitational constant (a universal constant), and r is the distance between the centres of the two stars – *this is also the radius of the relative orbit*.

Suppose that the orbital period of m is τ. How do we expect τ to depend on M, m and r? First, if r is kept fixed, then from Equation 2.12 we see that (reasonably enough) as M or m increases, F increases. Thus there will be a more rapid change of direction, and so τ should decrease. Second, if M and m are kept fixed, then from Equation 2.12 we see that (again reasonable) as r increases, F decreases, and moreover the distance around the orbit, $2\pi r$, increases. Therefore, τ should increase. Summarizing:

•   as M or m increases, we expect τ to decrease

•   as r increases, we expect τ to increase.

These expectations are borne out by the mathematical details, which won't concern us, but which lead to

$$\tau = 2\pi \left(\frac{r^3}{G(M+m)} \right)^{1/2} \qquad (2.13)$$

We have thus reached the point where, for a circular orbit, if we measure τ and r, then we can obtain the sum of the two masses.

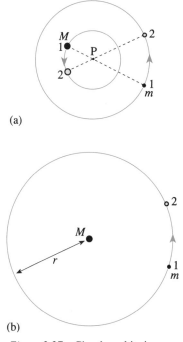

(a)

(b)

Figure 2.27   Circular orbits in a binary system: (a) relative to the centre of mass P of the system; and (b) of m relative to M.

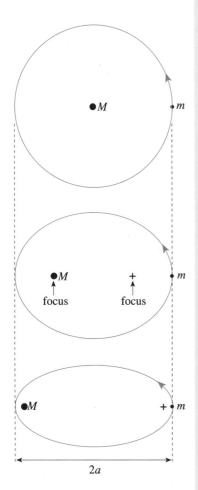

ITQ 2.12 Rearrange Equation 2.13 to obtain the explicit form for $M + m$ (i.e. $M + m = \ldots\ldots$).

Elliptical orbits

A circular orbit is rather a special case. In general, the orbit of m relative to M is an ellipse, with M at one of two special points called the **foci** of the ellipse. Various **elliptical orbits** are shown in Figure 2.28. The size of an ellipse is given by the **semimajor axis** a, which is half of the long dimension, and which is the average separation between the two masses. The extent of the departure from circular form is called the **eccentricity** of the ellipse, and is defined as half the distance between the two foci of the ellipse (Figure 2.28) divided by the semimajor axis. In a circle, both foci coincide at the centre, and so the eccentricity of a circle is zero.

The generalization of Equation 2.13 to elliptical orbits is remarkably straightforward: we simply replace the constant separation r in a circular orbit by the average separation a in an elliptical orbit. Thus

$$\tau = 2\pi \left(\frac{a^3}{G(M + m)} \right)^{1/2} \tag{2.14}$$

This equation can be rearranged (ITQ 2.12) to give

$$M + m = \frac{4\pi^2 a^3}{G\tau^2} \tag{2.15}$$

We would have obtained the same result had we considered the orbit of M relative to m, rather than m relative to M.

Thus by measuring τ and a we can get $(M + m)$.

Obtaining M and m separately

To obtain M and m separately we need to identify the position of the centre of mass of the binary system. Recall from Figure 2.27a that this lies on the straight line connecting the stars. We obtain its position on this line by making at least two observations, well separated in time. The centre of mass lies on both straight lines, and so must lie where they intersect: Figure 2.29 illustrates this procedure for the case of Sirius, where the centre of mass orbits are shown (elliptical in this case). These orbits are obtained by observing the motion of each star with respect to a non-accelerating frame of reference, which for practical purposes is provided by stars that are much farther away than the binary.

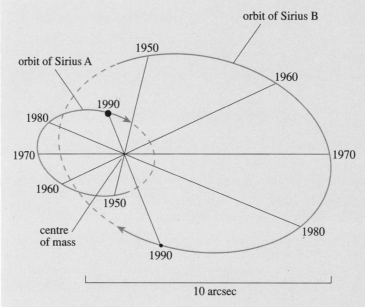

Figure 2.29 Sirius, a binary system, showing the position of the centre of mass.

Consider an instant when the distances of the two stars from the centre of mass are d_m and d_M. It can be shown that the ratio d_m/d_M is constant throughout the orbital motion, and is related to the masses via

$$M/m = d_m/d_M \qquad (2.16)$$

This equation is reasonable: if $M \gg m$, then $d_M \ll d_m$; that is, the centre of mass is close to the larger mass, as we might expect.

We have now achieved our goal: from Equations 2.15 and 2.16 we can obtain the masses M and m.

ITQ 2.13 Suppose that observations have revealed that, for a binary system, $M + m = 12M_\odot$, and $M/m = 3$. Calculate the values of M and m.

Note that Equation 2.15 requires that stars behave as rigid bodies, so that they don't deform each other. In fact, stars are not at all rigid! However, provided that they are small compared with their separation then the deformations are negligible. For all visual binaries, this condition is met.

This wide separation also means that the stars do not interfere with each other's evolution. Therefore, they are representative of the majority of stars (Subsection 2.4.2).

Before we turn to the star masses obtained from observations of binary systems, there are three observational details to point out.

First, it is important to realize that in Figures 2.26 and 2.29, as for any visual binary, we are observing the relative orbit as a projection onto a plane perpendicular to our line of sight, as illustrated in Figure 2.30. We thus observe the true shape of the relative orbit only if the actual relative orbit happens to lie in this plane. Furthermore, the semimajor axis a is shorter in the projection plane than it really is. Fortunately, the true value of a, for use in Equation 2.14, can be deduced from the observational data: in essence, we are able to 'unproject' the relative orbit, though the details will not concern us. Note that the ratio d_m/d_M in Equation 2.16 is unaffected by the projection; d_m and d_M are each shortened by the same factor. The orbital period τ is also unaffected.

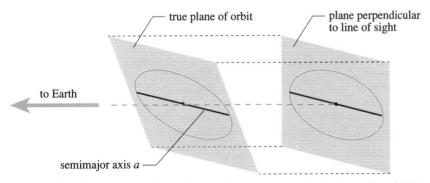

Figure 2.30   The projection of an orbit on to the plane perpendicular to our line of sight.

Second, in order to obtain a we also need to know the distance to the binary: what we actually measure is the *angular* separation of the two stars, which gives us the angle α corresponding to a.

ITQ 2.14 Write down an equation that relates a, α, and the distance d from the Earth to the binary.

The distance can be obtained by one of the methods that you met earlier in this chapter, or by various other methods.

Third, note that the method of obtaining masses from binary systems outlined in Box 2.2 requires that both stars be seen as distinct points of light, that is, we must be dealing with a *visual* binary system. Unfortunately, most binary systems are not of the visual kind. In some cases, we can detect the radiation from only one of the two stars. However, the second star makes its presence felt through its effect on the proper motion of the other star: the proper motion is not a smooth line but displays orbital wiggles. These pairs of stars are called astrometric binaries. Indeed, before Alvan Clark saw Sirius B in 1862, its existence had been inferred by Bessel in 1844 from such wiggles in the proper motion of Sirius A.

Other binaries reveal their binary nature only through the changing Doppler shifts (Subsection 2.2.1) in the spectral lines of one or both stars as they orbit each other. These are called spectroscopic binaries. There are also eclipsing binaries, in which we view the orbit so close to edge on that one star passes in front of the other, and the observed brightness of the 'star' will dip. These are rare, but a famous example that can be seen with the unaided eye is Algol (Plate 1.25a), which exhibits a rough halving of its luminosity for a few hours every 69 hours. In some mythologies, Algol is the winking eye of a demon.

Can we learn anything about stellar masses from these non-visual binaries? The answer is that we can, but less readily than in the case of visual binaries, and usually less completely too.

So, from the various techniques, what values *do* we find for stellar masses?

2.5.2 Stellar masses and stellar evolution

Measured masses range from about $0.08M_\odot$ to about $50M_\odot$, a large range, with the Sun again showing up as an average sort of star. At the upper end we have some true monsters, but even at the lower end we have bodies that are still far more massive than the planets.

☐ What is the mass of a $0.08M_\odot$ star, in Earth masses?

■ Nearly 30 000 Earth masses.

The lower the mass the greater the number of stars, and so the monsters are rare, and stars less massive than the Sun are commoner than stars of around solar mass. These relative numbers, and the upper and lower mass limits, are all things that the stellar theories in Chapter 3 and 4 have to explain.

We can, however, throw some light on stellar evolution right here if we plot stellar masses on an H–R diagram. This is done in Figure 2.31, where a handful of representative stellar masses have been included. Note the following important features.

1 The supergiants tend to be more massive than the red giants, which in turn tend to be more massive than the white dwarfs.

2 Within each of the supergiant, red giant, and white dwarf classes, there is no correlation of mass with luminosity or photospheric temperature – the relationship is jumbled.

3 Among the main sequence stars, mass correlates closely with luminosity, and hence with temperature: as mass increases, luminosity and temperature increase. (The increase in luminosity is enormous: the 600 to 1 increase in mass along the main sequence corresponds to a 10^{12} increase in L.)

4 In the lower part of the main sequence, the masses are comparable with the red giants, and in the upper part, with the supergiants.

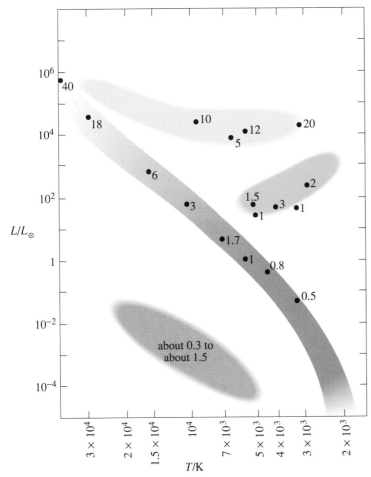

Figure 2.31 Stellar mass and the H–R diagram: masses are given in multiples of $M_\odot$.

Before we try to construct a model of stellar evolution based on these striking features, we have to address the question 'do stars change their mass during their evolution?' There is a good deal of observational evidence to help us to answer it. Thus, we observe main sequence stars, red giants and supergiants losing mass in the form of stellar winds streaming outwards. However, the accumulated totals are estimated to be only a small fraction of the initial mass of a star. A more impressive mass loss is shown in Plate 1.27, where you can see shells of material that have been flung off by the central star. These shells are misleadingly called **planetary nebulae**, because they look a bit like planetary discs when viewed under low magnification. They can account for a large fraction of the central star's mass. The central star occupies a region in the H–R diagram somewhat hotter and more luminous than the white dwarfs, and it is plausible that it could cool to become a white dwarf.

 Some stars end their lives more violently than by shedding a planetary nebula.

☐ What stars are these, and how do they end their lives?

■ Supergiants, which end their lives as Type II supernovae.

In fact, in a Type II supernova (Plate 1.28), most of the star's mass is blown away, resulting in a variety of debris patterns, some of which are shown in Plates 1.29–1.31.

It thus seems to be the case that throughout most stars' lives, severe mass loss occurs only when a planetary nebula is shed, the stellar remnant becoming a white dwarf, or when a massive star ends its life, as a Type II supernova.

We are now in a position to suggest a plausible model of some of the stages of stellar evolution based on the features 1 to 4 above, and on what we know about mass loss. Here it is. During its main sequence phase, a star does not change its luminosity or photospheric temperature very much, otherwise it would move a good way along the main sequence, and this does not fit in with the large differences in mass along the main sequence. After the main sequence phase the less massive stars become red giants, and the more massive stars become supergiants: you can see that this is consistent with the masses in Figure 2.31. It is also consistent with the rarity of supergiants: there are simply too few main sequence precursors. Finally, red giants evolve to the point where they shed planetary nebulae, the stellar remnant evolving to become a white dwarf. Supergiants become star-destroying Type II supernovae.

We are thus continuing to unfold the story of stellar evolution. But there is one huge aspect of the story that, as yet, we have barely touched, and this is whether stars of different mass all evolve at about the same rate. The final Section of this chapter describes observational data that strongly suggest an answer.

Summary of Section 2.5 and SAQs

1   Stellar masses can be obtained from observations of binary systems. This is most directly accomplished using visual binaries, the masses being given by

$$M + m = \frac{4\pi^2 a^3}{G\tau^2} \tag{2.15}$$

$$M/m = d_m/d_M \tag{2.16}$$

2   Measured stellar masses range from about $0.08 M_\odot$ to about $50 M_\odot$, with stars of lower mass being more common.

3   Stars lose a rather small fraction of their masses during much of their lifetimes, but much more impressive fractions when they shed planetary nebulae, and in supernovae.

4   When stellar masses are placed on an H–R diagram, and coupled with observations of mass loss, we obtain important clues to stellar evolution, leading us to a plausible model of some of the stages, as follows:

   •   after the main sequence phase the less massive stars become red giants, and the more massive stars become supergiants

   •   red giants evolve to the point where they shed planetary nebulae, the stellar remnant evolving to become a white dwarf

   •   supergiants end their lives as star-destroying Type II supernovae.

SAQ 2.8 (Objective 2.8)   In the Sirius binary system, the orbital period is 50 years, and the semimajor axis of the relative orbit is 20 AU. From these data, and from Figure 2.29, calculate the masses of Sirius A and Sirius B, expressing your answer in solar masses.

SAQ 2.9 (Objectives 2.10 and 2.11)   Discuss whether we can rule out the evolution of red giants to form supergiants.

2.6 Star clusters and stellar evolution

Many groups of stars contain far more than two stars, even as many as several million. Any group with more than a few members is called a **star cluster.** Clusters are very common, and some examples are shown in Plates 1.22 and 3.6. Detailed observations of clusters suggest that a cluster is the outcome of the stars in it forming at about the same time, in a volume of space about equal to that of the cluster. Moreover, the compositions of the stars are similar. Isolated stars (including isolated binary stars), result from the later partial or complete dispersal of a cluster.

The crucial points for us here are that all the stars in a cluster formed at about the same time, and all have similar compositions.

☐ Why are these the crucial points?

■ If the stars in a cluster have different masses, then we can discover the relative rates of evolution of stars that differ only in their mass.

These relative rates are conveniently revealed by plotting the H–R diagram of a cluster. Figure 2.32 shows two contrasting cases: The Pleiades ('ply-a-dees', Plate 1.22b), and a cluster that has only a catalogue number, M67 (Plate 1.22c). In the case of The Pleiades, almost all the stars are on the main sequence, suggesting that this cluster is not old enough for many stars to have reached the end of this phase. The stars that are not on the main sequence are lying towards the supergiant region. These stars have masses that would have placed them at

You should have seen The Pleiades in the project *In and around Orion*

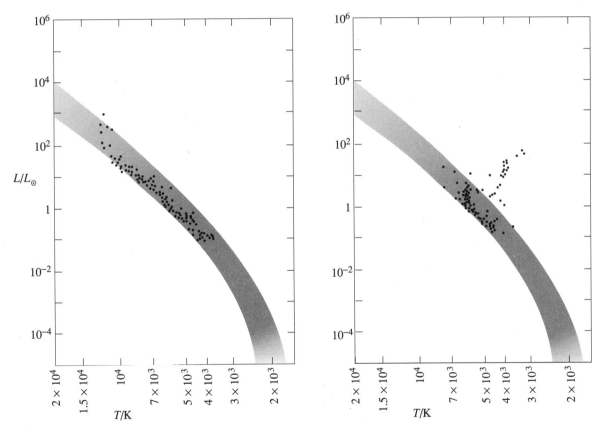

Figure 2.32 The H–R diagrams of two star clusters: (a) The Pleiades; (b) M67.

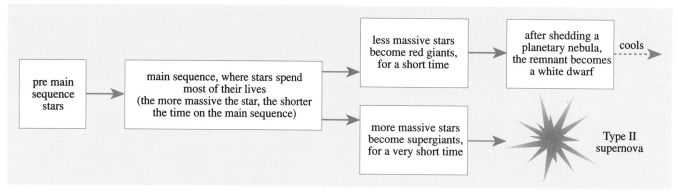

Figure 2.33 A model for stellar evolution.

the upper end of the main sequence, where the massive stars lie (Figure 2.31), and this is just where the main sequence for this cluster is unpopulated. A good interpretation is thus that the more massive a star, the shorter its main sequence lifetime. The case of M67 is the subject of SAQ 2.10.

We have come a long way in constructing a plausible model of stellar evolution, and it is summarized in Figure 2.33. We have described some of the observational basis of this model, and we assure you that further observations not only support it, but fill in some of the missing details. However, the time has now come to move away from pure observations as the sole basis for model building, and to involve a powerful body of physical theory in the modelling process. In the next two chapters we thus continue to develop the story of the stars, and of their evolution, but with considerable reliance on physical theory. This will necessarily involve us in modelling not only external events, but also stellar interiors.

SAQ 2.10 (Objectives 2.10 and 2.11)   Figure 2.32b shows the H–R diagram of the star cluster M67. Discuss whether this is consistent with the model of stellar evolution in Figure 2.33. Why is it reasonable to conclude that M67 is older than The Pleiades?

Objectives for Chapter 2

After studying Chapter 2 (and any associated audio, video or TV material), you should be able to:

2.1   Give brief definitions of the terms, concepts and principles listed at the end of the Objectives.

2.2   Perform calculations involving proper motion, transverse velocity, and radial velocity.

2.3   Outline how to obtain stellar distances by the methods of trigonometric parallax and spectroscopic parallax; calculate stellar distances using these two methods.

2.4   Outline how to obtain stellar radii from stellar angular diameters and distances, and from stellar luminosity and photospheric temperature; calculate stellar radii using these two methods.

2.5   Outline how to obtain photospheric temperatures from flux density ratios, and from spectral classes; obtain rough estimates of temperature using the latter method.

2.6   Outline how to obtain stellar luminosities from stellar radii and temperatures, and from various absorption lines in stellar spectra; calculate stellar luminosities using the former method.

2.7 Outline how stellar compositions are obtained from spectral line studies, and describe in broad terms the composition of the stars.

2.8 Outline how stellar masses are obtained from binary systems; calculate stellar masses using this method.

2.9 Prepare a Hertzsprung–Russell diagram from a table of stellar properties.

2.10 Describe and comment on the main features of a Hertzsprung–Russell diagram of stars in general, and of stars in a cluster.

2.11 Outline a broad model of stellar evolution based on the observed properties of large numbers of stars.

List of scientific terms, concepts and principles used in Chapter 2

Term	Page	Term	Page	Term	Page
absolute visual magnitude	67	Harvard Spectral Classification	62	spectrometric method	61
apparent visual magnitude	67	Hertzsprung–Russell diagram	72	spectroscopic parallax	66
astronomical unit	56	irregular variable	77	star cluster	87
Balmer absorption lines	61	light year	58	Stefan's constant	64
binary system	77	luminosity	63	stellar parallax	56
blue shift	55	main sequence	74	supergiant	76
centre of mass	81	nova	77	supernova	52
Cepheid	77	parsec	56	T Tauri star	77
cosmic relative abundances of the elements	69	photometric method	61	transverse velocity	53
Doppler effect	54	planetary nebula	85	trigonometric parallax	56
Doppler shift	55	proper motion	53	Type II supernova	77
eccentricity	82	radial velocity	53	variable star	77
elliptical orbit	82	red giant	75	visual binary system	80
flux density	65	red shift	55	white dwarf	76
foci	82	regular variable	77		
giant	76	semimajor axis	82		

Appendix

The chemical elements and their cosmic relative abundances

The cosmic relative abundance for hydrogen is arbitrarily set at 10^{12}. The relative atomic mass, A_r, is the average mass of the atoms of the element as it occurs on Earth. It is thus an average over all the isotopes of the element. To sufficient accuracy here, the scale is fixed by giving the carbon isotope $^{12}_6 C$ a relative atomic mass of 12.000 0.

Atomic number, Z	Name	Chemical symbol	Relative atomic mass, A_r	Cosmic relative abundance	
				By number	By mass
1	hydrogen	H	1.008 0	1.0×10^{12}	1.0×10^{12}
2	helium	He	4.002 6	8.5×10^{10}	3.4×10^{11}
3	lithium	Li	6.941	$<1 \times 10^{1\ b}$	$<7 \times 10^{1\ b}$
4	beryllium	Be	9.012 2	1.4×10^1	1.3×10^2
5	boron	B	10.811	$<1.3 \times 10^{3\ b}$	$<1.4 \times 10^{4\ b}$
6	carbon	C	12.011 1	4.2×10^8	5.0×10^9
7	nitrogen	N	14.006 7	8.7×10^7	1.2×10^9
8	oxygen	O	15.999 4	6.9×10^8	1.1×10^{10}
9	fluorine	F	18.998 4	3.6×10^4	6.8×10^5
10	neon	Ne	20.179	1.3×10^8	2.6×10^9
11	sodium	Na	22.989 8	1.9×10^6	4.4×10^7
12	magnesium	Mg	24.305	3.2×10^7	7.8×10^8
13	aluminium	Al	26.981 5	3.3×10^6	8.9×10^7
14	silicon	Si	28.086	4.5×10^7	1.3×10^9
15	phosphorus	P	30.973 8	3.2×10^5	9.9×10^6
16	sulphur	S	32.06	1.6×10^7	5.1×10^8
17	chlorine	Cl	35.453	3.2×10^5	1.1×10^7
18	argon	Ar	39.948	1.0×10^6	4.0×10^7
19	potassium	K	39.102	1.4×10^5	5.5×10^6
20	calcium	Ca	40.08	2.2×10^6	8.8×10^7
21	scandium	Sc	44.956	1.1×10^3	4.9×10^4
22	titanium	Ti	47.90	1.1×10^5	5.3×10^6
23	vanadium	V	50.941 4	1.0×10^4	5.1×10^5
24	chromium	Cr	51.996	5.1×10^5	2.7×10^7
25	manganese	Mn	54.938 0	2.6×10^5	1.4×10^7
26	iron	Fe	55.847	3.2×10^7	1.8×10^9
27	cobalt	Co	58.933 2	3.2×10^4	1.9×10^6
28	nickel	Ni	58.71	1.9×10^6	1.1×10^8
29	copper	Cu	63.546	1.1×10^4	7.0×10^5

30	zinc	Zn	65.37	2.8×10^4	1.8×10^6
31	gallium	Ga	69.72	6.3×10^2	4.4×10^4
32	germanium	Ge	72.59	3.2×10^3	2.3×10^5
33	arsenic	As	74.921 6	2.5×10^2	1.9×10^4
34	selenium	Se	78.96	2.5×10^3	2.0×10^5
35	bromine	Br	79.904	5.0×10^2	4.0×10^4
36	krypton	Kr	83.80	2.0×10^3	1.7×10^5
37	rubidium	Rb	85.467 8	4.0×10^2	3.4×10^4
38	strontium	Sr	87.62	7.9×10^2	6.9×10^4
39	yttrium	Y	88.905 9	1.3×10^2	1.2×10^4
40	zirconium	Zr	91.22	5.6×10^2	5.1×10^4
41	niobium	Nb	92.906	7.9×10^1	7.3×10^3
42	molybdenum	Mo	95.94	1.4×10^2	1.3×10^4
43	technetium	Tc[a]	98.906	$-$[c]	$-$[c]
44	ruthenium	Ru	101.07	68	6.9×10^3
45	rhodium	Rh	102.905	32	3.3×10^3
46	palladium	Pd	106.4	32	3.4×10^3
47	silver	Ag	107.868	4	4.3×10^2
48	cadmium	Cd	112.40	71	8.0×10^3
49	indium	In	114.82	45	5.2×10^3
50	tin	Sn	118.69	100	1.2×10^4
51	antimony	Sb	121.75	10	1.2×10^3
52	tellurium	Te	127.60	250	3.2×10^4
53	iodine	I	126.904 5	40	5.1×10^3
54	xenon	Xe	131.30	210	2.8×10^4
55	caesium	Cs	132.905	<80 [b]	$<1.1 \times 10^4$ [b]
56	barium	Ba	137.34	120	1.6×10^4
57	lanthanum	La	138.906	13	1.8×10^3
58	cerium	Ce	140.12	35	4.9×10^3
59	praseodymium	Pr	140.908	4	5.6×10^2
60	neodymium	Nd	144.24	18	2.6×10^3
61	promethium	Pm[a]	146	$-$[c]	$-$[c]
62	samarium	Sm	150.4	5	7.5×10^2
63	europium	Eu	151.96	5	7.6×10^2
64	gadolinium	Gd	157.25	13	2.0×10^3
65	terbium	Tb	158.925	2	3.2×10^2
66	dysprosium	Dy	162.50	11	1.8×10^3
67	holmium	Ho	164.930	3	4.9×10^2
68	erbium	Er	167.26	7	1.2×10^3
69	thulium	Tm	168.934	2	3.4×10^2

70	ytterbium	Yb	170.04	8	1.4×10^3
71	lutetium	Lu	174.97	6	1.0×10^3
72	hafnium	Hf	178.49	6	1.1×10^3
73	tantalum	Ta	180.948	1	1.8×10^2
74	tungsten	W	183.85	50	9.2×10^3
75	rhenium	Re	186.2	<2 [b]	$<3.7 \times 10^2$ [b]
76	osmium	Os	190.2	5	9.5×10^2
77	iridium	Ir	192.2	28	5.4×10^3
78	platinum	Pt	195.09	56	1.1×10^4
79	gold	Au	196.967	6	1.2×10^3
80	mercury	Hg	200.59	<100 [b]	$<2.0 \times 10^4$ [b]
81	thallium	Tl	204.37	8	1.6×10^3
82	lead	Pb	207.19	85	1.8×10^4
83	bismuth	Bi	208.981	<80 [b]	$<1.7 \times 10^4$ [b]
84	polonium	Po[a]	209	—[c]	—[c]
85	astatine	At[a]	210	—[c]	—[c]
86	radon	Rn[a]	222	—[c]	—[c]
87	francium	Fr[a]	223	—[c]	—[c]
88	radium	Ra[a]	226.025	—[c]	—[c]
89	actinium	Ac[a]	227	—[c]	—[c]
90	thorium	Th[a]	232.038	2	4.6×10^2
91	protoactinium	Pa[a]	231.036	—[c]	—[c]
92	uranium	U[a]	238.029	<4 [b]	$<9.5 \times 10^2$ [b]
93	neptunium	Np[a]	237.048	—[c]	—[c]
94	plutonium	Pu[a]	244	—[c]	—[c]
95	americium	Am[a]	243	—[c]	—[c]
96	curium	Cm[a]	247	—[c]	—[c]
97	berkelium	Bk[a]	247	—[c]	—[c]
98	californium	Cf[a]	251	—[c]	—[c]
99	einsteinium	Es[a]	254	—[c]	—[c]
100	fermium	Fm[a]	257	—[c]	—[c]
101	mendelevium	Md[a]	257	—[c]	—[c]
102	nobelium	No[a]	259	—[c]	—[c]
103	lawrencium	Lr[a]	260	—[c]	—[c]
104	unnilquadium	Unq[a]	~261	—[c]	—[c]
105[d]	unnilpentium	Unp[a]	~262	—[c]	—[c]

[a] No stable isotopes.

[b] Detected, but value given is upper limit.

[c] Far too scarce to have been detected beyond the Earth, and probably very scarce.

[d] A further five elements are known (1993), from $Z = 106$ to $Z = 110$.

Chapter 3
Life cycles of the stars

Prepared for the Course Team by John Zarnecki

Contents

3.1 Introduction

As with so many astronomical phenomena, the life cycle of a star takes place over a time-scale that appears infinitely long in comparison with a human lifetime, or even with the entire duration of recorded human history of perhaps several thousand years. Zoologists or botanists are able to study the complete life cycles of the animals or plants in which they are interested, but astronomers are not afforded that luxury where the stars are concerned. The changes that occur in stars are, with a few notable exceptions, much too slow to be observed. The evolutionary pattern has to be deduced by observing a wide range of stars at different stages of their lives, and combining these observations with theory and models based on the laws of physics as determined in other environments. The fact that a credible model of the entire life cycle of most types of star has been developed can surely be regarded as one of the triumphs of 20th century astrophysics. This doesn't mean, however, that all the problems are solved – far from it. There is still much to understand.

What, then, are the questions to pose in this chapter? We have chosen the following:

- How are stars made?
- What powers them?
- What is their ultimate fate?

In answering these questions, we shall make extensive use of our knowledge of the observed properties of the star that we know best, namely our Sun, which we have already discussed in detail in Chapter 1. However, it would be dangerous to use only our Sun as a model, as we would have no idea how typical of the whole population of stars it might be. Therefore, we also make extensive use of observations of all stars, as described in Chapter 2, to guide us in our development of a theory. Although we don't know as much about any individual star as we do about the Sun, the power of the collective data on thousands or even tens of thousands of stars is crucially important. It doesn't matter too much if the information that we have on a few stars is wrong, as it undoubtedly is in some cases; what is important is that the overall characteristics that emerge from observations of a large number of stars will push us in the right direction in our search for a description and explanation of the life story of a star. This kind of statistical approach is one that is often used in astrophysics. It is to some extent forced on us when we are in a situation where we can study a very large population but, perhaps because of their great distance or faintness, we are not able to make measurements on individual members of that population with great precision (and remember that some parameters can't be measured directly at all). However, the power of this technique applied to a fundamental scientific problem should not be underestimated.

3.2 Starbirth

Where should we be looking to find starbirth taking place? This question was first considered in detail by the British physicists Sir James Jeans (1877–1946) and Sir Arthur Eddington (1882–1944). Jeans in particular studied the gravitational instability of extensive masses of gas. At this stage, we are going to jump ahead a small way in our journey through the Universe and consider some of the areas of the interstellar medium that we shall look at in more detail in Chapter 5. When we study the distribution of stars within the Milky Way, we find that it is far from even. You can easily see this in Plate 3.3, which shows a panoramic view of the sky: apart from the general 'splash' of stars across the sky indicating the position of our own galaxy, the Milky Way, there are, even within the Milky Way, many regions from where stars appear to be 'missing'. An example can be seen in Plate 1.14, the Coal Sack region of the Milky Way, so-called because of the lack of stars. However, we now know that this apparent lack of stars is not what it at first appears. There is strong evidence that these 'gaps' arise because our view of the stars is obscured in some directions by intervening clouds of gas (consisting mainly of hydrogen) and dust (about 1% of the mass of the gas and consisting mainly of heavy elements and their compounds). These are the **dense clouds**, of which there are several types; you'll be looking at these in detail in Chapter 5. For the present, all you need to know is that they are characterized by a low temperature, a high density (at least by the standards of the interstellar medium) and a rich collection of molecules – and that such clouds are relatively common. Although the typical number density, n, of gas in the interstellar medium is of the order of 10^6 particles m^{-3}, in the dense clouds n varies from about 10^9 to about 10^{12} particles m^{-3}.

We should at this point put into context the term 'dense'. For example, if we could compare a cubic metre of material from a dense interstellar cloud with a cubic metre of the Earth's atmosphere at sea-level, we would find that the sample of atmosphere would have about 10^{15} (a thousand million million) times more gas molecules and atoms than the sample of the same volume from the dense cloud. Even if we took a similar sized sample from what we would describe as 'a good laboratory vacuum', we would still find that our sample from the vacuum would have a factor of about 10^6 (a million) more particles than our sample from the dense cloud. So the term 'dense' must be taken in context. However, the clouds are large, and if we multiply the large volumes by the low densities, we do end up with a significant amount of material. The dense clouds make up perhaps 45% of the total mass in the interstellar medium. It is the dense clouds where it appears that conditions are particularly favourable for stars to form.

Let's look at the evidence that supports the belief that dense clouds are the seat of starbirth.

Some young star clusters seem to be surrounded by the remnants of the original cloud from which they formed. Plates 1.16 and 1.17 show the Orion Nebula. It is visible to the naked eye as a haze surrounding the star θ Orionis (Greek theta) in the sword of Orion. Observations with a telescope show this region to be one of the most magnificent, visually, in the sky. There is plenty of evidence to suggest that star formation took place here very recently, at least on the astronomical time-scale. For example, if we look at a Hertzsprung–Russell (or H–R) diagram (Section 2.4) of the stars in the central region of the nebula (Figure 3.1), we see that they mostly lie above the main sequence.

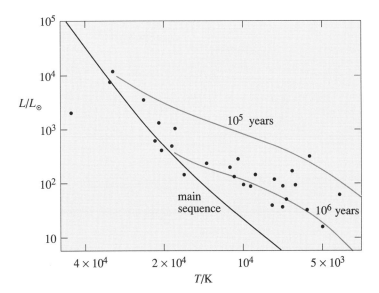

Figure 3.1 H–R diagram for stars in the Orion Nebula, showing that most of them fall above the main sequence. The dashed lines show the predicted positions of stars 10^5 and 10^6 years after their formation.

☐ What does this suggest about the stars in this region?

■ You saw in Chapter 2 that stars spend most of their life, maybe 90% of it, on the main sequence. The fact that the stars associated with the Orion Nebula aren't on the main sequence suggests therefore that they are at either the beginning or the end of their lifetime.

All other evidence points to these stars being very young. What interests us here, though, are the vast clouds of glowing gas and obscuring dark clouds of dust and gas. These are almost certainly the remnants of the dense cloud from which the young stars in the nebula formed. Lit up by the intense radiation from these stars (four of which at the centre of the nebula form the well-known Trapezium), the hydrogen in the cloud is ionized and glows in its characteristic light.

Another example is in Plate 1.22a, where the star cluster NGC 2264 is seen to be intimately associated with the remnants of a dense cloud. Most of these stars also lie above the main sequence, though they seem to be rather older than those in the Orion Nebula. Theoretical age estimates yield about 5×10^6 years for the stars in NGC 2264, and about 10^6 years for those in the Orion Nebula.

Another strand of evidence is that some dense clouds are found to contain a large number of compact infrared sources. A good example is shown in Plate 1.17b, which is an infrared image of the Orion Nebula. It is thought to contain some very young stars, unobservable in visible light but detectable in the infrared part of the spectrum.

ITQ 3.1   Why should we expect very young stars to emit in the infrared part of the spectrum? (*Hint*: Think of Wien's displacement law.)

It seems that the infrared radiation comes not from the young star itself but from the cocoon of dust still surrounding it. Heated to a temperature of a few hundred kelvin by the recently formed star, the warm dust re-radiates in the infrared part of the spectrum.

The theoretical models of stellar evolution that we shall look at in more detail shortly all point to regions of low temperature and high density as being the most likely sources of starbirth. The dense clouds seem to fit the bill quite well.

By way of a brief introduction to these models, recall that, according to Isaac Newton's 17th century formulation of the theory of gravity, each piece of matter attracts every other piece with the force of gravity. The Earth attracts the Moon, forcing it to follow a circular orbit; the Moon attracts the Earth, producing the ocean tides; the Earth attracts an apple, making it fall down from a tree; one apple also attracts another apple hanging on an adjacent branch, but in this case both of the masses are so small that a very sensitive device would be needed to measure the force. Just as the force between adjacent apples on a tree can be neglected for most practical purposes, so can that between molecules in the Earth's atmosphere. However, when we are dealing with the gas and dust clouds spread through the vast expanses of the interstellar medium, we cannot ignore this force and must consider the Newtonian gravitational attraction between different sections of these interstellar clouds. Jeans was able to show that, under appropriate conditions, a cloud (or part of one) would start to contract under the influence of the gravitational force. He derived a simple formula for calculating the mass and size that a cloud would have to reach, as a function of its temperature and density, before gravitational contraction could start. It is the details of this and subsequent processes, leading to the formation of stars, that form the subject matter for the remainder of this Section.

3.2.1 Contraction of a dense cloud

We have pointed out that all atoms, molecules and particles in a cloud are attracted to each other by the gravitational force. However, observations show that many clouds appear to be in a state of equilibrium – in other words, they don't seem to be in a state of contraction. Why is it then, that the particles don't all collapse into a very small volume?

☐ Can you suggest a possible source of energy to oppose gravitational contraction?

■ You have seen in Section 2.4 of *Preparatory science* that each gas atom or molecule has thermal kinetic energy of $\frac{3}{2}kT$. This results from the particle's continuous motion, sometimes striking others and creating an outward pressure that counteracts the tendency of the gas to contract.

The basis of the approach used by Jeans was to consider the balance between the two forces. He proposed that if the force due to gravity was the greater, then gravitational contraction could occur. Using this simple criterion, Jeans was able to show that, for a given set of conditions of temperature and particle number density, there is a value for the mass of a uniform spherical cloud at which the force of gravitational attraction will overcome the force due to the motion of the particles, and contraction will occur. This critical mass is known as the **Jeans mass** and is given by the following expression:

$$M_J = \frac{9}{4} \times \left(\frac{1}{2\pi n}\right)^{1/2} \times \frac{1}{m^2} \times \left(\frac{kT}{G}\right)^{3/2} \tag{3.1}$$

where n is the particle number density, m the mass of the 'average' gas particle in the cloud, and T the gas temperature. Figure 3.2 shows how the Jeans mass, M_J, varies with temperature, T, and number density, n, when the particle mass, m, equals that of a hydrogen molecule. If the actual cloud mass exceeds M_J, then contraction is predicted.

> You needn't memorize Equation 3.1, but you should remember that the Jeans mass *increases* with increasing temperature and *decreases* with increasing particle number density. This information can also be seen in Figure 3.2

ITQ 3.2 According to the Jeans criterion, Equation 3.1, (or alternatively from Figure 3.2), what conditions of temperature, T, and number density, n, are likely to promote gravitational contraction? (A qualitative answer only is required.)

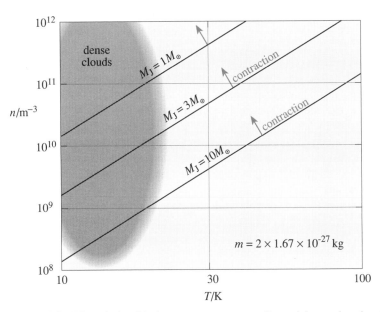

Figure 3.2 The relationship between temperature, T, particle number density, n, and the mass required in a spherical cloud for the gravitational force to cause contraction to occur. This is the Jeans mass, given by Equation 3.1. It is assumed that the particles are hydrogen molecules.

You will see in Chapter 5 that the dense clouds are the densest and coolest regions in the interstellar medium, and so, on the Jeans criterion, would contract at lower mass than other types of region. Figure 3.2 shows that dense clouds of only a few solar masses would contract. Many dense clouds are far more massive than this. Moreover, there are yet denser regions within dense clouds (called cores and clumps), with masses between about $0.3 M_\odot$ and about $10^3 M_\odot$, that can therefore satisfy the Jeans criterion on their own. Thus, gravitational contraction of dense clouds is to be expected.

The picture that has been painted so far, however, is a highly simplified one.

☐ What are the factors that could complicate this simplified approach to the gravitational contraction of a dense cloud?

■ We wouldn't necessarily expect a typical cloud to be spherical or to have the same temperature and density throughout.

In addition, no account has been taken of rotation or of magnetic fields, which almost certainly play an important part. These two factors may well inhibit a cloud's tendency to contract under gravity.

Despite its over-simplifications, the Jeans approach is a good starting point for more sophisticated, and perhaps more realistic treatments of the early stages of star formation. Whatever approach is adopted, we can speculate as to what might be the trigger mechanism that is probably needed to cause a cloud, or a region inside it, to change from an equilibrium state to one in which contraction has been initiated. The following are among the mechanisms that have been suggested, and each appears plausible:

- **Supernovae**, about which you will learn more later, are responsible for generating shock waves that travel through the interstellar medium and compress the material in their path.

- In order to maintain the spiral shape of our galaxy, a so-called **spiral density wave** sweeps around the galaxy, compressing all the material that it passes, including clouds.

- The close approach, or collision, of another cloud, or even a star, may be sufficient to produce a local gravitational disturbance that could trigger gravitational contraction.

Given that, somehow, a dense cloud, or a region inside it, starts to contract, we must now consider the question of what happens next.

3.2.2 Fragmentation

It was pointed out in Section 2.6 that stars are often found in groups, referred to as clusters. Examples can be seen in Plate 1.22. You also learnt that the stars in a cluster appear to have formed at about the same time. How can this be consistent with the picture of gravitational contraction that we've painted so far?

The answer is believed to lie in the phenomenon of **fragmentation**. We left our dense cloud beginning to contract under the influence of gravitational forces, triggered by some external influence. Does that collapse produce a single condensed cloud? The answer is almost certainly no. As the cloud contracts, it is thought that it starts to break up into fragments, each fragment having the potential to continue collapsing separately from the other fragments. Why does fragmentation occur? Well, it could be as a result either of the initial 'clumpiness' of the cloud, or of rotation. Whatever the cause, the result is that the cloud, rather than contracting into a single centre, produces numerous centres towards which different parts separately contract. These fragments might break up into yet smaller parts. This qualitative description certainly appears consistent with the observation that star clusters are common, and is also consistent with the Jeans criterion in the following sense: as contraction continues, the particle number density will clearly increase.

☐ What effect will this have on the Jeans mass at a point in the cloud (assuming a roughly constant temperature)?

■ From Equation 3.1, you can see that an increase in n will cause the Jeans mass, M_J, to decrease.

This means that, if a fragment breaks away from the main body of the cloud, it is still quite possible that the Jeans criterion is satisfied in the fragment, and so gravitational contraction can continue. In this way you can see, at least qualitatively, how a cloud initially with a mass of hundreds or even thousands of solar masses can ultimately produce a large number of small fragments, each collapsing on its own, to yield a cluster. Star clusters formed in this way are called **open clusters**, reflecting their open structure (Plate 1.22). They typically contain a few hundred stars.

3.2.3 Protostars

From a fragment to a protostar

We have now reached the stage where our dense cloud is contracting, probably in the form of many fragments. Let's now concentrate on the development of a typical fragment. The best way to understand its subsequent evolution is to look at the energy balance. Consider a single gas molecule in a contracting fragment. Initially, it will possess both gravitational energy and thermal kinetic energy. From Section 1.5 in *Preparatory science,* we can see that for a molecule near the surface of the fragment, its gravitational energy is given by $e_g = -GMm/R$, where M is the total mass of the fragment, m is the mass of the molecule, R is the radius of the fragment and G is the universal gravitational constant. Its thermal kinetic energy is given by $e_k = \frac{3}{2}kT$, where T is the temperature and k is Boltzmann's constant.

☐ Assuming that the contracting fragment can be treated as an isolated system, what can we say about the total energy of the fragment as contraction progresses?

■ The law of conservation of energy (Subsection 1.5.4) tells us that the total energy of an isolated system remains constant.

What does this mean for the contracting fragment? As contraction continues, the distance R of our molecule from the centre of the fragment will decrease. This results in a decrease in gravitational energy (if you are surprised by this, remember that there is a minus sign in the expression for the gravitational energy). Because the total energy remains constant, this reduction in gravitational energy must be accompanied by an increase in the molecule's kinetic energy. The molecules collide, and so the increase in the individual kinetic energies can be expressed as an increase in the thermal kinetic energy, $\frac{3}{2}kT$. This means that the temperature near the cloud surface will increase. Had we considered a molecule inside the cloud the expression for its gravitational energy would have been slightly different, but we would have reached the same conclusion.

Overall, therefore, as the fragment contracts, the gravitational energy of the particles is converted via mutual collisions into thermal kinetic energy, and the temperature rises.

However, there are various complications. One is that collisions between molecules can leave them in excited states, which can emit characteristic radiation. In this case, the radiation is most likely to be in the radio wave, microwave or infrared part of the spectrum (see Box 1.3). Initially, this radiation tends to escape from the collapsing cloud and the resultant overall rise in temperature is minimal – perhaps only from 10 K to 20 K! However, as the contraction progresses, the number density of the molecules increases and this makes it more difficult for the emitted radiation to escape; it tends to be trapped by the surrounding layers. In other words, the gas becomes opaque to the radiation and now the internal temperature can rise more rapidly.

So the fact that, during the collapse process, some molecules will be excited to emit radiation, will only have the effect of initially slowing down the inexorable rise in temperature of the cloud fragment.

Section 2.4 introduced you to the Hertzsprung–Russell diagram and the role it plays in our understanding of stars.

☐ Where does a contracting fragment of a dense cloud fall on the H–R diagram at the beginning of its life?

■ If the H–R diagram is plotted as in Figure 2.23, we would expect the fragment to be at the bottom right because of its low temperature and, at least initially, low luminosity.

The track of the contracting cloud fragment across the H–R diagram is far from certain and is difficult to observe directly for two reasons. One is that the process is taking place behind a shield of gas and dust, which effectively screens the fragment from view. The second reason is the subject of ITQ 3.3. For both reasons, we are forced to fall back on theoretical calculations and computer models of this phase. These seem to show that, after only a few thousand years of gravitational contraction, the surface has heated up to between 2 000 and 3 000 K. The fragment is still quite large at this stage and therefore the luminosity can reach a healthy level. The exact track depends on the balance between the increasing surface temperature, which tends to increase the luminosity, and the decreasing surface area, which has the opposite effect (Equation 2.7). At this stage, the chain of events has started that will lead the fragment, almost inevitably, to become a normal main sequence star. For this reason, we are now justified in calling the fragment a **protostar**.

From a protostar to the main sequence

Figure 3.3 shows the predicted tracks for protostars of various masses as they evolve towards the main sequence region on the H–R diagram. Also shown is the time-scale for this early stage of a star's evolution (from when the fragment that becomes the protostar breaks away from the parent cloud). It's clear from this that the more massive the protostar, the quicker it reaches the main sequence. For example, a protostar of $15M_\odot$ takes only about 10^5 years to reach the main sequence, less than 1% of the time that it would take a protostar of $1M_\odot$ to reach the same stage. Virtually all fragments that ultimately become main sequence stars take less than about 10^8 years to pass through the protostar phase – rather short on the astronomical time-scale.

ITQ 3.3   What does this fact mean for our ability to observe this phase of stellar evolution?

Several interesting features can be seen in Figure 3.3. For example, for protostars of intermediate and low mass, the early drop in luminosity is due to the effect of the increase in surface temperature T being more than offset by the effect of the decrease in radius R: remember Equation 2.7, $L = 4\pi\sigma R^2 T^4$.

The subsequent sharp rise in temperature for all but the least massive protostars results from changes in internal conditions that will not concern us. The result is that, for protostars more massive than about $2M_\odot$, the effects of increasing surface temperature and decreasing surface area just about balance so that the luminosity changes little as the temperature increases – this is indicated by an approximately horizontal track on the H–R diagram for these protostars. Shortly before joining the main sequence, the tracks generally show a drop in luminosity as the effect of the contraction of the protostar tends to dominate over temperature effects.

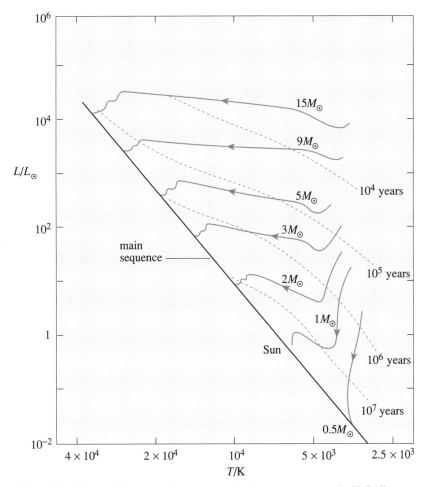

Figure 3.3 Theoretical tracks of protostars of various mass across the H–R diagram as they evolve towards the main sequence. Also shown are the times for the protostars to reach different stages of their evolution.

Our knowledge of the protostar phase of stellar evolution has been enhanced in the past 10 to 15 years by observations made by radio astronomers. They have discovered a large number of protostars that show evidence of a phenomenon called **bipolar outflow** – that is gas flowing at high velocities, typically 50 km s^{-1}, in two streams moving in opposite directions. An example is shown in Plate 1.18b, where the outflow shows up in the form of Doppler shifts in opposite directions, one a blue shift and the other a red shift (Subsection 2.2.1). Observations seem to indicate that the flows carry a significant amount of mass and require a lot of energy to sustain them – but they are believed to last for only a relatively short time, perhaps 10^4 years. How can these observations be explained?

The key to the proposed explanation lies in the probable formation of a disc of material around a protostar, shown schematically in Figure 3.4. It seems likely that this consists of material that somehow became left behind as the cloud fragment contracted. Modelling suggests that rotation of the fragment plays an important part in this process. It may be that the material farthest from the rotation axis of the fragment, around the equator, which therefore has the highest rotational motion, is not able to collapse with the rest of the fragment, and instead takes up the shape of a **circumstellar disc** or torus. If, at this stage, the protostar starts for some reason to produce a strong **stellar wind** – something that happens at various stages of a star's life, as we shall see later – then the disc will tend to channel the outflowing material so that it streams out preferentially along the axis perpendicular to the disc in the form of two streams.

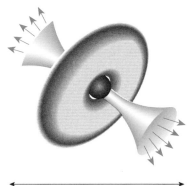

100 AU

Figure 3.4 Schematic representation of bipolar outflow showing a central protostar, a circumstellar disc or torus and a strong stellar wind. The torus confines the wind to flow predominantly in two opposing directions.

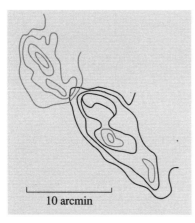

Figure 3.5 Observations of the region around IRS5 in L1551, showing measurements of Doppler-shifted emission from carbon monoxide molecules. These indicate a red shift (coloured lines) on one side and a blue shift (black lines) on the other. Plate 1.18b shows the same region.

10 arcmin

Well over 100 such objects have now been observed by radio astronomers. A good example is the young stellar object that has the catalogue number IRS5, and lies in a dense cloud, catalogue number L1551. The contour lines in Figure 3.5 show the variation of the intensity of radio waves emitted in the region around L1551. The coloured contours show where the frequency has undergone a red Doppler shift, and the black contours indicate a blue shift. This is very indicative of bipolar outflow. The model as shown in Figure 3.4 may explain the principal observed features in such sources, although current thinking suggests that the disc alone cannot channel the outflows, and that magnetic fields probably play a part too.

Another class of objects that is thought to be relevant to the early stages of evolution are the **T Tauri** stars, named after the first to be discovered, the star T in the constellation Taurus. They show several telltale signs of instability and youth, including:

- They generally lie to the right of the main sequence on the H–R diagram, just where protostars are supposed to lie;
- They usually appear in or near dense clouds;
- Many show an infrared excess (a higher flux in the infrared part of the spectrum than would be expected from a main sequence star at the appropriate temperature), suggesting a surrounding dust shell, probably in the process of being blown away;
- They often show irregular variability.

Other evidence indicates that they are young stars of age 10^5 to 10^8 years and that they are losing mass through stellar winds of high speed (up to 100–200 km s^{-1}). This is consistent with the previously discussed model of bipolar outflow sources that requires a strong stellar wind. It is thought that stars can lose as much as $0.5M_\odot$ in the form of a stellar wind during the T Tauri stage. Some T Tauri stars also show evidence of thin discs of circumstellar material, again consistent with the models of bipolar outflow sources, though in T Tauri stars the outflow is in all directions. From these observed properties, it is concluded that T Tauri stars are pre main sequence stars, in the mass range from about $0.2M_\odot$ to about $2.0M_\odot$, which are in their final spasmodic stage of birth and approaching the main sequence. If this interpretation is correct, they can be used as tracers of the behaviour of pre main sequence stars of these masses.

Let's attempt to bring together some of this observational evidence on the ever-useful H–R diagram. In Figure 3.6 a series of evolutionary tracks for pre main sequence stars of various masses is plotted. They are called **Hayashi tracks** after the Japanese astrophysicist Chushiro Hayashi (1920–) who was pre-eminent in studying the evolution of pre main sequence stars in the 1960s. You may notice, incidentally, that these tracks differ in detail from those for a similar part of a star's life shown in Figure 3.3. This emphasizes that astronomers are not sure about the detailed evolution of a protostar onto the main sequence. Although the broad features are generally agreed on, the fine detail depends on various assumptions made in appropriate models. The line marked as 'birthline' represents the positions on the various Hayashi tracks where, according to one of the models, stars become optically visible. The dots in Figure 3.6 mark the positions of observed T Tauri stars and stars that show evidence of major outflow (mostly in the form of bipolar outflow). They do indeed fall mostly in the region between the birthline and the main sequence. In addition, there seem to be more lying on Hayashi tracks for the lower masses, consistent with our knowledge that low mass stars are more common than high mass stars. The general interpretation of both T Tauri stars and stars showing major outflow being associated with the early stages of stellar evolution is well borne out by these observations.

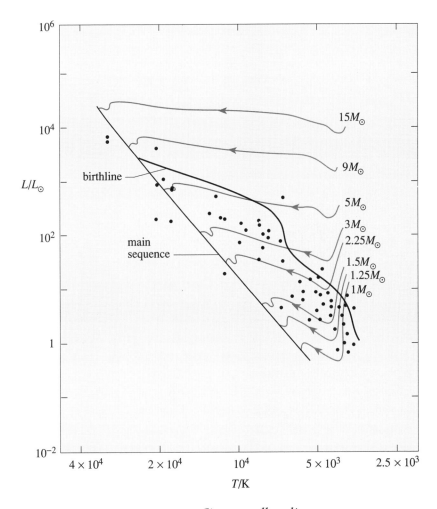

Figure 3.6 H–R diagram for a selection of T Tauri stars and stars showing evidence of major outflow.

Circumstellar discs

The suggestion that discs of material may be associated with bipolar outflow sources and with some T Tauri stars poses the exciting possibility that this might be the material from which a planetary system may form, and that planetary formation might therefore be a widespread phenomenon in our galaxy. Further exciting evidence has been collected in the past decade on this subject by the Infrared Astronomical Satellite (IRAS). IRAS discovered that the spectra of various stars showed an infrared excess, probably because the stars are surrounded by a shell or disc of solid particles or dust. This material absorbs radiation from the central star and re-radiates at infrared wavelengths corresponding to the lower temperature ($T < 100$ K) of the dust. For some stars, the observations implied that the dust was in the form of a disc rather than a shell, giving support to the belief that what was being observed was the early stages of planetary system formation. One example of infrared excess observed by IRAS was from the bright star Vega ('vee-ga'). The data imply that the dust grains responsible for the infrared radiation are about a thousand times larger than typical interstellar dust grains. The shell or disc has a diameter of roughly 170 AU, about twice the diameter of our Solar System. Vega is a young star, perhaps only 20% of the Sun's age, so the observations seem consistent with the suggestion that the dust is a sign of recent planetary formation.

Exciting data are also emerging from ground-based observations. Plate 1.19a shows an image of the region close to the star β Pictoris (Greek beta). The light from the star itself has been blocked out as it would otherwise swamp the much fainter light from the disc, which appears to extend out to 400 AU from the star. An artists's impression is shown in Plate 1.19b. We shall return briefly to β Pictoris in Book 2.

It is time, however, to return to the protostar, which is now about to enter one of the most important stages of its entire life. Although there are differences in the details of the various models of this stage, they all essentially show a continuous rise in temperature (though losses through radiation may slow this down) as the gravitational energy decreases. The critical point comes when the temperature in the centre, or **core**, of the protostar becomes sufficient for nuclear fusion to be triggered in the core. *The energy released raises the core temperature sufficiently to halt contraction, and marks the protostar's arrival as a new main sequence star.* You learned in Subsection 1.5.4 that it is nuclear fusion that is the power source in the Sun, so you shouldn't be surprised to hear that this is thought to be so for all main sequence stars.

This would be a good place for you to watch video sequence 3, Formation of protostars. *Remember to read the associated notes.*

Summary of Section 3.2 and SAQs

1 Stellar evolution occurs on such a long time-scale that it cannot be directly observed.

2 Observational and theoretical evidence points to dense interstellar clouds as being the place where star formation begins.

3 An external trigger mechanism is believed to cause a cloud to start contracting under the influence of gravitational forces.

4 The Jeans criterion, despite being a simplified approach, makes useful predictions of the mass that a cloud, or part of one, must achieve before gravitational forces overcome those due to the thermal kinetic energy of the gas and contraction is able to start. The Jeans mass is given by

$$M_{\mathrm{J}} = \frac{9}{4} \times \left(\frac{1}{2\pi n}\right)^{1/2} \times \frac{1}{m^2} \times \left(\frac{kT}{G}\right)^{3/2} \qquad (3.1)$$

5 As contraction of a dense cloud continues, it is thought that the cloud fragments into smaller parts, each of which may continue to contract, as long as the Jeans criterion is satisfied for that particular fragment.

6 Gravitational contraction is accompanied by a rise in the temperature throughout the fragment, though this is moderated by the escape of radiation from the fragment, particularly until the fragment becomes opaque.

7 The temperature continues to increase and the size to decrease, both at a rate and in a way that depend predominantly on the mass of the fragment – now a protostar.

8 Some protostars show evidence for bipolar outflow, material flowing out in opposite directions at high speed.

9 T Tauri stars are pre main sequence stars of mass below about $2M_{\odot}$, showing strong stellar winds and variations in luminosity.

10 Observational evidence points to the existence of discs of material around certain young stars, and some of these may be planetary systems in the process of formation.

11 When the temperature in the core of the protostar rises sufficiently, nuclear reactions are triggered. This provides the energy source to prevent further contraction, and at this stage the protostar has joined the main sequence and become a fully fledged star. The time for a fragment to reach this stage is generally less than about 10^8 years; the more massive the fragment, the shorter the time.

SAQ 3.1 (Objective 3.3)   A particular spherical dense cloud has a radius of 3 pc and a particle number density of $10^9 \, m^{-3}$. Calculate whether this cloud contains enough material for a star or stars to form from it. (Assume that all the material in the cloud is in the form of H_2 molecules.)

SAQ 3.2 (Objectives 3.6)   What observational evidence from Doppler shifts can distinguish the mass outflow in a typical T Tauri star from that in bipolar outflow?

SAQ 3.3 (Objective 3.3 and 3.4)   A dense cloud is compressed, such that a denser core of solar mass inside it increases in density and temperature, as in the table below. Assuming that the core consists mostly of H_2 molecules, and by considering the Jeans mass in each case, discuss whether the core will contract to form a star.

	Uncompressed	Compressed
number density/m^{-3}	5×10^9	8×10^{11}
temperature/K	10	25

3.3   Main sequence lifetime

3.3.1   Stellar structure

We shall start our investigation of main sequence stars by looking at the physical conditions that exist inside a typical star – the pressure, the density and the temperature, for example – and the way in which these parameters vary with position within a star. If we take our Sun as an example, we saw in Chapter 1 that these parameters can be measured for the outer layers, the corona, chromosphere and photosphere. How they change deeper in the Sun, however, can't be known from direct observation as those regions are essentially inaccessible. We have to rely on indirect information, which leads to theoretical models of the variation of temperature, pressure, density and composition with depth, as shown in Figures 1.27 and 1.28.

The situation with stars other than the Sun is clearly much more problematic. Yet, in order to understand the way that different stars evolve we *do* need to have an understanding of these interior conditions, because it is these that dictate, to a large extent, the nature, the rate and the extent of the nuclear processes.

The study of these conditions involves the construction of a set of equations, known as the **equations of stellar structure**, which allow us to predict the variation of the various physical properties in a star. The development of these equations has absorbed a great deal of effort by astronomers and physicists over the past 50 years and is still continuing, with an ever-increasing degree of sophistication being achieved. The complete equations and the associated theory are quite complex but, by making various simplifying assumptions, it is possible to study basic properties of stars and to derive some limited quantitative information about their structure. We shall briefly look at the way in which some of the equations are derived, without in any sense attempting a rigorous determination.

Before we do that, however, we can make some general observations. Because energy appears to be lost from the surface of a star, in the form of radiation and perhaps particles, and is released within a star, it appears likely that the temperature generally increases as we go deeper into a star. A temperature gradient in this direction is needed to maintain an outward flow of energy. Also, the pressure must increase with increasing depth because of the increasing amount of overlying material. However, properties such as pressure, temperature, density, and various of the intrinsic properties of the material that constitutes the star, such as composition, thermal conductivity, opacity (the degree to which the gas absorbs radiation), and the rate of energy generation, are all intricately inter-related, and it is one of the challenges of stellar physics to find, and solve, these relationships.

☐ Is our assertion that temperature and pressure increase with depth true for the Sun?

■ Yes, definitely! Figure 1.27 shows that both parameters increase quite sharply with depth.

What we are now proposing is simply an extension of the solar model to cover main sequence stars of all types. The physical principles involved are the same. What must be done, however, is to make the model more general in order to cope with a wide range of conditions, especially that of different stellar masses.

Temperature

In order to set up the equations that describe the flow of energy, the pressure balance and other properties of a star, astronomers often resort to the stratagem of considering a small volume at an arbitrary position within the star. They then write down the appropriate equations for that small volume only. By applying what are called boundary conditions – for example, the fact that the temperature of a small volume at the edge of the star is simply the observed surface temperature – and other constraints, such as the fact that the masses of all small volumes added up is the total mass of the star, they look for consistent solutions to the equations that yield, amongst other things, profiles of temperature and pressure against depth in the star.

If we make the assumption that the star is spherically symmetric – in other words, that its properties vary in the same way in any radial direction away from the centre – then the small volume that we should consider is a thin spherical shell, as shown in Figure 3.7. In this figure, Q is the flux of energy flowing outwards in the radial direction through the shell. It has the units of energy per unit cross-sectional area perpendicular to the direction of flow per unit time. In order to maintain this flow of energy, there must be a temperature difference between the faces of our imaginary shell; so, referring to Figure 3.7, in order to maintain an outward flow of energy, it's necessary to have T_1 greater than T_2. Thus, we expect temperature to increase with depth.

The exact difference between T_1 and T_2 depends not only on the rate of energy flow (a higher rate of energy transfer generally requiring a larger temperature difference), but also on the properties of the gas itself, such as its composition and pressure.

Pressure

One of the simplifying assumptions that is made is that the stellar material, at least for main sequence stars, behaves as a so-called perfect or **ideal gas**. If you have come across the concept of an ideal gas before, you may be surprised to hear that we can apply it at the high densities that are believed to exist deep inside a main sequence star. The reason that we can do so with confidence is because of the very high temperatures inside a star, which ensure that, at least for a main sequence star, the concept is valid. This means that we can use simple equations, such as the **ideal gas law,** which states, in one form:

$$P = k\rho T/m \tag{3.2}$$

where P is the gas pressure, ρ is the gas density, m is the average mass of the gas particles, k is Boltzmann's constant, and T is the gas temperature. Because m is

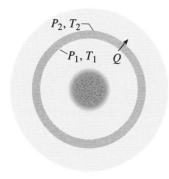

Figure 3.7 A thin spherical shell within a star to which calculations of various stellar properties are applied. The pressure and temperature at the inner and outer surfaces of the shell are calculated, as well as the heat flowing through it.

dependent on the composition of the star, this form of the equation reinforces the fact that certain of the physical properties, such as pressure, do depend on composition.

But how does the pressure vary with position in the star? To answer this question, we return to our imaginary shell in Figure 3.7. In a stable main sequence star, we assume that this shell will be stationary, or at least moving only slowly – in other words in general there will not be rapid movement of mass on a large scale, so the forces acting on the shell must approximately balance. Gravity acting on the shell will cause the material to be pulled towards the centre of the star. Opposing this will be the force due to the pressure in the gas. If P_1 and P_2 are the pressures on the inner and outer faces of the shell, then as long as P_1 is greater than P_2, the pressure difference will result in a force acting outwards, opposing that due to gravity. The pressure in a body always increases with depth, because of the growing overburden, and so P_1 must be greater than P_2. However, this gradient need not be sufficiently large to stop contraction. But if there is an internal energy source generating a temperature gradient, then, as Equation 3.2 shows, this will increase the pressure gradient. In a main sequence star the internal energy source is, of course, the nuclear power house in the core. It enables the star to achieve stable equilibrium. The variation of pressure with depth can then in principle be calculated.

Energy release and flow

We have seen when considering temperature that a temperature variation across the shell maintains a flow of energy across that shell. If the shell considered is outside the region where energy is being released then the energy flowing into the shell is equal to that flowing out. However, if the shell is in the region where energy is being released, then the rate at which energy flows out exceeds the rate at which it flows in by an amount equal to the rate of energy release within the shell.

Other equations can also be established. Rather than attempting to derive any of these equations – they can get quite complex and are beyond the scope of this Course – we shall instead show you that, by making some very simple assumptions, it is possible to make a surprisingly accurate estimate of the internal conditions in a star – temperature in this particular example.

A simple calculation of temperature in a stellar interior

Consider a star of mass M and radius R, composed of an ideal gas. Imagine it as being divided into two hemispheres, each of mass $0.5M$, as indicated in Figure 3.8.

The two hemispheres gravitationally attract each other with a force of magnitude given approximately by

$$F = \frac{G(0.5M)(0.5M)}{R^2}$$
$$= \frac{GM^2}{4R^2}$$

It has been assumed that the two hemispheres can be considered as point masses separated by a distance of R (*Preparatory science*, Subsection 1.4.1). Balancing this gravitational force on each hemisphere, which tends to make the star contract, is the outward pressure, P, of the hot gas. The pressure gradient here is provided by the difference between P inside the star, and zero pressure outside it. Let us assume that P acts over the inner surface of the hemisphere, of surface area πR^2 (see Figure 3.8). So, remembering that pressure times area is force (*Preparatory science*, Section 2.3)

$$P\pi R^2 = \frac{GM^2}{4R^2} \tag{3.3}$$

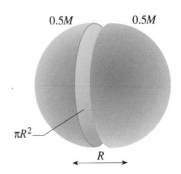

Figure 3.8 Schematic diagram of a star divided into two hemispheres for the purpose of estimating the central temperature.

We now need to use the ideal gas law:

$$P = k\rho T/m \qquad (3.2)$$

The density, ρ, is equivalent to M/V, or Nm/V, where V is the volume containing N particles each of mass m. Equation 3.2 then becomes

$$P = \frac{kNmT}{mV} = \frac{NkT}{V} \qquad (3.4)$$

For a sphere, $V = \tfrac{4}{3}\pi R^3$, so

$$P = \frac{3NkT}{4\pi R^3} \qquad (3.5)$$

Thus, eliminating P from Equations 3.3 and 3.5,

$$\frac{3NkT}{4\pi R^3} \times \pi R^2 = \frac{GM^2}{4R^2}$$

which can be rearranged to give

$$T = \frac{GM}{3kR} \times \frac{M}{N}$$

The factor M/N represents the total mass of the star divided by the total number of particles – in other words it is the average mass of a particle, m_{av}, in the whole star. Thus we have the final result

$$T = \frac{GMm_{av}}{3kR} \qquad (3.6)$$

For a so-called order of magnitude calculation such as this one, where physicists are happy to get an answer correct to 50% or so, we won't go far wrong if we assume that the star is composed entirely of ionized hydrogen, and so m_{av} is approximately equal to m_H. If we substitute values appropriate for the Sun, we find $T \approx 4 \times 10^6$ K. We should expect this to be only an approximation to the true temperature; furthermore, the actual temperature varies considerably through the star, being highest in the core, and falling towards the edge. In the case of the Sun, for example, more detailed calculations indicate a temperature in the core of the order of 1.5×10^7 K. Our very simple calculation, therefore, which has made no assumption of the method of energy release, but has used only some simple laws of physics, has given the core temperature accurate to within a factor of four. What this calculation has done is to show that the temperatures that are likely to be attained in a typical star are sufficiently high to trigger the types of nuclear reaction that are discussed in Subsection 3.3.3.

Equation 3.6 is also important because it indicates the way in which we might expect the temperature of a star to change with changing mass. From this equation we can write $T \propto M/R$. Now, if the mass of a star were to be doubled, we would expect its radius to increase by perhaps only 25%. This follows from $M = \tfrac{4}{3}\pi R^3 \rho$, provided that ρ remains roughly constant, which it does. Try it! In other words, the mass increases more rapidly than the radius, causing the ratio M/R to increase with increasing mass. It therefore follows that the temperature is predicted to rise with increasing stellar mass. This is very important and is at the root of the observation that luminosity increases dramatically for more massive main sequence stars – this **mass–luminosity relationship** was established in the 1920s by Eddington, on theoretical grounds. From it, it follows that the lifetime is expected to decrease with mass. We shall return to this later.

Energy release and transport in main sequence stars

If we accept that nuclear processes (which differ depending on a star's mass) are responsible for energy release within main sequence stars, where do we believe that these processes take place within a star? It has to be stressed that we have essentially no direct information on this question even for the Sun – but armed with the results of the modelling of the interiors of stars through the equations of stellar structure, and with our knowledge of the relevant nuclear processes, progress with this matter is possible.

☐ Why can't we assume that nuclear processes are occurring throughout the volume of most main sequence stars?

■ The surface temperatures of stars (Chapter 2) are too low for nuclear processes to be taking place at the surface, so clearly these reactions do not take place throughout a star.

For stars of all masses, nuclear reactions take place where the temperatures are greatest, which is at the centre and in a surrounding region, called the core. Because the nuclear reaction rates vary so much with temperature, this means that, moving out from the centre of a star, the boundary defining the limit of nuclear reactions is fairly sharp. What do vary with mass are the size of this region, the types of reaction that predominate, and the mechanism by which energy is transported to the outer layers of a star.

☐ Can you recall, from Chapter 1, the mechanisms by which energy can be transported from one place to another, and which do you think play an important part in main sequence stars?

■ There are three mechanisms – conduction, convection and radiation. If we regard the Sun as typical of main sequence stars, then we would expect, as we saw in Subsection 1.5.5, that convection and radiation are the dominant mechanisms of energy transfer in these stars.

Let's consider stars of low mass on the main sequence. The rate of energy release does not increase sufficiently towards the centre to set up the temperature gradient necessary to initiate convection in the core. In other words, the core is non-convective. Immediately outside the core, the temperature gradient is still too small to cause convection, and so radiation is the primary mechanism by which energy is transferred. Farther out, however, there is a region in which convection does take place, in the form of a convective shell or envelope.

Once the mass of a star exceeds about $1.5M_\odot$, the temperature of the core has risen sufficiently for a different set of nuclear reactions (we'll be looking at these shortly) to become predominant, and energy release in the core is sufficiently concentrated to trigger convective instability. Therefore the centre of the star is convective – in fact, this convective zone may extend beyond the core in which nuclear reactions are taking place. The situation for both upper and lower main sequence stars is shown in Figure 3.9.

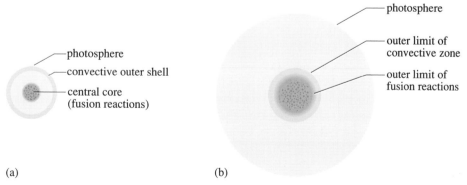

(a)   (b)

Figure 3.9   Schematic cross-section of a star of (a) $1M_\odot$ and (b) $5M_\odot$, showing the difference between the location of the convective regions.

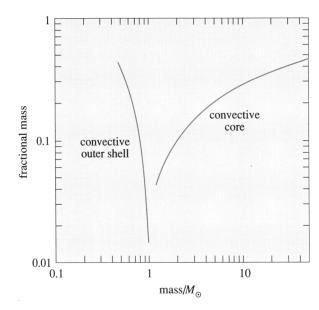

Figure 3.10 The fractional mass in the convective core or shell as a function of stellar mass.

To show you how the situation varies with the changing mass of a star, Figure 3.10 is a plot of the fractional masses in either the **convective core** or the **convective shell** as a function of the mass of a star.

ITQ 3.4   In a star of low mass, will the composition of the core change during its main sequence lifetime? If so, how?

The stability of main sequence stars

Before we leave the subject of stellar structure and related properties, it is worth considering briefly the **stability** of stars on the main sequence.

☐   What do you expect would happen to the pressure in a star if that star were to be 'stretched', so that its radius increased at constant temperature?

■   Since $P = k\rho T/m$ (Equation 3.2), the pressure will clearly fall everywhere as the density ρ falls.

Thus the force due to the variation of pressure with depth will also fall. The gravitational force will also be reduced if a star is 'stretched', but not by as much as the force due to the pressure in the gas. So the gravitational force will temporarily 'win' and cause the star to shrink again back to its original dimensions. This means that a star on the main sequence is very stable against any dimensional changes, and this contributes to the longevity of most stars on the main sequence.

Why is there a main sequence?

Finally, we shall address briefly the fundamental matter of why there is a main sequence in the first place! In 1926, Henry Norris Russell and the German physicist Heinrich Vogt ('voit') (1890–1968) derived a result, sometimes called the **Russell–Vogt theorem**, which can be stated in the following way: 'The equilibrium structure of an ordinary star is determined uniquely by its mass and chemical composition'. To put it into another form, we can say that a certain mass of stellar material of fixed composition can reach only *one stable configuration*. This stable configuration will correspond to one point on the H–R diagram. If now the mass alone changes, the star will move to a different point. This is exactly what we see along the main sequence, as in Figure 2.31. Thus, we have a main sequence because the stars on it are stable, with similar chemical compositions, but of different masses.

How can we reconcile the Russell–Vogt theorem with the fact that the H–R diagram, apart from the main sequence, also contains other regions, for example red giants, supergiants and white dwarfs. The existence of these regions would seem at first to undermine the theorem. But, as we shall see later, their existence is not necessarily contradictory, for it is the chemical composition of these stars that is different, and this allows them to occupy different regions on the H–R diagram.

3.3.2 Main sequence lifetimes

Consider the duration of a star's life on the main sequence.

☐ You have already come across some evidence in Chapter 2 that gives a clue as to how a star's lifetime on the main sequence varies with the star's properties. Can you remember the source of that evidence and what it tells us?

■ The evidence comes from looking at the H–R diagram for star clusters (Section 2.6). These show that the more massive a star, the shorter is its main sequence lifetime.

Let's try to be slightly more quantitative about the matter of main sequence lifetime. The lifetime is given by the energy available divided by the luminosity. Modelling shows that, for stars of mass less than about $1.5M_\odot$, the nuclear reactions are such that the main sequence luminosity depends on a high power of the mass, in fact $L \sim M^5$. This means that if the mass is doubled, the luminosity is increased 2^5 or 32 times! The reason for this sensitive dependence on mass is the temperature of the core – the relevant nuclear reaction rates are *very* sensitive to temperature.

In order to estimate the lifetime of a star on the main sequence, we shall make the assumption that the energy available is proportional to the total mass. Therefore, the main sequence lifetime of a star of mass less than about $1.5M_\odot$ (usually termed a **lower main sequence star**) is given by $t \propto M/L$ or $t \propto M/M^5$, and so

$$t \propto M^{-4} \tag{3.7}$$

This tells us that the lifetime of a star on the main sequence decreases rapidly with increasing mass. The expression we have just derived is for lower main sequence stars. The comparable expression for more massive stars (**upper main sequence stars**) is

$$t \propto M^{-2} \tag{3.8}$$

We now have approximate relationships for the way in which the main sequence lifetime of a star depends on its mass – but the above relationships are not equalities but proportionalities. For example, a relationship like $t \propto M^{-2}$ tells us that if the mass of a star is doubled, its main sequence lifetime changes by a factor of $(2)^{-2}$ or $\frac{1}{4}$. In other words, the lifetime is one quarter of that of the less massive star. However, we still need to fix, or 'calibrate', the lifetime scale. We do that by a variety of means, usually consisting of a mixture of observational and theoretical approaches. Using the Sun for calibration gives a main sequence lifetime of about 1×10^{10} years for a mass of $1M_\odot$. Somewhat more detailed calculations give a dependence of main sequence lifetime on mass as shown in Table 3.1. The three most massive stars listed are upper main sequence, the remaining being lower main sequence. The calculations are based on a number of simplifying assumptions, including that of constant luminosity and pure hydrogen composition initially.

It follows from Table 3.1 that massive stars, such as those of $15M_\odot$, are predicted to have relatively short main sequence lifetimes, perhaps as brief as 15 million years. This means that many of the massive upper main sequence stars currently observed must have been formed fairly recently on the astronomical timescale, and therefore provide further evidence that new stars are being formed even today.

Table 3.1 Selected properties of main sequence stars of various masses

Mass/$M_\odot$	Luminosity/$L_\odot$	Surface temperature/K	Main sequence lifetime/yr
0.50	0.03	3 800	2×10^{11}
0.75	0.3	5 000	3×10^{10}
1.0	1	6 000	1×10^{10}
1.5	5	7 000	3×10^9
3	60	11 000	5×10^8
15	17 000	28 000	1.5×10^7
25	80 000	35 000	6×10^6

3.3.3 Nuclear reactions

Before we look at some of the details of nuclear fusion in main sequence stars, we should ask whether we know of any other way in which the luminosity of these stars could be explained. In the following two ITQs you are asked to consider two particular alternative energy sources and to work out for how long each could keep the Sun shining at its present rate.

ITQ 3.5 Suppose that it is chemical energy that is responsible for the luminosity of the Sun. Assuming that 1 kg of material in the Sun yields an energy output of 3.5×10^7 J (a value typical for coal-burning on Earth), determine for how long this mechanism could sustain the Sun's present luminosity.

ITQ 3.6 Assuming that a star like the Sun contracts to a tenth of its present size, and in doing so releases gravitational energy, for how long could this power the Sun at its present luminosity? (You can assume that the gravitational energy of a sphere of radius R and mass M is approximately $-GM^2/R$.)

The answers to ITQs 3.5 and 3.6 show that these two methods of releasing energy couldn't have powered the Sun through its lifetime of about 5×10^9 years, which is still thought to be only about half of its entire main sequence lifetime. Before the development of nuclear physics in the early and middle part of the 20th century, the source of the luminosity of a typical star was something of a mystery. It was not until the development of our ideas on the structure of matter and on nuclear processes that it was eventually appreciated that nuclear fusion could provide the vast amount of energy needed to power most stars – in fact, it appears to be the only possible energy source that we know of that will do the job.

In Section 2.2 of *Preparatory science* and in the study of the Sun and its power source in Chapter 1, you were introduced to some basic ideas concerning atoms, nuclei and nuclear processes. We shall call heavily on some of these ideas and concepts in our study of the evolution of stars both in this chapter and in Chapter 4. However, you will need to know just a little bit more about nuclear processes, so this is an appropriate time to study Box 3.1.

Box 3.1 More on nuclear reactions

In Subsection 1.5.4 you met Einstein's famous equation, namely $E = mc^2$, which links mass and energy. When applied to a nucleus, of mass m, it enables us to determine the *rest energy*, mc^2, of any nucleus. This can be thought of as the energy that would be released if the nucleons (protons and neutrons) were annihilated and converted into energy alone. It is possible for us to measure the rest energy of most nuclides to high accuracy (see *Preparatory science* Section 2.2 for the definition of a nuclide). Figure 3.11 shows a plot of the rest energy *per nucleon*, mc^2/A, as a function of the mass number A, the number of nucleons in the nucleus. The general property of the curve is that the rest energy per nucleon initially decreases fairly rapidly with increasing mass number; there is then a broad minimum around values of A between 50 and 60. Then the rest energy per nucleon gradually increases for nuclei with higher values of A. The nuclide with the *lowest* rest energy per nucleon is $^{56}_{26}$Fe.

We can use Figure 3.11, or more detailed tabulated data, to work out whether a reaction is **exothermic** or **endothermic** – in other words, does the reaction release energy or does it require an input of energy in order for it to take place?

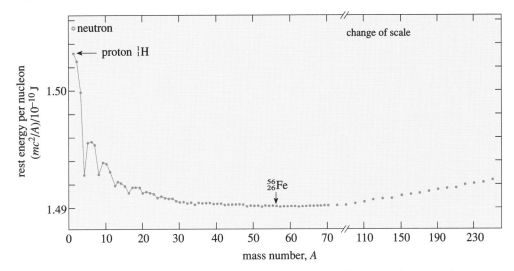

Figure 3.11   The variation of rest energy per nucleon as a function of mass number. At each mass number, the nuclide with the lowest rest energy per nucleon is shown. Beyond $A = 70$, only some mass numbers are shown.

☐   Without *calculating* rest energies, use Figure 3.11 to decide whether the reaction

$$^{12}_{6}C + {}^{4}_{2}He \longrightarrow {}^{16}_{8}O + \gamma$$

is exothermic or endothermic. (At each of the mass numbers 4, 12 and 16, these are the nuclides with the lowest rest energy per nucleon.)

■   Figure 3.11 shows that the rest energy *per nucleon* is *lower* in the product $^{16}_{8}$O than in either of the reactants $^{12}_{6}$C or $^{4}_{2}$He. With the same number of nucleons (16) in the product as in the reactants, it follows that the sum of the rest energies of the reactants exceeds that of the product, and so the reaction *releases* energy, i.e. it is exothermic. [*Comment*: That the number of nucleons in the reactants equals that in the product is in accord with the law of conservation of baryon number.]

To find the energy released in the reaction we make a quantitative calculation.

☐ Calculate the energy released in the reaction. (The rest energies for the carbon, helium and oxygen nuclei are $1.790\,4 \times 10^{-9}$ J, $5.972\,0 \times 10^{-10}$ J and $2.386\,5 \times 10^{-9}$ J, respectively*).

■ The sum of the rest energies of the reactants on the left-hand side of the reaction is $2.387\,6 \times 10^{-9}$ J. For the product, on the right-hand side, the rest energy is $2.386\,5 \times 10^{-9}$ J. There is thus an excess of 1.1×10^{-12} J in the reactants.

The translational kinetic energy of the reactants is not very different from that of the product, and so nearly all of the energy released goes into the photon – the gamma ray. You can check that 1.1×10^{-12} J corresponds to a gamma ray. Use $\varepsilon = hf$ (Equation 1.3) to convert this energy value into a frequency, and then use Figure 1.23 to check in which part of the electromagnetic spectrum it falls. It should be right in the middle of the section marked 'gamma rays'.

The fusion of two light nuclei to form a single nucleus with $A < 56$ is exothermic for nearly all pairs of reactants. However, can we determine which nuclear reactions are fast enough to be significant in the interior of stars? Various factors contribute to the rate of a particular nuclear reaction. We shall look at those factors in a qualitative way only.

First, we would clearly expect the rate to depend on the concentration (the number density) of the reactants. For the simplest case of a reaction between two particles, the rate, and thus the energy release per unit volume, is proportional to the *product* of the concentrations of the two interacting particles.

Another crucial factor is the ability of two nuclei to get close enough to each other to react.

☐ What normally prevents two nuclei from approaching very close to each other?

■ As nuclei are positively charged, it is the repulsive electrical force that tends to keep them apart.

The electric charge on a nucleus is Ze, where Z is the atomic number of the nucleus, and e is the charge on the proton. From *Preparatory science*, Subsection 1.4.2, the *magnitude*, F_e, of the repulsive electrical force between nuclei with atomic numbers Z_1 and Z_2 is given by

$$F_e = A_0(Z_1e)(Z_2e)/r^2 \tag{3.9}$$

where A_0 is a universal constant, and r is the separation of the nuclei. Nuclear reactions can occur if the particles approach close enough to each other in spite of the repulsive electrical force; this occurs if the relative velocity of the two particles is high enough. Of course, the temperature is the main factor that dictates the relative velocity of particles in a gas. Although for a given temperature, particles in a gas will exhibit a range of speeds, the average speed is proportional to the square root of the temperature (see *Preparatory science*, Subsection 2.4.1). This means that for the velocity of the nuclei to be high enough for the repulsive electrical force to be overcome in an appreciable number of encounters, the temperature also generally needs to be high.

---

* For historical (and practical) reasons, physicists often use the unit of the electronvolt (abbreviated to eV) and its derivatives, kilo- and mega-electronvolt for rest energy rather than the SI unit of energy, the joule (J). You needn't be concerned about this, but should be aware of it. The conversion is $1\,\text{eV} = 1.602 \times 10^{-19}$ J.

We can also see from Equation 3.9 that the higher the electric charges of interacting nuclei, the greater is the repulsive electrical force between them. This generally means that nuclear reactions between light elements occur at an appreciable rate at lower temperatures than reactions between heavy elements.

With this information, you should begin to see that light elements in a star can be gradually converted into heavier elements as a star evolves, and that, if the temperature within the star rises, these heavier elements can also undergo nuclear reactions. Figure 3.11 shows that most of these fusion reactions are exothermic until the product nucleus has a mass number of about 56.

You have already learnt in Subsection 2.3.5 that the majority of stars have a remarkably similar composition to each other and to the Sun: 92% of all nuclei are hydrogen, about 7.8% are helium and the remaining 0.2% is made up of the other elements. In view of the great preponderance of hydrogen, and that $Z = 1$ for hydrogen, it is clear that we should be looking to hydrogen for the source of nuclei to take part in the exothermic nuclear fusion reactions described in Box 3.1. It is now firmly believed that the most important series of nuclear reactions occurring in main sequence stars are those that convert hydrogen into helium. This is termed **hydrogen burning**.

There are a various routes by which hydrogen can be converted into helium. However, some reactions are excluded by the conservation laws.

☐ Can you remember which conservation laws are relevant to nuclear reactions?

◼ They are the conservation of charge, baryon number and energy.

The hydrogen burning routes that are not excluded by the conservation laws each involve a chain of reactions, whose overall effect is the conversion of hydrogen nuclei into helium nuclei. Several such chains are believed to play an important part in the cores of main sequence stars. The particular temperature in the Sun's core dictates that the **ppI chain (or cycle)** (Subsection 1.5.4) should dominate, but that isn't necessarily the case in other stars. In stars with cores of progressively higher temperature than the Sun, we find that two other chains become important. These two are called the **ppII** and the **ppIII chains (or cycles)**.

☐ What do the names ppII and ppIII tell you about these particular nuclear reaction chains?

◼ By analogy with the ppI chain, these reaction chains start with the interaction of two protons.

Moreover, for each of the pp chains, the net effect is the production of a helium nucleus, $^4_2$He, from four protons ($^1_1$H), as follows (see also Subsection 1.5.4):

$$4\,^1_1\text{H} \longrightarrow\ ^4_2\text{He} + 2\text{e}^+ + 2\nu + 2\gamma$$

The neutrinos produced in the pp chains, by virtue of their very low probability of interacting with other matter, essentially all escape from the star in which they are produced. They carry off about 2% of the energy released in the formation of every helium nucleus. Incidentally, the neutrinos detected in the underground detector described in Subsection 1.5.6 are those produced in the ppIII chain. They are of higher energy than those released in the ppI or ppII chain, making them easier to detect. Unfortunately, in the case of the Sun, reactions in the ppIII chain are relatively rare because it is the ppI chain that dominates.

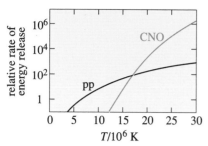

Figure 3.12 The rate of energy release for the three pp and CNO reaction chains as a function of temperature. A relative abundance of the elements as for the Sun has been assumed.

As we move to stars with yet hotter cores, we find a different set of reactions becoming important. These are reactions that involve the nuclei of carbon, nitrogen and oxygen. As in the pp cycles, the net effect of this set of reactions is the production of a $^4_2$He nucleus from four protons; however C, N and O act as *catalysts* – that is, they help the reactions to take place. Although the relative abundances of the various isotopes of C, N and O may change, the combined concentration of these three elements, which is anyway low in main sequence stars, remains unchanged. This set of reactions is termed the **CNO chain (or cycle)**.

Figure 3.12 shows the rate of energy release as a function of temperature for both the pp and CNO reaction chains (the three pp chains have been added together for this purpose). As we can see, up to a temperature of about 17×10^6 K, it is the pp cycles that contribute most to energy generation within stars. Above that temperature, even though the pp cycles generate energy at an increasing rate, they are outstripped by the rate due to the CNO cycle. It is clear that the rate of energy generation depends heavily on the temperature – note the log scale. In the region where the two sets of reactions (pp and CNO) contribute equally to energy generation, the rates of energy production can be approximated by the following simple relations. For the pp chains

$$R_{pp} \propto nT^5 \tag{3.10}$$

and for the CNO cycle

$$R_{CNO} \propto nT^{17} \tag{3.11}$$

where R is the appropriate rate of energy generation, n is the number density of the reactant nuclei, and T is the temperature. The very high powers to which the temperature is raised in these equations go some way to explaining why certain stellar properties are so sensitive to a star's temperature. For example, in Subsection 2.5.2 you were told that for a 'mere' increase in mass along the main sequence by a factor of 600, the corresponding stellar luminosity increased by a factor of 10^{12}! This incredibly sensitive dependence of luminosity on mass can now be understood in the light of Equations 3.10 and 3.11, if you recall from Subsection 3.3.1 that the greater the mass the greater the temperature of the core.

The designation of upper and lower main sequence is a reflection of the division in mass (and therefore temperature) between those stars in which the pp cycles dominate and those in which it is the CNO cycle that takes a dominant role. This division occurs at a mass of around $1.5 M_\odot$, corresponding to a core temperature of about 17×10^6 K. For more massive stars, in other words upper main sequence stars, the mass is greater and the temperature is higher, and the CNO cycle provides most of the energy generated. For less massive stars, lower main sequence stars, the temperature is lower and it is therefore the pp cycles that are the main source of energy. The Sun falls into this latter category with a temperature nowhere higher than 15×10^6 K. In these circumstances, it is thought that the ppI cycle is predominant over the others.

3.3.4 The masses of stars

What can we say, if anything, about the *distribution* of the masses of stars? For example, do stars all tend to have a similar mass or do they cover a wide range of masses? If so, are we equally as likely to find a low mass star as to find a massive star?

☐ Can you recall from Section 2.5 the only technique we have for the direct determination of the masses of stars?

■ The only direct method of measuring the mass of a star is by studying the dynamics of a binary system. This can then directly give us the masses of the component stars.

116

For all other stars, the techniques are less direct.

Although the measurement of mass of any one star might not be possible to high precision, if we observe a large number of stars, we can expect the overall trend to be known to a reasonably high degree of accuracy. A plot of the mass distribution function is shown in Figure 3.13. This confirms what was stated in Section 2.5 – namely that star masses cover the approximate range from $0.08M_\odot$ to $50M_\odot$. The figure also indicates that far more stars have a low mass than a large mass. While we can believe that the relative rarity of massive stars is a genuine feature, at the other end of the mass range, the observations that contribute to Figure 3.13 may be suffering from a selection effect: if we observe stars at random, there is clearly a bias towards observing brighter stars. The less massive a star is, the less luminous it is and the harder it is to observe, so that we might be underestimating the true number.

Despite this difficulty, it appears that no star of mass less than about $0.08M_\odot$ has been found, and we have solid theoretical grounds for believing that there is a lower limit to the mass of a conventional main sequence star. We have already seen that the smaller the mass of the star, the lower the core temperature.

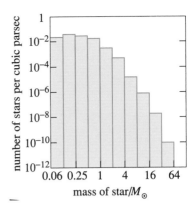

Figure 3.13 The number of stars observed as a function of stellar mass (based on observations of stars in the vicinity of the Sun).

☐ What will be the effect on nuclear processes, such as the pp cycles, of reducing the temperature of a star?

■ Figure 3.12 shows that the rate of energy generation will be reduced. Eventually, a temperature will be reached at which the nuclear reaction rate is insignificant.

So we have good reasons for believing that the mass distribution function (Figure 3.13) should have a cut-off at the low mass end of the scale, and calculations show that this should occur at around a value of $0.05M_\odot$.

Objects that are more massive than planets but do not have sufficient mass (approximately $0.05M_\odot$) to trigger nuclear reactions are usually referred to as **brown dwarfs**: brown because at the predicted surface temperature of these objects, they would be expected to glow with a dim, brownish red light, and dwarf, clearly, because of their size. Some astronomers believe that they might be very common objects in our galaxy. If the distribution of masses indicated by Figure 3.13 were to continue to lower masses, this would be the case. However, if they do exist, their extreme faintness makes them very difficult to detect with certainty. Over recent years, several brown dwarf candidates have been discovered, but there are difficulties associated with all of them, and to date, most astronomers agree that no brown dwarf has yet been observed with any certainty.

The likely evolutionary track of a brown dwarf on the H–R diagram is shown in Figure 3.14. It evolves straight past the main sequence because significant nuclear reactions are never triggered.

What about the situation at the other end of the mass range?

☐ Have you learnt of any reason why the mass of a star should have an upper limit?

■ From the discussion so far, the only obvious limitation comes from the mass of the original contracting cloud. As typical clouds can have masses of several thousand solar masses or more, this is not a severe limitation.

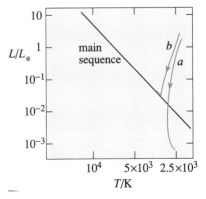

Figure 3.14 The path, a, of a star of very low mass ($<0.05M_\odot$), which evolves straight past the main sequence, and the path, b, of a star of mass $\approx 0.3M_\odot$, as it evolves on to the main sequence.

However, there is a process that is not important in most stars but which plays a crucial part in the most massive stars. This process is **radiation pressure**, the pressure exerted by photons of light, or of any other form of electromagnetic radiation. For photons, the radiation pressure is given by

$$P_{rad} = \tfrac{1}{3}\alpha T^4 \qquad (3.12)$$

where α is a constant, 7.55×10^{-16} Pa K^{-4}.

We can use a variant of Equation 3.4 to write the gas pressure as

$$P_{gas} = nkT \qquad (3.13)$$

where we have used the fact that the number density $n = N/V$.

ITQ 3.7   Estimate the ratio of the radiation pressure to the gas pressure at the core of the Sun. (*Hint*: in order to calculate n, determine an average value by using the mass and radius of the Sun; also assume that the Sun is composed entirely of ionized hydrogen.) Use Figure 1.27 for a more realistic estimate of the density at the centre of the Sun. How does this affect the answer? (A qualitative assessment will do.)

We see therefore that radiation pressure is almost negligible in comparison with the gas pressure, at least in a star like the Sun. However, is this likely to be the case for all stars?

☐   What do you think will happen to the effect of radiation pressure in relation to the gas pressure as the temperature increases?

■   In ITQ 3.7, it was shown that $P_{rad}/P_{gas} = \alpha\, T^3/3nk$. Therefore as T increases, the effect of radiation pressure compared with that of gas pressure will increase very quickly.

Whereas the stability of 'normal' main sequence stars results from a balance between the gravitational force and the force due to gas pressure, it appears that for more massive stars a balance between the force due to radiation pressure and the gravitational force is needed for a stable star. However, detailed modelling shows that radiation pressure increases so rapidly with temperature that such a star would be easily 'blown apart' by the radiation pressure. Detailed calculations show that the upper limit to the mass of a star falls somewhere in the range from $50M_\odot$ to $100M_\odot$. This is not inconsistent with the mass distribution shown in Figure 3.13.

3.3.5   Stellar winds

Subsection 1.4.3 introduced us to the idea of the solar wind. It was suggested that it originates from material that has 'boiled off' from the solar corona, perhaps from regions where the magnetic field does not confine the material. If we make the assumption that the Sun is a typical main sequence star, then we might expect that a similar wind is exhibited by most stars – in which case, it should be termed a stellar wind.

ITQ 3.8   Using the following data for the solar wind at a distance of 1 AU from the Sun, estimate the mass lost from the Sun per year in both kilograms and in units of solar mass. (Particles other than protons can be neglected for this calculation.) (*Hint*: a spherical shell, radius r and thickness Δr, has a volume $4\pi r^2 \Delta r$.)

number density of protons	$5 \times 10^6 \, m^{-3}$
outward speed from Sun	$250 \, km \, s^{-1}$

We see therefore that the rate of mass loss from a star like the Sun is small. Even if we integrate this mass loss over the Sun's main sequence lifetime, it comes to little more than 10^{-4} of the total mass. Observations of the mass loss from other stars are very difficult owing to the low rates of mass loss and the distance to the stars, so data are very sparse. What information there is, coupled with theoretical studies, shows that the rate of mass loss is expected to increase with increasing stellar mass such that for a massive star of $50M_\odot$, the rate of mass loss is expected to be of the order of $5 \times 10^{-7}M_\odot$ per year. In view of the very much shorter main sequence lifetime of such a star, the proportion of the total mass lost over the main sequence lifetime is still small.

Despite the relatively small amount of material involved in a typical stellar wind, it is one means by which material is returned from a star into the interstellar medium, and by virtue of this fact, it is a phenomenon that should be studied and well understood. What do we expect the composition of this material to be? You should recall from Figure 3.10 that whether convection takes place in a shell (for low mass stars) or in a convective core (for higher mass stars), the products of the nuclear reactions in the core of a star are not brought to the surface of the star by convection. This has the important consequence that the material being recycled by main sequence stellar winds is thought not to be enriched in heavy elements (predominantly helium) from the nuclear processes occurring in the core, but is representative of the material from which the star first formed.

The main sequence stellar wind isn't the only means by which a star loses material to the interstellar medium. We have already encountered one other episode when significant mass loss takes place – namely the T Tauri phase – and later we shall encounter others, including red giant stellar winds, planetary nebulae, novae and supernovae.

Summary of Section 3.3 and SAQs

1   Stellar models allow astronomers to predict the variation of such physical properties as temperature, pressure and density within a star during its main sequence lifetime. These properties can be verified only indirectly.

2   The mode of energy transfer within a star depends on its mass. For a star of mass less than about $1.5M_\odot$, convection is confined to an outer shell. In a more massive star, the temperature gradient in the core is sufficient to allow convection to take place there. In such stars convection is confined to the core and the adjacent region.

3   Nuclear fusion is the source of energy that powers main sequence stars. No other mechanism is known that can provide the observed luminosities over the main sequence lifetime.

4   The main sequence on the H–R diagram represents the stable configuration of stars of different mass but similar composition, converting hydrogen into helium through nuclear fusion.

5   The lifetime of a star on the main sequence decreases rapidly with increasing mass.

6   The detailed nuclear reactions that are responsible for converting hydrogen into helium depend on the core temperature, and therefore the mass of a star. For stars of mass less than about $1.5M_\odot$ (lower main sequence stars), the pp cycles predominate. For more massive stars (upper main sequence stars), reactions involving carbon, nitrogen and oxygen as catalysts are dominant, and comprise the CNO cycle.

7   The observed masses of main sequence stars lie between approximately $0.08M_\odot$ and $50M_\odot$ with the least massive stars being most common. Theory shows that stars of mass less than about $0.05M_\odot$ never reach sufficient temperature to trigger nuclear reactions and so become brown dwarfs. At the other extreme ($\geq 50M_\odot$), radiation pressure is too great to allow a stable star to exist.

8   Stellar winds during the main sequence lifetime lead to a small proportion of a star's mass being ejected into the interstellar medium.

9   Some of the main properties of stars on the main sequence for a variety of masses are shown in Table 3.1.

SAQ 3.4 (Objective 3.7)   Outline the different means involved in the transport of energy from the centre of the Sun to the skin of a person standing on the surface of the Earth.

SAQ 3.5 (Objective 3.8)   Discuss whether the fusion reaction

$$^{12}_{6}C + {}^{12}_{6}C \longrightarrow {}^{24}_{12}Mg + \gamma$$

(a) is possible and (b) could be an appreciable source of energy in main sequence stars. (At each of the mass numbers 12 and 24, these are the nuclides with the lowest rest energy per nuclide.)

SAQ 3.6 (Objective 3.9)   Assuming that the age of the Earth is 4.5×10^9 years, determine the mass of the most massive star now on the main sequence that was also on the main sequence at the time of the Earth's formation.

SAQ 3.7 (Objective 3.9)   Using data from Table 3.1, and the logarithmic graph paper provided, (a) draw a graph of luminosity against mass for main sequence stars and estimate the mass of a star that has a luminosity of $300L_\odot$, and (b) draw a graph of lifetime against mass, and hence confirm the more sensitive dependence in lower main sequence stars.

3.4   Post main sequence lifetime of low mass stars

3.4.1   The giant phase

In Table 3.1, the lifetime of a main sequence star is shown as a function of mass.

☐   What determines the end of a star's lifetime on the main sequence?

■   When the hydrogen in the core is exhausted.

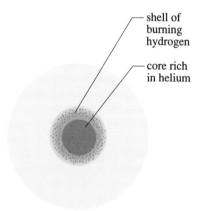

shell of burning hydrogen

core rich in helium

Figure 3.15   Schematic drawing of a star with a shell of burning hydrogen.

Remember that, generally, it is only in the core that it is hot enough for fusion reactions to occur. So the question arises – does the core get replenished with hydrogen through convective mixing between the core and the rest of the star? Convection in the core region occurs only in the more massive stars, but even there, as Figures 3.9 and 3.10 show, it does not extend much beyond the core. The rate at which hydrogen is depleted in the core is thus determined by the rate at which nuclear reactions take place there, and a critical point will be reached when the hydrogen has all gone. Once this stage has been reached, nuclear reactions in the core will stop. The core will then start to contract (slowly) as it is no longer releasing energy at a sufficient rate to generate a pressure gradient sufficient to support the surrounding layers. As a result of this contraction, gravitational energy is converted into thermal kinetic energy and a shell of unprocessed material will undergo hydrogen burning. This is illustrated in Figure 3.15. Meanwhile the core continues to contract and, in doing so, continues to heat up as more gravitational energy is converted into thermal energy. When a temperature of around 10^8 K is reached, a new range of nuclear reactions becomes possible.

☐   Bearing in mind what you know of the composition of the core at this stage and what you learned from Box 3.1, what do you think may be the next set of nuclear reactions?

■   The core now consists predominantly of helium, and from Box 3.1, we suspect that **helium fusion** reactions should now occur – these would be exothermic (Figure 3.11).

We might expect therefore that two helium nuclei would combine in some way to produce $^8_4$Be However, $^8_4$Be is very unstable and almost immediately decays back

120

to two helium nuclei. So is there any way in which helium burning can take place and nuclear reactions continue? It was as recently as the 1950s that the full details were worked out. It was appreciated that, at the temperature and density likely to prevail in the helium core of a post main sequence star, it would occasionally happen that the short-lived beryllium nucleus would meet another helium nucleus before it decayed. The result is the formation of a $^{12}_{6}C$ nucleus. The overall scheme is therefore as follows:

$$^{4}_{2}He + {}^{4}_{2}He \longrightarrow {}^{8}_{4}Be + \gamma$$
$$^{8}_{4}Be + {}^{4}_{2}He \longrightarrow {}^{12}_{6}C + \gamma$$

This chain is known as the **3α process**, α being the commonly used symbol for the helium nucleus, because the net effect is the conversion of three helium nuclei into a $^{12}_{6}C$ ucleus. The onset of the 3α process – helium burning – halts the contraction of the core and stabilizes the star.

Helium burning is initiated at temperatures of around 10^8 K but is remarkably sensitive to temperature: the rate of energy release by this process is proportional to the 40th power of temperature!

The 3α process releases 1.17×10^{-12} J of energy per $^{12}_{6}C$ nucleus, or 3.9×10^{-13} J per $^{4}_{2}He$ nucleus. This latter figure is only about 10% of the energy released in forming the helium nucleus from hydrogen. (You can check this statement from the answer to ITQ 1.12a.) This fact, coupled with the higher luminosity during this phase, ensures that the time until the helium in the core is exhausted, which we take to define the end of this phase, will be considerably shorter than the main sequence lifetime. As a rough rule of thumb, the length of the helium-burning phase is about 10% of the main sequence lifetime.

External appearances

What has been happening to the rest of the star during this post main sequence phase? The contraction of the core, which was initially slow, has speeded up under the pressure of the outer regions of the star. Simultaneously, however, the radius of the star as a whole *increases*. Although this surface expansion which accompanies the core contraction is predicted by the equations of stellar structure, the explanation is not straightforward or even completely understood. It is also predicted that this expansion is not accompanied initially by a significant change in luminosity.

ITQ 3.9   What will happen to the temperature of the outer layers of the star at this *initial* phase, bearing in mind the comment above about the star's luminosity in this immediate post main sequence phase?

As hydrogen burning in the shell around the core progresses, the luminosity is expected eventually to increase as convection carries energy to the surface. Once the core temperature has risen sufficiently, helium starts to burn in the core and the star is now a fully fledged red giant.

As an example, for a star of $1M_{\odot}$, the core will be compressed to about 1/50th of its original size and the core temperature will rise from 15×10^6 K to about 100×10^6 K. At the same time, the diameter of the star will increase by about a factor of 10, with a surface temperature of about 3 500 K. This causes the star to glow with an orange hue, and this, together with its size, gives it its (somewhat perverse!) name: red giant.

What about the paths of these stars on the H–R diagram? These are shown in Figure 3.16 for stars of different masses. The line marked A denotes the onset of hydrogen core fusion – the start of main sequence life. The dashed line B denotes the cessation of hydrogen core fusion – the end of main sequence life, and the onset of hydrogen shell fusion. Subsequent stages are labelled on the $3M_{\odot}$ track only: (C) hydrogen shell fusion continues; (D) helium core fusion starts; (E) helium core fusion continues; (F) helium shell fusion starts. Notice that as the red giant phase is approached, the tracks tend to crowd together. This indicates a fairly narrow range of conditions for red giants.

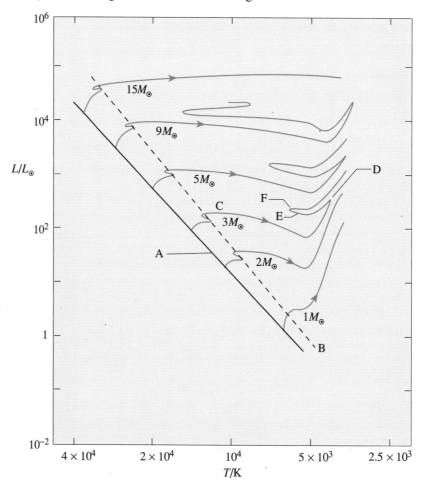

Figure 3.16 The predicted paths of stars on the H–R diagram as they evolve off the main sequence to the red giant (or supergiant) phase. The loop to the left for the $1M_\odot$ and $2M_\odot$ stars has been omitted for clarity.

After helium fusion starts in the core, the tracks retreat from a peak value of luminosity and wander backwards and forwards on the H–R diagram as the red giant readjusts to its new source of energy. You can see from Figure 3.16 that part of the track (E) is horizontal, and this is called the **horizontal branch**.

Figure 3.16 also shows that post main sequence stars are not always at temperatures that give them an orange hue – they can be far hotter than this. Such stars, with luminosities comparable with those of red giants, plus the red giants themselves, are the *giant* stars introduced in Subsection 2.4.1. Stars lying on the H–R diagram between the main sequence and the giants are, unsurprisingly, called **subgiants**. In evolutionary terms, subgiants consist largely of stars en route to becoming red giants.

The helium flash

The manner in which the helium burning starts depends on the *mass* of the star, with an important difference between stars with masses below and above about $2.25M_\odot$.

At the root of this difference is a phenomenon known as **degeneracy**. A detailed description of degeneracy is beyond the scope of this Course – it requires a knowledge of quantum mechanics. However, we do need to know something about this phenomenon in order to understand several features of the evolution of stars after they leave the main sequence. Up to now we have been able to assume that the gas inside a star behaves like an ideal gas. For such a gas, simple equations, such as Equation 3.2, can be used to describe the relationships between pressure, temperature and density for example. At the extreme densities that exist deep inside some stars, the matter may be so compressed that a different set of equations must be used to describe the physical properties of the *electrons* in the gas – remember that the atoms are ionized, so we have an electron gas mixed up with a gas of atomic nuclei. This is the so-called degenerate electron gas. It has various properties that differentiate it quite clearly from the more normal gases that we are familiar with.

We shall focus on one property in particular and see how this affects the behaviour of red giants of low mass. Equation 3.2 shows that, if the temperature of an ideal gas is increased, its pressure will increase proportionally if other properties remain unchanged. The increase in pressure leads to expansion, and hence to cooling. For a degenerate gas, however, the situation is different. When the temperature changes, the pressure is hardly affected. The pressure depends mainly on density and composition rather than temperature.

Why is this relevant to the situation we find in red giants? Well, if helium burning starts in an ideal gas, this is basically a stable process. Let's investigate this statement in slightly more detail. Suppose that a small temperature rise occurs in the helium-burning core. Because the nuclear reaction rate depends on a high power of the temperature, we can expect an increased rate of release of energy. If the stellar material is fairly opaque, the energy may not be able to escape. Therefore, the local temperature will rise – in an ideal gas, this will result in the pressure rising, the gas expanding and cooling, and therefore the rate of nuclear reactions falling. There is, in other words, an in-built stability to the whole process.

However, if helium burning starts in a degenerate gas, the situation can be very different. Because the pressure in a degenerate gas is now nearly independent of temperature, the rise in temperature on initiation of nuclear processes does not produce a consequent rise in pressure, expansion and cooling to control the initial rise in temperature. This rise in temperature therefore causes the helium burning to continue even faster. This is an unstable situation – the process can start to 'run away' and produce an explosive release of energy in the degenerate core of these lower mass stars. This is usually termed the (core) **helium flash.** This is, incidentally, believed to be one of the few cases in the history of a star where an event occurs over a time-scale perhaps as short as a matter of hours or less. However, although the helium flash happens very quickly in the core, the release of energy probably takes thousands of years to reach the surface.

One result of the helium flash is to raise the core temperature to the point where the degenerate conditions are removed (Figure 3.17). Once degeneracy is removed in this way, then the core can expand and cool and the situation will be stabilized.

Under exactly what conditions does degeneracy occur? Figure 3.17 shows a plot of density against temperature divided into two regions corresponding to normal (i.e. non-degenerate) and degenerate conditions. The transition between the two is not sharp and so is indicated by a fuzzy boundary. The region occupied by the cores of main sequence stars is indicated. Stars of lower mass, after their main sequence lifetime, evolve into the region corresponding to degenerate conditions, whereas higher mass stars achieve core temperatures at which helium burning is initiated before degenerate conditions are reached.

To summarize, the evolution of stars immediately after they leave the main sequence depends on whether degeneracy sets in before helium burning (the 3α process) is initiated. If the mass is greater than about $2.25M_\odot$, the helium reactions start before the core can become degenerate. For stars with masses less than about $2.25M_\odot$, helium burning starts in a degenerate core in a violent reaction known as a helium flash. This will probably remove the degenerate state of the core.

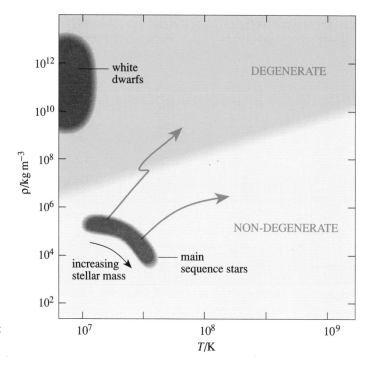

Figure 3.17 Conditions for degeneracy in an electron gas. The conditions in the cores of main sequence stars are shown, along with the directions in which the core conditions evolve in the post main sequence phase. White dwarfs are dealt with in Subsection 3.4.5.

Internal structure

The changes in the structure of a star during the post main sequence phase are qu:
complicated. In Figure 3.18, these changes are shown for a star of $5M_\odot$ as a functi
of time after leaving the main sequence. The quantity plotted on the vertical axis
the mass fraction, M_R: this is the fraction of the total mass involved as we mov
outwards from the centre of the star; $M_R = 0$ corresponds to the centre and $M_R = 1$
the surface of the star. This quantity is used rather than the radius because the nucle
reactions are taking place in a region that is very small and yet contains
appreciable proportion of the star's total mass. The compact nature of the heliur
burning inner core is clear from Figure 3.18. It is also clear that (a) hydrogen burni:
will continue in a thin shell, which will be at the surface of the helium core, thou,
well away from the helium-burning inner core, and (b) after depletion of helium
the core, helium burning will continue in a shell that moves progressively outwar
as further helium is used up. These factors are partly responsible for the tortuous pa
predicted for some stars across the H–R diagram during the giant phase (Figure 3.1(

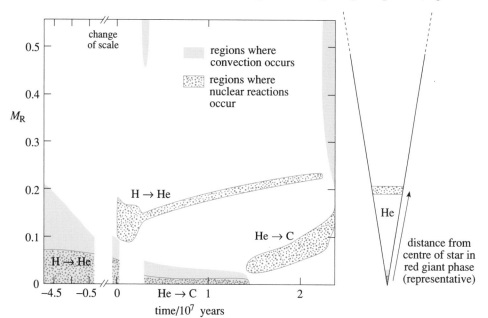

Figure 3.18 Schematic representation of the internal structure of a star of mass $\simeq 5M_\odot$ during and after its main sequence lifetime. (The main sequence lifetime ends at time zero.)

Winds from red giants

Before we finish discussing the main phase of the life of a giant, we should consider one important effect of its increased radius. The star's gravity at its surface will be very much less than what it was during its main sequence lifetime (*Preparatory science*, Subsection 1.4.1), particularly for red giants, being larger. This means that atoms in the red giant's atmosphere can more easily escape, resulting in a copious stellar wind, though at a lower velocity than that of the main sequence stellar wind. Winds from red giants can therefore be responsible for a more significant loss of the star's total mass, in contrast to the very small loss by this mechanism during the main sequence lifetime.

Very low mass stars

For stars of mass less than about $0.5M_\odot$, we find a very different story. Theoretical calculations show that the critical mass below which helium burning is unlikely to start is around $0.5M_\odot$. The evolutionary track of a star with a mass somewhere between $0.1M_\odot$ and $0.5M_\odot$ is shown in Figure 3.19. Initially, the star evolves in a similar direction (compare with Figure 3.16) to a star of slightly higher mass. However, because helium burning never starts in such a star, the luminosity soon peaks and then declines rapidly.

3.4.2 Further reactions in giants

Is there anything more that can happen to a star in the giant phase? The answer is certainly yes. In addition to the helium-burning reactions, there is another reaction that is thought to occur in all giants. The $^{12}_{6}$C nuclei produced by helium burning can capture an additional α-particle in the following reaction

$$^{12}_{6}\text{C} + ^{4}_{2}\text{He} \longrightarrow ^{16}_{8}\text{O} + \gamma$$

to produced the heavier nucleus, $^{16}_{8}$O. This reaction and the 3α process in red giants are thought to be the main sources of carbon and oxygen in the Universe.

Giants with a mass less than about $3M_\odot$ or $4M_\odot$ do not develop core temperatures high enough to trigger any further nuclear reactions beyond that which produces oxygen. The cores of such stars accumulate carbon and oxygen, the remnants of helium burning. When the helium in the core is exhausted, the core therefore begins to contract again. This heats the helium surrounding the core sufficiently to trigger helium burning, the 3α process, in the shell. This situation is shown schematically in Figure 3.20.

Shell helium burning has caused the giant to expand further and move upward on the H–R diagram for the second time. The star is now even larger – its size can be as large as the orbit of Mars! However, this situation isn't stable. The helium-burning shell is rather thin and this causes a thermal runaway to occur. The result is another helium flash, but quite different from the core helium flash that we have already met. In that case, the cause was degeneracy but now, in the helium-burning shell, the material is not compressed enough for degenerate conditions to be reached. These **shell helium flashes** are due to the fact that the shell is too insubstantial to lift the material above it. Thus, as shell helium burning gets underway, the shell cannot expand and so the temperature rise is not moderated. The helium burning rate increases, increasing the temperature further. This leads to a rapid release of energy. These flashes are thought to be approximately periodic events but separated by intervals of 10^5 years or more. These violent events may play a part in the ejection of large amounts of material, a phenomenon observed to take place towards the end of the lives of some stars, but more of that later.

For stars of intermediate mass – more than about $3M_\odot$ or $4M_\odot$ but less than about $8M_\odot$ – further reactions are possible. (The fate of the highest mass stars is so different that we shall defer discussion of them until Chapter 4.) For these intermediate stars, **carbon burning** occurs to produce neon and magnesium;

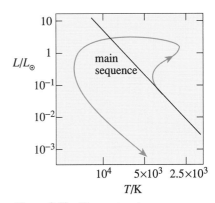

Figure 3.19 The post main sequence evolutionary track of a star of mass between approximately $0.1M_\odot$ and $0.5M_\odot$.

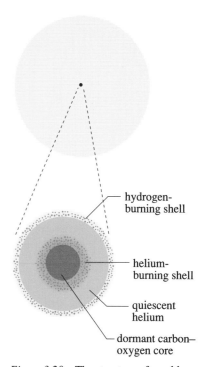

hydrogen-burning shell

helium-burning shell

quiescent helium

dormant carbon–oxygen core

Figure 3.20 The structure of an old red giant of low mass ($<4M_\odot$). The star has a size comparable with the orbit of Mars.

neutrons are also produced in substantial numbers, which allows further nuclear reactions to take place.

☐ Why should neutrons be able to react easily with a nucleus?

■ They are neutral particles, so there will be no electrostatic repulsion as would be the case if they possessed a positive charge. Thus reactions can take place at low temperatures.

The neutrons initiate a series of reactions, known as **s-process reactions** (s for slow). These build up the concentration of intermediate mass nuclides, i.e. mass number up to 56, and they also create some nuclides that are yet more massive. However, others of these more massive nuclides can be created only by reactions that do not occur in giants – you will meet such reactions in Chapter 4.

The various processes that have been discussed in the giant phase explain why the evolutionary track on the H–R diagram at this time is predicted to be quite complicated (Figure 3.16). Every time a new energy source dominates the star's evolution, the direction on the H–R diagram is likely to change. We should remember, however, that this part of a star's lifetime is short compared with the main sequence lifetime – for a $1M_\odot$ star, 10^9 years as opposed to 10^{10} years. This is why we would expect to observe relatively few stars at this stage of their evolution.

3.4.3 Variable stars

What happens next to the giant? Well, it appears that many stars at this stage become variable. You have already been introduced to such stars in Subsection 2.4.2. The observed effects are believed to be due to some kind of instability in the structure of the star. It is thought that this occurs in the outer layers, which are alternately compressed and expanded. This may result from self-sustaining oscillations due to the changing opacity (a measure of the absorption of radiation) of the atmosphere. Calculations show that, for certain combinations of stellar parameters, these oscillations are to be expected.

ITQ 3.10   If the outer layers of a star oscillate so that the radius changes by ± 2%, by how much would you expect the observed luminosity to change (assume that the surface temperature does not change)?

Other causes of variability are known (including those involving mass transfer in binaries, inhomogeneous atmospheres, etc.), but the type involving oscillations of the atmosphere are primarily associated with this particular late stage of stellar evolution. Because this phenomenon appears to require a particular combination of atmospheric parameters, we shouldn't be surprised to learn that these stars appear to occupy certain well-defined regions of the H–R diagram. The pulsating classes of stars include the Cepheids and RR Lyrae stars. (The names arise from those given to the first star of each particular type to be discovered.)

The region on the H–R diagram in which the pulsating stars lie is termed the **instability strip**, and it corresponds to the conditions of temperature and density under which self-sustaining oscillations are predicted (Figure 3.21). The instability strip extends from the supergiant region to the white dwarf region. During the course of its evolution, probably almost every star will pass through this region and thus display this type of instability. Comparison of Figures 3.16 and 3.21 shows that, in the post main sequence phase, the part of the instability strip that will be crossed depends on a star's mass, and thus stars of different mass might be expected to fall into different pulsating classes. A recent star catalogue lists about 6 800 stars that are believed to be variables of the pulsating atmosphere type, so they clearly are relatively common.

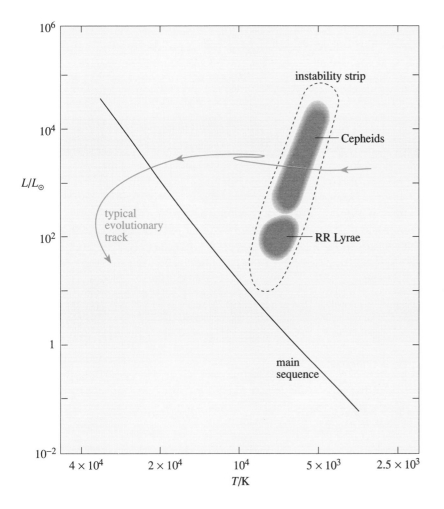

☐ Because this type of variability involves the periodic movement of the outer layers of a star, state an effect that you met earlier that might be detectable in these stars.

■ The Doppler effect, which involves a shift in the wavelength of a spectral line if the source is moving with respect to the observer. [*Comment*: This is sometimes detectable for pulsating stars.]

Figure 3.22 shows the variations observed for the star δ Cephei. In the case of Cepheids, it is believed to be the variation of surface temperature, resulting from changes in the stars' size, that is primarily responsible for the luminosity changes.

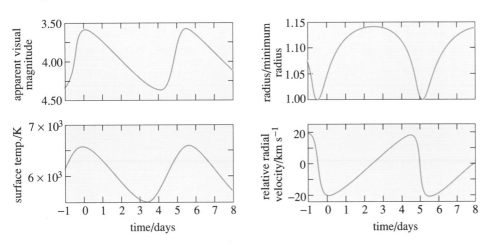

Figure 3.22 The variation of (a) apparent visual magnitude, (b) surface temperature, (c) radius and (d) relative radial velocity over one complete oscillation of period 5.4 days for the star δ Cephei.

The study of variable stars is a very important tool that enables astronomers to probe the structure of stars, and can potentially yield more information than observations of non-varying stars. The time a star spends on the instability strip is thought to be not particularly long, and ends once the causes of instability are removed by the continued evolution of the star.

3.4.4 Planetary nebulae

Extended gaseous envelopes of the type shown in Plate 1.27, when observed in the 18th century, were given the name **planetary nebulae** because of the apparent similarity of their disc-like appearance in small telescopes to planets. However, the name, although universally accepted, is entirely inappropriate. These objects have nothing to do with planets! They are now known to be large, somewhat tenuous gas shells, also containing some dust, expanding with typical velocities of a few tens of kilometres per second. Their mass is typically between $0.1M_{\odot}$ and $0.2M_{\odot}$, and they often seem to be associated with hot stars that are contracting while the envelopes themselves are expanding. Observations also seem to indicate that planetary nebulae are generally 'disconnected' from the star. They are also relatively common, with of the order of a thousand having been detected.

How do planetary nebulae fit into the picture of stellar evolution? All the evidence points to their being generated during the giant phase or afterwards. The exact method of their expulsion is not completely clear. Is it possible, perhaps, that they result from the pulsations of the outer layers of a star during its time in the instability strip, maybe being the result of pulsations that have grown very large? Or perhaps their release is triggered by the shell helium flashes discussed in Subsection 3.4.2. Or, rather than a sudden expulsion of matter, they may simply represent the continuing expansion and ultimate mass loss from a giant during its advanced stages of evolution. Whatever the generating mechanism, it seems that planetary nebulae are dissipated into the interstellar medium after a time of at most 10^5 years after ejection from the parent star.

3.4.5 White dwarfs

After a star has shed a planetary nebula it is rapidly approaching the final stages of its life. It is at this stage that the **white dwarfs** are believed to fit into our evolutionary picture. You have already been briefly introduced to white dwarfs (Subsection 2.4.1) and seen their position on the H–R diagram (Figure 2.23).

☐ What properties of white dwarfs can you recall?

■ They are very small (Earth-sized) and have surface temperatures of about 10^4 K.

Why should we connect these objects with the late stages of stellar evolution? One clue comes from looking at the central stars of planetary nebulae on the H–R diagram. These are shown in Figure 3.23, together with the positions of typical white dwarfs. If we assume that the star at the centre of a planetary nebula is the hot core of a giant that is running out of nuclear fuel, and that the only course left open to it is to cool and contract under gravity, then we can predict that it would evolve along the track shown, ending in the region of the white dwarfs. This is the type of evolutionary picture that is generally accepted today by astronomers. Let's assume that this is broadly speaking correct, and take a closer look at some properties of white dwarfs.

It is widely believed that the core of a white dwarf consists of electron degenerate material. With no possibility of initiating any further nuclear reactions, the giant remnant, possibly devoid of its outer layers through a combination of the copious stellar wind in the giant phase and the ejection of a

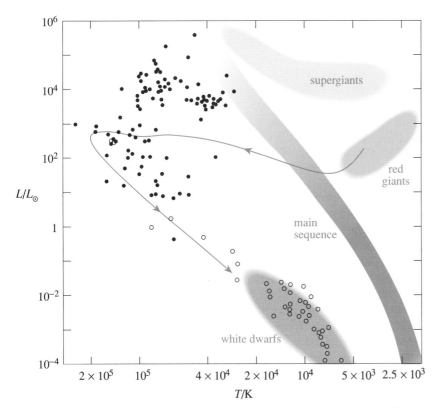

Figure 3.23   The positions of central stars associated with planetary nebulae (dots) and of white dwarfs (open circles) on the H–R diagram. Also shown is a predicted evolutionary track for a star of around $0.8M_{\odot}$.

planetary nebula, contracts under the force of gravity. The density in the core shoots up until electron degenerate conditions are created. This assertion is supported by reference to Figure 3.17. The density and temperature conditions believed to pertain in the cores of white dwarfs are shown – they are clearly in the area where material is electron degenerate.

What implication does the fact that a white dwarf is probably composed of electron degenerate material have? In any body of degenerate matter, if *gravity* is the dominant force holding the body together, the increase of pressure with depth is *much* more rapid than if the material were non-degenerate. This gives us a clue as to the mechanism that is likely to counteract the collapse of the cooling remnant of the dying red giant. It is the pressure gradient resulting from electron degeneracy; this is often called **degeneracy pressure**. However, this halted contraction doesn't prevent a typical white dwarf from having some fairly exotic properties. One of these is the subject of ITQ 3.11.

ITQ 3.11   Assuming that a typical white dwarf has a radius of 2 000 km and a mass of $0.8M_{\odot}$, calculate its average density. How does this compare with the value for the Sun?

In principle, the equations of stellar structure can be solved for a white dwarf just as for a main sequence star.

☐   What are the main differences in the data used for solving the equations of stellar structure for a white dwarf, as opposed to a main sequence star?

■   The major differences are in the size and the composition.

What emerges from solving these equations for a typical white dwarf? First, it is found that for a surface temperature of about 10^4 K, the core temperature will be in the region of 10^7 K. At first sight this might appear anomalous, as we have already seen that a temperature of this order is able to trigger nuclear fusion reactions in a star like the Sun.

☐ Why shouldn't this also occur in a white dwarf? (*Hint*: Think of the likely composition.)

■ A white dwarf, being essentially the collapsed core of a giant, is likely to be almost devoid of hydrogen, much of it having been used during the main sequence lifetime or thrown off into the interstellar medium in the form of a planetary nebula. The white dwarf, depending on the mass of its 'progenitor' or parent, is likely to consist largely of carbon, nitrogen, oxygen or heavier nuclei. Such nuclei require higher temperatures before fusion reactions can occur.

Solution of the relevant equations does show, not surprisingly, that the outer layers of a white dwarf are not degenerate and must therefore be treated with different equations for certain properties. Perhaps more surprising is the prediction that as the mass increases, the radius decreases. Following from this is the prediction of an upper limit to the mass of a white dwarf, above which electron degeneracy pressure can't halt the contraction. This value is about $1.4 M_\odot$ and it is known as the **Chandrasekhar limit**. How does this rather surprising prediction compare with observations? Actually quite well – no white dwarfs have been found above this mass limit.

What about the frequency of occurrence of these objects? We run into the problem again of selection effects. Because white dwarfs are rather faint, we probably are not able to observe many of them. When we take account of this fact, it appears that white dwarfs are really rather common, perhaps constituting 10% of all stars in our galaxy. We should therefore regard a white dwarf as being a rather common feature of late stellar evolution.

What about stars with intermediate mass, above the Chandrasekhar limit of $1.4 M_\odot$ and below about $8 M_\odot$? Remember the prediction that white dwarfs cannot have a mass above $1.4 M_\odot$. Therefore, if these intermediate mass stars are to become white dwarfs, as seems to be the case, they must lose mass. The shedding of mass, as we have seen, plays a significant part in these later stages of stellar evolution, through stellar winds and planetary nebulae. However, from what we know of them, it doesn't seem that these mechanisms are able to account for the loss of enough mass to bring the more massive stars below the Chandrasekhar limit. So some difficulties still remain to be explained in this picture of the final stages of evolution of intermediate mass stars.

Is there any future for a star after the white dwarf phase? The answer is almost certainly 'no'. The white dwarf cools over a time scale of 10^9 years or more and moves to the lower right on the H–R diagram. It is generally regarded as a final resting point in stellar evolution, and its material is now essentially lost from taking any further part in the cosmic cycle. This is to be the final fate of our Sun – a dark, cold, dense sphere of degenerate material, rich in carbon and oxygen and only about the size of the Earth!

You should watch video sequence 4, A delicate balancing act, *before you move on to Chapter 4. Remember to read the associated notes first.*

130

1   When the hydrogen in the core of a main sequence star is exhausted, the core contracts and the temperature rises. At a temperature of around 10^8 K, helium burning is initiated. This is the 3α process. In stars of mass less than $2.25M_\odot$, the electrons in the core first become degenerate. This leads to a core helium flash.

2   This transition phase is accompanied by a contraction and heating of the core but a swelling of the diameter by typically a factor of 10, and a cooling of the surface. The star becomes a red giant.

3   After depletion of helium in the core, helium burning continues in a shell surrounding the core, accompanied by periodic shell helium flashes. This shell helium burning causes a further swelling of the red giant.

4   The giant phase lasts for approximately 10% of the main sequence lifetime and is accompanied by a copious stellar wind.

5   In giants, fusion reactions can also produce oxygen. In giants more massive than $3M_\odot$ or $4M_\odot$, further fusion reactions can occur, some involving neutrons, to produce heavier elements.

6   During and after the giant phase, most stars pass through a region on the H–R diagram called the instability strip. Here a star undergoes pulsations that lead to a regular variation in the star's luminosity.

7   At around this stage, some stars eject a shell of material, of mass $0.1M_\odot$ to $0.2M_\odot$, called a planetary nebula.

8   After depletion of all nuclear fuels, the core again collapses until electron degeneracy sets in. Degeneracy pressure is able to prevent further collapse.

9   With no further nuclear reactions possible, the white dwarf cools and disappears from view.

10 White dwarfs cannot have a mass above the Chandrasekhar limit of $1.4M_\odot$.

11 The late-stage evolution of stars more massive than about $8M_\odot$ is quite different from that of less massive stars, and will be considered in Chapter 4.

SAQ 3.8 (Objectives 3.11–3.16)   In the form of a list, outline the post main sequence evolution of a star of initial mass $0.8M_\odot$. Be sure to cover its external appearance and interior events.

SAQ 3.9 (Objective 3.12)   List the various ways in which stellar matter can be returned to the interstellar medium, and for each mechanism state and comment on the amounts of matter returned, and whether it is enriched in heavy elements.

SAQ 3.10 (Objective 3.15)   If the luminosity of a white dwarf drops by a factor of 10^4, and its radius stays constant (a feature of degenerate matter), what has happened to its surface temperature? (Answer this question from theory, and check your answer by referring to Figure 3.23.)

Objectives for Chapter 3

After studying Chapter 3 (and any associated audio, video or TV material), you should be able to:

3.1   Give brief definitions of the terms, concepts and principles listed at the end of the Objectives.

3.2   Outline the scheme of stellar evolution for stars of intermediate and low mass.

3.3 Describe the main properties of dense clouds and their role in the formation of protostars.

3.4 Explain the roles of gravity and thermal kinetic energy in the formation of a protostar.

3.5 Describe the part played by cloud fragmentation in the formation of stars.

3.6 Understand the properties and roles of bipolar outflow sources and T Tauri stars in early stellar evolution.

3.7 Differentiate between the various means of heat transfer in stellar matter.

3.8 Understand some basic ideas about nuclear reactions, including energy release, and the rest energy curve.

3.9 Describe the properties of main sequence stars, including an explanation of the role of the pp and CNO reactions, and the importance of temperature in these reactions.

3.10 Understand the ideas of equations of stellar structure.

3.11 Explain the main characteristics of the giant phase of evolution.

3.12 Identify the main periods of mass ejection from stars including stellar winds from main sequence and red giant stars, T Tauri stars and planetary nebulae.

3.13 Explain the role of the instability strip in stellar evolution.

3.14 Describe the main properties of degenerate matter.

3.15 Describe the main properties of white dwarfs.

3.16 Describe the later stages of the evolution of stars of low and intermediate mass.

List of terms, concepts and principles used in Chapter 3

Term	Page	Term	Page	Term	Page
3α process	121	fragmentation	98	ppIII chain (or cycle)	115
bipolar outflow	101	Hayashi track	102	protostar	100
brown dwarf	117	helium flash	123	radiation pressure	117
carbon burning	125	helium fusion	120	Russell–Vogt theorem	110
Chandrasekhar limit	130	hydrogen burning	115	s-process reactions	126
circumstellar disc	101	horizontal branch	122	shell helium flash	125
CNO chain (or cycle)	116	ideal gas	106	spiral density wave	98
convective core	110	ideal gas law	106	stability	110
convective shell	110	instability strip	126	stellar wind	101
core (of a star)	104	Jeans mass	97	subgiant	122
degeneracy	122	lower main sequence star	111	supernova	98
degeneracy pressure	129	mass–luminosity relationship	108	T Tauri star	102
dense cloud	95	open cluster	99	upper main sequence star	111
endothermic	113	planetary nebula	128	white dwarf	128
equations of stellar structure	105	ppI chain (or cycle)	115		
exothermic	113	ppII chain (or cycle)	115		

Chapter 4
Supergiants, supernovae and black holes

Prepared for the Course Team by Jocelyn Bell Burnell

Contents

4.1 Introduction: what happens to the massive stars?

We have seen that stars like the Sun, and those of up to a few times the mass of the Sun, when they run short of hydrogen in their cores, swell to become red giants. This phase, we believe, is often followed by one in which the star varies in brightness. This can lead to the shedding of the outer layers as a planetary nebula; the core of what was the red giant becomes a white dwarf.

What is the fate of stars much more massive than the Sun? That is the subject for this chapter. Astrophysicists are now much less certain of the answer to this question (qualitatively or quantitatively) than they were twenty years ago! The description that follows is the best understanding of what probably happens, but the importance of mass loss from the star through stellar winds has only recently been appreciated. The consequences of this for the evolution of massive stars are not yet fully worked out.

It is now suspected that for the most massive stars (those with masses more than $50M_\odot$) there are copious stellar winds, so copious that the outer layers of these stars are peeled off during their lifetime. This may expose the helium-rich core of the star; it certainly has a drastic effect on the evolution of the star. However, stars of this mass are relatively rare, and won't be further considered here. In this chapter we shall be concerned with stars of mass greater than about $8M_\odot$ and less than about $50M_\odot$.

In studying this chapter, you will need to complete your viewing of video sequence 4, A delicate balancing act, *if you have not already done so.*

4.2 Supergiants

You saw in Subsection 3.3.2 that massive stars have a much shorter lifetime on the main sequence than lighter stars. Because they are more massive they have a higher central temperature, and so the hydrogen-burning nuclear reactions proceed faster. Because their nuclear reactions proceed faster, energy is released more quickly and so these stars are also brighter. For a short while they are hot and bright, and are found in the top left-hand part of the H–R diagram.

Some stars (the relatively recently formed ones) are still to be found in that part of the H–R diagram. But where are those that formed earlier?

☐ From what you have learnt about the way lighter stars evolve off the main sequence, can you guess where in the H–R diagram the massive stars move to when they evolve off it?

■ They move to the right, and upwards a little.

Stars that were once on the main sequence in the top left-hand corner of the H–R diagram are today's **supergiants**. Look at Figure 4.1 to remind yourself where the supergiants are located in the H–R diagram.

Two of the prominent stars in the constellation of Orion are supergiants. Betelgeuse, which to the northern hemisphere observer is the bright star in the top left-hand corner of the constellation, is termed a red supergiant. The colour is perceptible, but is not very dramatic; as one's eyes become dark-adapted after 15 minutes or so, an orange tint becomes noticeable. A colour photograph taken with an ordinary camera will show it clearly (Plate 1.15a). Rigel, at the opposite corner of the constellation, is a blue supergiant, shining with a blue-white light.

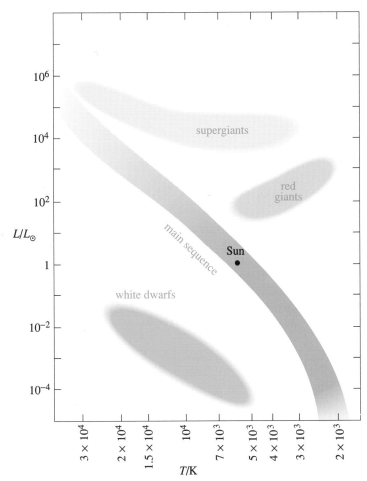

Figure 4.1 The H–R diagram, showing where the stars tend to congregate.

ITQ 4.1 If a star moves from the upper main sequence in the top left-hand part of the H–R diagram to become a supergiant, what changes take place in its luminosity and surface temperature?

ITQ 4.2 A main sequence star initially has a surface temperature of $25\,000\,K$ and radius $10R_{\odot}$. The temperature drops (without change of luminosity) to $5\,000\,K$ as it becomes a (yellowish-white) supergiant. Use Equation 2.7 to determine its new radius.

4.2.1 After the main sequence

As with the less massive stars, the reason for the massive star moving off the main sequence is that a significant fraction of the hydrogen in the core has been consumed and converted into helium by nuclear fusion reactions.

☐ What is the name of the set of nuclear fusion reactions that dominate in the heavier main sequence stars?

■ The CNO cycle (Subsection 3.3.3).

ITQ 4.3 Can you suggest a reason why there are so few stars in that part of the H–R diagram between the upper main sequence and the area where the supergiants lie?

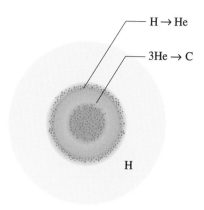

H → He

3He → C

H

Figure 4.2 The structure of a helium-burning supergiant (not to scale).

The colours (as perceived) of some stars do not well match their names. For example, the stars called red giants often appear orange-white.

The evolution of a massive star to a supergiant parallels the evolution of a less massive star to a red giant (Chapter 3). The main difference is that in the lower mass stars it is the pressure of the hot gas that supports the star, whereas in more massive stars (over about $5M_\odot$) radiation pressure provides the supporting force (Subsection 3.3.4).

As you saw in Chapter 3, the nuclear burning slows as the fuel in the centre of the star is used up. There is still burning where fresh material is available in a shell around the outer edge of the core, but the core is becoming choked with 'ash', the product of the burning. As the nuclear reactions diminish, there is no longer the pressure gradient from the escaping radiation to balance the gravitational force and so the core contracts under gravity.

A consequence of this contraction is that the density and the temperature of the core of the star rise, and there comes a point where what has been inert 'ash' can itself start to burn. Another nuclear fusion reaction can start, converting the material in the core into yet more massive nuclei, and once again producing energy. So the star keeps shining and again is in balance.

The first time this happens it is the fusion of helium to carbon (the 3α process, described in Subsection 3.4.1) that starts. While this phase lasts the star has two sources of energy from nuclear reactions (Figure 4.2): the fusion of helium to carbon in the core, and the fusion of hydrogen to helium in a shell outside the core.

By this stage the star has become a supergiant. Its surface temperature (and hence whether it is called blue, yellow or red) depends on the star's mass and the rate at which it loses mass through its stellar wind. Future changes in luminosity and temperature also depend on these properties. Some supergiants are always blue, some track from blue to red and stop there, and some will track back again from red to blue.

4.2.2 Astronomical alchemy

What happens next in the star, when the amount of helium available in the core for conversion into carbon diminishes noticeably? As the nuclear reaction wanes and the pressure gradient due to the escaping energy diminishes, the star once again contracts under gravity. The core temperature goes up yet again and, at temperatures of about 3×10^8 K, the reaction

$$^{12}_{6}\text{C} + ^{4}_{2}\text{He} \longrightarrow ^{16}_{8}\text{O} + \gamma$$

can commence. The star then has three sources of energy from nuclear reactions.

☐ What are these three sources of energy?

■ $^{12}_{6}\text{C} + ^{4}_{2}\text{He} \longrightarrow ^{16}_{8}\text{O} + \gamma$ in the core; the 3α process in a shell around the core; and $4\,^{1}_{1}\text{H} \longrightarrow ^{4}_{2}\text{He} + 2e^+ + 2\nu + 2\gamma$ in a shell outside that again.

ITQ 4.4 Sketch the structure of the star at this stage. (You might find it helpful to have Figure 4.2 in front of you as you do this.)

The supergiant star goes through this pattern of steps a number of times as successive elements become scarce in the core. In contrast to lower mass stars, in stars over about $8M_\odot$ each new burning starts in a non-degenerate core. However, these later stages of evolution of a supergiant star are not well understood, and what follows should be treated with caution; as our understanding grows the picture will change in detail, and may change in larger matters too.

As the core temperature rises towards 6×10^8 K, the new reactions that come into play are:

$$^{16}_{8}\text{O} + ^{4}_{2}\text{He} \longrightarrow ^{20}_{10}\text{Ne} + \gamma$$

$$^{20}_{10}\text{Ne} + ^{4}_{2}\text{He} \longrightarrow ^{24}_{12}\text{Mg} + \gamma$$

and increasingly the carbon burning is through the reaction

$$^{12}_{6}C + ^{12}_{6}C \longrightarrow ^{24}_{12}Mg + \gamma$$

At temperatures of about 10^9 K, the reactions

$$^{24}_{12}Mg + ^{4}_{2}He \longrightarrow ^{28}_{14}Si + \gamma$$

and, possibly, if there is any O left in the core

$$^{16}_{8}O + ^{16}_{8}O \longrightarrow ^{32}_{16}S + \gamma$$

take place.

The culmination comes when the central temperature is about 7×10^9 K and the core consists mainly of iron. Surrounding this core, like the layers in an onion, are shells consisting mainly of S and Si, O and C, He, and H, as shown in Figure 4.3.

ITQ 4.5 In each of the stages of a supergiant's life cycle the conversion of hydrogen into helium has been taking place somewhere in the star. Describe how the site of this reaction moves as the star evolves.

The higher temperatures also mean there are more neutrinos produced, and these carry away a growing proportion of the energy generated. Nearly all the neutrinos escape without interacting with the outer layers of the star (Subsection 1.5.4) so do not contribute to its pressure balance. We shall next see that each new reaction is less efficient than the previous at releasing energy, so reactions have to go faster to produce the necessary radiation to balance gravity. So the star goes through its life cycle at an ever-increasing pace, squandering its reserves faster and faster.

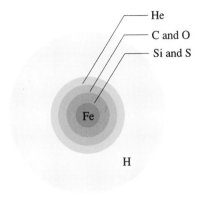

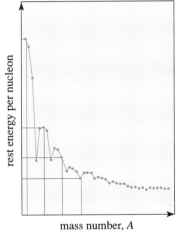

Figure 4.3 The structure of a highly evolved supergiant (not to scale).

Diminishing returns

Broadly speaking, as the star progresses to the fusion of more massive elements, the energy released per kilogram of material undergoing reaction diminishes. The full proof of this statement is beyond the scope of this Course, but one can sense the correctness of it by looking at Figure 4.4, which is the left-hand part of Figure 3.11.

You learnt in Chapter 3 that the fusion of light elements is exothermic, i.e. energy is released. In terms of Figures 3.11 and 4.4, energy is released by a reaction if the product is at a lower value of rest energy per nucleon than the reactant(s). However, the curve in Figure 4.4 is gradually flattening – its gradient is becoming shallower. To see this, look at the straight lines on the graph. The vertical lines mark out equal intervals of A along the horizontal axis. But the intervals marked out on the vertical axis by the horizontal lines decrease as the values of A increase. The vertical intervals are a measure of the energy released in fusion; because the curve is flattening as more massive elements (i.e. elements with large A) are produced, the energy released in the reaction diminishes.

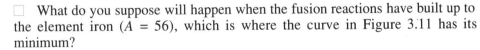

Figure 4.4 The variation of rest energy per nucleon with mass number, up to $A = 40$.

☐   What do you suppose will happen when the fusion reactions have built up to the element iron ($A = 56$), which is where the curve in Figure 3.11 has its minimum?

■   In some sense, yet to be spelled out, the star has reached the end of the road. Fusion to an element of higher A would *consume* energy, not release it. Also, the opposite process (called fission), which produces an element of smaller A, would consume rather than produce energy.

With the recent developments in infrared astronomy came the discovery that many stars, especially those in their later stages of evolution, are much brighter in the infrared than would be expected from their optical emission. Supergiant and giant stars, it seems, are often surrounded by cocoons of dust and gas (Plate 1.26). This material absorbs some (sometimes almost all) of the optical emission from the star, becomes warmed to temperatures of several hundred to a thousand kelvins, and then emits infrared radiation.

These circumstellar shells are created in the later stages of evolution by increased mass loss through stellar winds from giants and supergiants. The mass losses have been estimated to be from $10^{-5}M_\odot$ to $10^{-7}M_\odot$ per year, and the wind speeds to be tens or hundreds of kilometres per second. The material gathers in a shell that surrounds the star with a radius of ten to a hundred times the radius of the star, and expands typically at $15\,\mathrm{km\,s^{-1}}$.

The shells contain gas atoms, gas molecules (mostly H_2, but also molecules like CO and H_2O) and dust grains. In a column of area $1\,\mathrm{m}^2$ stretching through the thickness of the shell there would be 10^{22} to 10^{24} particles. The dust grains appear to be made up of graphite and silicates, and to be typically tens of nanometres in size (but that quantity is particularly uncertain). The densities are so low in interstellar space that to form grains even as small as $1\,\mathrm{nm}$ would take longer than our galaxy has been in existence! It is now understood that the dust grain formation takes place in the cool outer atmospheres of giants and supergiants. Here, as the material flows steadily outwards, for about a month on the outward journey the conditions are suitable for the formation of grains through condensation. Having formed, the dust grains are expelled by radiation pressure out into the shell. When the environment is cool enough the grain acquires a mantle of ice (water, methane or ammonia ice) and grows to hundreds of nanometres in size. From the outer edge of the shell material is steadily lost into the interstellar medium; this part of the story is continued in Chapter 5.

Summary of Section 4.2 and SAQs

1   Massive stars spend less time on the main sequence than less massive stars, and then evolve across the H–R diagram more quickly.

2   When a significant fraction of the hydrogen in the core of a massive star has been converted into helium, the star moves off the main sequence to become a supergiant.

3   In stars of mass greater than about $8M_\odot$, nuclei as massive as iron are formed.

4   Each new reaction produces energy less efficiently than the previous; to compensate, the reaction rate is greater.

5   A number of supergiant (and giant) stars are surrounded by dust shells, which emit at infrared wavelengths. It is thought that the dust condenses in the cooler, outer parts of a supergiant's atmosphere.

SAQ 4.1 (Objective 4.1)   Sketch an H–R diagram and on it mark the area occupied by the supergiants, identifying the positions of red, yellow and blue supergiants. Show the evolutionary tracks of supergiants that evolve from blue to red, and of supergiants that change from blue to red and back again. Show from what part of the main sequence the supergiants have come.

SAQ 4.2 (Objective 4.2)   Explain in your own words why a massive star goes through its life cycle at an ever-increasing pace.

If you have not yet looked at video sequence 4 this would be an appropriate time to do so.

When the reactions that produced iron diminish, the iron core must contract. The temperature and density increase still more, but now with no hope of further nuclear reactions that can release energy. The collapse brings the central regions to a sufficiently high density that the electrons become degenerate. However, large though the electron degeneracy pressure is, in these heavy stars it is unable to halt the collapse; there is a maximum mass that can be supported by electron degeneracy pressure, which as you saw in Chapter 3 is called the Chandrasekhar limit: once the iron core has grown to more than about $1.4M_\odot$ it has exceeded this limit. Most stars whose main sequence mass was greater than about $8M_\odot$ form, in their last stages of evolution, iron cores that exceed this limit.

So the electron degeneracy pressure will only temporarily delay the collapse, and then the core continues shrinking inexorably. At about 10^{10} K, iron nuclei are broken up by photons in the form of gamma radiation producing alpha particles and neutrons. (These neutrons are of importance for a process that will shortly be described: the r-process.) This break-up, too, absorbs energy. The core collapse gets faster and faster, reaching supersonic velocities. As the collapse continues the density rises, as does the energy of the degenerate electrons. There comes a point where these electrons (e^-) have enough energy to make possible the reaction

$$e^- + p \longrightarrow n + \nu$$

where p stands for proton and n for neutron. This reaction removes electrons so the electron degeneracy pressure drops and the core collapse proceeds in earnest. It stops, finally, when the core density becomes comparable with the density of the nucleus of the atom! The core temperature has risen to 10^{12} K and the core density has become approximately $3 \times 10^{17}\,\text{kg m}^{-3}$!

At these densities a new form of degeneracy pressure, **neutron degeneracy pressure**, comes into play. This pressure, due to the neutrons, builds up quite quickly, causing the collapse of the inner part of the core to come to a sudden halt and rebound slightly. The rebound launches a shock wave out through the overlying layers of the star, layers that are still falling inwards at speeds that may be as high as $70\,000\,\text{km s}^{-1}$ – 150 million miles per hour!

ITQ 4.6   The Earth has a mass of 6×10^{24} kg. What would be its radius if it had a density of $3 \times 10^{17}\,\text{kg m}^{-3}$, like the collapsed core of the star?

Exactly what happens next is still not completely clear, but it seems that some, or all, of the following things happen:

- The shock wave itself may blow apart the outer layers of the star, which consist mainly of lighter elements;
- The shock wave may heat the outer layers to a temperature of about 10^{10} K initiating explosive nuclear fusion reactions, which release enormous amounts of energy and throw off the outer layers of the star;
- Enormous numbers of neutrinos are produced and, although most of them escape without interacting with the outer layers of the star, sufficient may interact to lift off the material.

Whatever the detailed mechanisms, the net result is that the star suffers catastrophic self-destruction. The inner core of the star has collapsed to an incredible density, and the outer layers have been blown off in a gigantic explosion. The star spent millions of years evolving to the point where it had a massive iron core, and then went through these last stages in seconds. The energy released by the core collapse is about 10^{46} J. At least 99% of this is carried away by neutrinos; the remainder goes into the kinetic energy of expansion (10^{44} J) and into the sudden brightening of the star (10^{42} J), with a little bit probably also going into the production of high energy particles called cosmic rays. Typically, the star's luminosity brightens by a factor of 10^8 (Plate 1.28a), and it may for a while outshine the entire galaxy in which it is situated. If the star is in the Milky Way then it may be bright enough to be seen in daylight for a few weeks. It is called a **supernova**; nova means new (star) in Latin and a supernova (plural supernovae) is an extra-bright new star. This is a misnomer because it is the death throes of an *evolved* star that we are witnessing, but the name does remind us that what was previously an inconspicuous star suddenly brightens up and becomes noticeable.

Type I and Type II supernovae

Astronomical nomenclature can be perverse, and one such instance is found in the classification of supernovae. They are divided into two broad groups depending on whether or not their spectra show hydrogen lines. The supernova resulting from the explosion of a supergiant will contain hydrogen spectral lines and is known as a Type II supernova. Astrophysicists are beginning to appreciate that both groups incorporate a variety of conditions, but the most common kind of Type II supernova is the kind just described above.

For stars more massive than 30–$40 M_\odot$, it is suspected that radiation pressure and the stellar wind may cause the star to shed its hydrogen envelope. If such a star subsequently undergoes a supernova explosion it will lack hydrogen in its spectrum and will be classed as Type I.

However, most Type I supernovae are found in those areas of galaxies where there are old, slowly evolving stars, whereas Type II supernovae are associated with massive, young stars that have evolved rapidly to the supernova stage.

☐ What does this suggest about the mass of most objects that become Type I supernovae?

■ Because slowly evolving stars have low mass it suggests that most Type I supernovae are the explosions of low mass stars.

This much is clear about Type I supernovae, but what exactly the original star was and what caused the explosion is not clear. In Subsection 4.5.1 the effects on stellar evolution of a close binary companion will be discussed; it may be that some of the Type I supernovae are explosions of stars whose evolutionary history has been seriously affected by a close companion star.

4.3.1   Creation of heavy elements in supernova explosions

We have seen that fusion of light elements in stars can build nuclei as far as the iron group ($A \sim 56$), but cannot build further, and in Chapter 3 you learnt that some elements can be built by another process, the s-process (s for slow), in which neutrons are added to nuclei. Some of the nuclei beyond the iron group may be built this way, but this process will be successful only if the neutron is added to a relatively stable nucleus.

☐ Can you guess what happens when the process has built up, step by step, to a nucleus that is relatively unstable, one that decays radioactively before there is time for the capture of a neutron through the s-process?

■ Either the process stops there, or (possibly) the product of the radioactive decay may be stable enough for neutron capture via the s-process to work on it.

However, sooner or later there will arise a situation where an unstable nucleus and all its decay products are sufficiently unstable that they decay before the slow process can operate. How can nuclei heavier than this be built? How does nature 'work around' such an unstable stepping stone?

Let's stay with the analogy of stepping stones for a minute. Imagine you are crossing a river using a set of stepping stones. One of the stones (far from either bank!) is unexpectedly wobbly and you begin to lose your balance. Putting a foot down in the river is one way to recover; the drier alternative is to jump quickly to the next stone, hoping it is stable and that you can pause there to recover your poise.

☐ Suppose the step of adding a neutron to a particular nucleus results in an unstable nucleus. By analogy, can you see how the situation might be saved?

■ If it were possible quickly to jump ahead to the next (and hopefully stable) nucleus by adding a neutron to the unstable nucleus before it had time to decay, then the situation might be recovered.

In creating the more massive elements nature does just this. It is possible to add rapidly another neutron to an unstable nucleus before it has time to decay. This technique works where there is an abundant supply of neutrons, and involves a mechanism that allows the rapid absorption of neutrons by nuclei. Reactions embodying this mechanism are called **r-process reactions** (r for rapid), and occur in supernova explosions. The supply of neutrons comes from the break-up of the iron nuclei in the core, giving a flood of neutrons (10^{36} neutrons per square metre per second!). The r-process occurs for a few seconds only during the explosive expansion of the outer layers of the star, which have been heated to over 10^{10} K, and builds elements beyond iron. During these few seconds the s-process will also be operating. Moreover, the outer layers of the star, which are rich in hydrogen and helium, will very probably undergo a rapid sequence of nuclear fusion reactions, building elements predominantly of the iron group. Heavier elements ($A > 56$) are created in the explosion by the r-process, and certain of these, such as gold and plutonium, are created predominantly by this means (remember that other heavy elements can also be created by the s-process).

4.3.2 Brighter and brighter

A Type II supernova explosion provides not only the environment in which these heavier elements ($A > 56$) are created but also the mechanism for distributing them through a large volume of space. And because the explosion shatters the star, also ejected into space are the elements, such as silicon, sulphur and magnesium, formed earlier by nuclear fusion in the star. Supernova explosions are the most important way in which the chemical composition of the interstellar medium is enriched with elements heavier than iron.

Type II supernovae have hydrogen emission lines in their spectra; Doppler shifts (illustrated in Figure 2.4) of these lines observed in recently exploded supernovae show material expanding outwards at speeds of up to $10\,000$ km s^{-1}. For about a month the visible surface of the star expands steadily at several thousand kilometres per second; as the surface area increases so the amount of light radiated increases. Then the brightness begins to fade. When the visible surface has expanded to a radius of about 2×10^{10} km it becomes transparent, and the amount of light produced drops markedly.

ITQ 4.7   How does this radius of 2×10^{10} km compare with the radius of a supergiant, the radius of the Solar System, and the distance to the nearest star?

4.3.3 Light curve

We discussed earlier how, when building heavier elements step by step from lighter ones, unstable (that is, radioactive) nuclei can bring the building to a halt. Radioactive nuclei have other effects too. In particular, the type of radioactive decay in which a gamma ray is emitted can be important for the brightness of a new supernova. It has been suggested that such gamma rays are the energy source governing the brightness of a supernova for the period starting six or eight weeks after the explosion. The most likely decay sequence is $^{56}_{28}Ni$ rapidly decaying to $^{56}_{27}Co$, which in turn decays more slowly to $^{56}_{26}Fe$ with the emission of gamma rays. We shall see later, when we discuss supernova 1987A, that this suggestion has been confirmed.

☐ The $^{56}_{28}Ni$ nuclei that head this process decay, typically, in 6 days; that is, half of the remaining nickel nuclei disintegrate some time during each subsequent 6-day interval. This period is called the **half-life** of the nickel nuclei. Where and when were these nuclei created?

■ Because this is a heavy element (comparable with iron), the nuclei could have been created only in a massive star or in the explosion of a massive star (a supernova). The gamma rays produced in the decay of its 'daughter', $^{56}_{27}Co$, for a time control the brightness of the supernova. The typical cobalt nucleus lasts about 2 months before decaying, i.e. it has a half-life of 2 months, so 2 months (on average) previously these cobalt nuclei were created by the decay of the nickel nuclei. However, these nickel nuclei are very short-lived, decaying typically in 6 days, so they must have been created only shortly before the cobalt nuclei appeared. Most probably the nickel was formed in the explosion.

Figure 4.5 shows how the brightness of a typical Type II supernova changes. This type of graph, showing how brightness (or luminosity) varies with time is called a **light curve**.

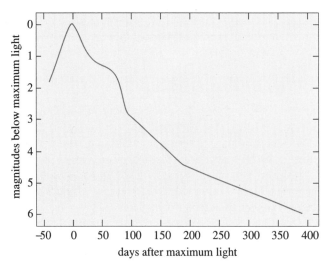

Figure 4.5 The light curve of a typical Type II supernova. (Magnitude is a measure of luminosity – see Subsection 2.3.4.)

Note the usage of the words visible and optical. Optical wavelengths are the visible wavelengths plus the near infrared wavelengths and the near ultraviolet.

Note that the brightness or luminosity plotted is that measured in the optical part of the spectrum. Why should it be the optical data that are used? Supernovae are rare occurrences and our understanding of them has been achieved by putting together all available data. Because optical telescopes have been and are more numerous than, for example, neutrino detectors or far-ultraviolet telescopes, most of the available data are from the optical wavelength band. Also, although most energy is lost through neutrino emission, for studying the evolution of the

142

supernova over the subsequent weeks and months the optical radiation emitted is a useful diagnostic.

Often we miss the initial rise in optical brightness as the photosphere of the star explodes, noticing the supernova only when it is close to maximum brightness, some weeks after the explosion. The shape of the light curve after maximum brightness depends on both the radius and the temperature of the visible surface (remember Equation 2.7). For the first 25 days or so after maximum brightness the visible surface is still expanding but, nevertheless, the effects of falling temperature dominate and the luminosity drops. The majority of Type II supernovae have a curious shoulder, or plateau, in their light curves between days 25 and 75 after the maximum. The outer layers of the star are thinning so we are seeing farther into it; but meanwhile the star is expanding in a way that just balances our ability to see deeper into it. Like walking down the up-escalator, the net result is that the surface we see does not appear to move much – the radius is roughly constant. So too is the temperature, and hence the brightness does not change much, giving the shoulder. After about day 75, the visible surface retreats rapidly and, although the temperature remains roughly constant, the shrinking radius causes the luminosity to fall abruptly. From 100 days after the maximum, radioactive heating by gamma rays controls the brightness, and the shape of the light curve is governed by the half-life of the radioactive decay.

4.3.4   How common are supernova explosions?

The last supernova seen in our galaxy was in AD 1604 – before the telescope was invented! And before that, we know of ones in AD 1572, AD 1054 and AD 1006. So, at first glance, a rate of roughly 4 in 1000 years would seem appropriate for our galaxy. However, supernovae at maximum brightness can be as bright as a whole galaxy, so we can find them also in other galaxies. For these, the rate seems to be one every 25 to 50 years per galaxy – a very different rate.

Why the difference? Are there factors that bias the numbers observed? It is believed that the discrepancy is caused by absorbing material that is concentrated in the plane of our galaxy. The supernovae that have been observed are all quite close to us in the galaxy; we suspect that ones farther away, near the plane of the galaxy, are not seen because of obscuration by material in the interstellar medium. Correcting this bias as well as possible suggests that the real rate in our galaxy is much the same as in other galaxies. There are approximately equal numbers of Type I and Type II supernovae.

4.3.5   Supernova!

For almost 400 years no bright, nearby supernova had given astronomers the chance to check out their conjectures about the death of massive stars. During these centuries the available instrumentation grew: first the optical telescope was invented, then the other wavelengths of the electromagnetic spectrum were recognized and, since the mid 1900s, telescopes have been developed to detect these too. Detectors of the elusive neutrinos were in place and gravitational wave detectors under development. What was really needed was a good supernova explosion to allow astrophysicists to check out their theories on how supernovae occurred, whether nucleosynthesis actually took place, and what happened to the core of the star.

Then on 24 February 1987 it happened. A Canadian astronomer, Ian Skelton, using a mountain-top telescope in Chile, found an unexpected splodge on a photographic plate he had just exposed, something that hadn't been there the previous night when he had also photographed that part of the sky. After 20 minutes trying to explain away the spot (OK, nobody's too bright in the cold at 9 000 feet at 3 o'clock in the morning) he looked outside and saw it was real. In a nearby galaxy in the southern sky, called the Large Magellanic Cloud (Plate

3.10), a star had exploded. Plate 1.28a shows this part of the sky before and after the explosion.

☐ Ian Skelton observed the supernova at about 3 am on 24 February 1987. If the Large Magellanic Cloud is 163 000 light years away, when did the supernova actually explode?

■ About 163 000 years previously; the light that he observed took that length of time to travel from the Large Magellanic Cloud to the Earth.

For every discovery there are, usually, several near misses. Some 19 hours earlier in Australia, Robert McNaught had photographed that part of the Large Magellanic Cloud at the Anglo-Australian Observatory. Although he developed the plate he did not examine it that night. Subsequently he found that he had the first photograph of the supernova – it was beginning to happen and at that stage was just becoming bright enough to be visible to the naked eye. Skelton is therefore credited with the discovery of **SN 1987A** (SN being the abbreviation for supernova, and 'A' indicating that it was the first one found in 1987.) However, McNaught's observation, combined with Skelton's negative observation the previous night, is scientifically important in pinning down the start of the event.

This supernova had already, unknowingly, been observed by neutrino detectors, and would be observed in all the major wavelength bands over the next few years. During the previous year, two underground neutrino detectors, not primarily designed for the detection of neutrinos from supernovae, had been sufficiently improved in sensitivity that they were able to play an important part in the study of this explosion. One of the detectors is in a zinc mine in Kamioka in Japan, the other in a salt mine near Lake Erie in Ohio, USA. Simultaneously they detected a short burst of a few neutrinos lasting about 10 seconds, and well above the normal background rates; about 3 hours before McNaught's observation 11 neutrinos were counted in the Japanese detector and 8 in the USA one. The number and energy of the particles in the neutrino burst fitted well with the prediction of what would be produced if the central core of a supergiant collapsed to nuclear densities. It appears that about 3×10^{46} J of energy were carried away by 4×10^{58} neutrinos and, 163 000 years after the explosion, 19 of these neutrinos interacted in the two large underground detectors.

About 1% of the energy of the collapsing star went into the shock wave, which slowly travelled out through the star and caused the increase in the luminosity. By that time the neutrinos had gone, at the speed of light, and so the neutrinos were detected a few hours before the star was seen to brighten.

ITQ 4.8 Is it necessary for a cosmic source of neutrinos to be above the horizon for the detection of neutrinos here on Earth? Was this source above horizon at the time of the detection?

It had been assumed that massive stars exploded as *red* supergiants, so it was something of a surprise when it became clear that the progenitor, the star that exploded producing SN 1987A, was the *blue* supergiant catalogued as Sanduleak − 69° 202, a $20M_\odot$ spectral class B star. Ultraviolet observations made when the supernova had faded somewhat established that Sk − 69° 202 no longer existed, confirming the identification. This stimulated new work on the evolution of massive stars.

The spectrum of the supernova contains hydrogen lines, and it must therefore be classified as a Type II supernova, but SN 1987A was fainter, by a factor of ten, than the Type IIs that, up till then, were thought to be typical.

The light curve in Figure 4.6 is a plot of the optical luminosity against time. It strikingly confirms the theory that gamma rays produced in the radioactive decay of $^{56}_{27}\mathrm{Co}$, heat the material. From about 100 days to about 700 days after the

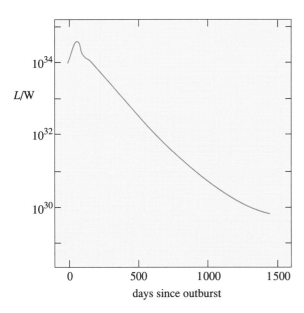

Figure 4.6 The light curve of SN 1987A.

outburst, the fading of the supernova follows the radioactive decay of cobalt nuclei. Further evidence that the nuclear reactions are reasonably well understood came from infrared and gamma ray observations. Infrared spectrometers found spectral lines due to iron and cobalt, while gamma ray telescopes detected gamma rays with the energies expected from the decay of $^{56}_{27}$Co. This was the first time that a direct check of the theory of element formation had been possible.

ITQ 4.9 If the decay of $^{56}_{27}$Co is solely responsible for a supernova's luminosity, and each decay produces two gamma rays, one of energy 1.3×10^{-13} J and one of energy 1.9×10^{-13} J, what mass of cobalt nuclei must decay per second to produce a supernova luminosity of 10^{33} W?

The central mystery of SN 1987A concerns the fate of the core of the original star. The neutrino flux detected is good evidence that the core collapsed to nuclear densities, but, apart from an exciting observation of rapid pulsations supposedly from the object, observations which later proved to be in error, there has so far (1993) been no sign of the central activity expected. Check the *Yearbook* for more recent information on this point. The next Section will deal in more detail with the nature and activity of the collapsed star produced in a supernova explosion.

In the absence of such activity, the brightness of the supernova will continue for decades to be governed by the decay of radioactive nuclei, such as $^{56}_{27}$Co and $^{44}_{22}$Ti. The one exception to this will be temporary brightenings as the expanding shock wave encounters and illuminates clumps of material in the space surrounding the supernova. For example, about five years after the outburst, it lit up a ring of material expelled by the supergiant some 10^4 years before the explosion (Plate 1.28b), and it is predicted that between the years 2000 and 2005 the shock will reach remnants of an earlier stellar wind from the supergiant, when there will be increased ultraviolet and optical line emission, increased X-ray and infrared emission from heated dusty material, and some increase in radio flux.

How will SN 1987A appear thousands of years hence? If there is a central, pulsed source in the supernova remnant then it may evolve to look like the Crab Nebula (Plate 1.29). More probably it will develop a circular structure, as in Plate 1.31. There will be more discussion of supernova remnants in Chapter 5.

1   In the last few seconds of the life of a supergiant, the iron core collapses to nuclear densities with the copious emission of neutrinos.

2   A shock wave is launched through the outer layers of the star; the effects of this, with assistance from the neutrinos, causes the outer layers to be explosively expelled. This is called a Type II supernova explosion.

3   In the explosion, rapid nuclear processes (fusion and r-processes) take place producing, in the main, iron group and heavier elements.

4   Subsequent radioactive decay of some of these elements affects the post-explosion light curve of the supernova.

5   SN 1987A confirmed that supergiants can become supernovae. The neutrino emission showed that collapse of the core to nuclear densities had taken place. The present nature of the central object remains a mystery.

SAQ 4.3 (Objective 4.3)   At its brightest, a hypothetical supernova has a luminosity of $5 \times 10^9 L_\odot$. It is sufficiently bright that it turns night into day – that is, it shines in the night sky as brightly as the Sun shines in the daytime sky, and delivers the same flux density to the Earth as does the Sun. How far away is it? Give your answer in astronomical units, light years and parsecs. How many supergiant stars are there within that distance from the Earth?

SAQ 4.4 (Objective 4.3)   If there were no supernova explosions, and massive stars quietly collapsed in on their iron cores, how would the chemical composition of the interstellar medium be different?

SAQ 4.5 (Objective 4.3)   Identify the following phases on the supernova light curve shown in Figure 4.5: (i) shock heating and expansion of the photosphere; (ii) temperature dropping but surface expanding; (iii) temperature and radius of visible surface approximately constant; (iv) visible surface shrinking at constant temperature; (v) gamma ray heating.

4.4   Endpoints of evolution: neutron stars and black holes

In this Section some of the most bizarre objects to be found in the Universe are introduced. The common threads in their remarkable nature are very high densities and strong gravitational fields. They are unusual radio sources, flickering X-ray sources, energetic gamma ray sources, and the powerhouses at the heart of active galaxies. Some were formed in the Big Bang that created this universe, most were formed later through stellar evolution, and some were formed in ways not yet understood.

Neutron stars are known to exist; black holes are less certain but are believed by most astrophysicists to exist. We start by considering the more normal neutron stars and progress to the more speculative black holes.

4.4.1   Neutron stars

What is left after a Type II supernova explosion? The explosion ejects the outer layers of the star into space; tons of debris, enriched with heavy elements, expand outwards at high speed. This becomes what is known as a **supernova remnant** – a shell of glowing gaseous material encircling the site of the explosion. We shall defer further discussion of the evolution of this exploding remnant of the star until Chapter 5, and instead ask what is left at the site of the explosion. (Note that the term supernova remnant is used by some authors to include any central object; here the term refers only to the material that is shed.)

In earlier Sections we followed the evolution of the core of the star as it collapsed rapidly. The implosion had been triggered by the reaction

$$e^- + p \longrightarrow n + \nu$$

which absorbed electrons (removing their contribution to the pressure supporting the star) and produced neutrinos (which carried away energy). You learnt that, if the core mass exceeds the Chandrasekhar limit of $1.4M_\odot$, the collapse could be brought to a sudden halt when the density became comparable with the density of an atomic nucleus, and a new form of degeneracy pressure due to the neutrons came into play.

Neutron degeneracy pressure is the same phenomenon as the electron degeneracy pressure that you met in Subsection 3.4.1, except that the particles providing the pressure in this case are neutrons, and the density is much higher. The existence of this force allows the presence of another stable form of matter, more dense than that of the white dwarf star, in which the strong forces of gravitational contraction are balanced by the pressure from the neutrons.

We saw earlier that the Chandrasekhar limit is the maximum mass that can be supported by the electron degeneracy pressure. Similarly in this case there is a limit, but because the composition of the star is different the limit is slightly different; it is estimated to be about $2.0M_\odot$. This is the most massive star that could be supported against gravity by neutron degeneracy pressure.

Neutron stars of mass greater than about $2.0M_\odot$, and white dwarfs of mass greater than about $1.4M_\odot$, are not expected to exist. But it is possible to have neutron stars of mass less than $1.4M_\odot$, provided that high enough densities can be produced.

☐ Suppose the mass of the collapsing core is bigger than this limit, what happens?

■ The collapse of the imploding core of the supergiant is not halted and it continues to shrink under gravity to even greater densities. What it becomes, we shall see in the next subsection.

In this subsection we shall concentrate on cores where the mass is less than $2M_\odot$. So, after the collapse, what do we have? Something small, something dense and very rich in neutrons! This is a **neutron star**, a body of up to $2M_\odot$, packed into a sphere about 10 km in radius.

ITQ 4.10 Calculate the average density of a $1.5M_\odot$ neutron star of radius 10 km. How many tons would a thimble-full contain? (Take the volume of a thimble to be 1 cm^3; to the same accuracy, 1 ton = 1 tonne = 1 000 kg.)

These densities are hard to envisage, and hard to believe! Something comparable would be achieved if Mont Blanc were compressed to thimble size, or if the whole Earth shrunk to a few hundred metres across.

The gravitational force at the surface of the neutron star is correspondingly enormous.

ITQ 4.11 What is the acceleration due to gravity at the surface of a neutron star of mass $1.5M_\odot$, radius 10 km? (Gravitational force is revised in Subsection 1.4.1 of *Preparatory science*.)

So neutron stars are small objects, rich in neutrons, with very high densities and huge surface gravitational fields. You may, justifiably, feel that this is already plenty of unusual properties for any type of astronomical object, but the account of the bizarre nature of these objects does not end here. The next property we shall consider is the rotation of the star, but first it is necessary to introduce angular momentum.

☐ In a fairytale country there is a children's playground with lots of attractive equipment and lots of adults prepared to push, pull, lift, hold and otherwise co-operate in enabling children to enjoy themselves. The equipment includes a friction-free roundabout. Children perch on the rim of the roundabout and an obliging adult sets it rotating. If all the children but one then move towards the centre of the roundabout, what does the one child remaining at the rim experience?

■ If most of the mass moves nearer the centre the mass distribution becomes more compact. This reduces the moment of inertia so, by the conservation of angular momentum, the angular speed must increase. The child at the rim will be travelling faster. (In real life, roundabouts are far from friction-free and the consequent spin-down is usually the overriding effect!)

There is a similar effect when the inner core of the supergiant collapses – it spins up. To give a feel for the size of the effect, suppose that the Sun collapsed to the size of a neutron star; how rapidly would it be rotating then? If angular momentum is conserved

$$I_\odot \omega_\odot = I_n \omega_n$$

where the subscript n denotes the quantities for the neutron star. The moments of inertia are:

$$I_\odot = 6 \times 10^{46}\,\text{kg m}^2 \text{ and } I_n = 10^{38}\,\text{kg m}^2$$

The Sun rotates on its axis once every 25.5 days

$$= 25.5 \times 24 \times 3\,600\,\text{s} = 2.2 \times 10^6\,\text{s}$$

Therefore

$$\omega_\odot(\text{number of revolutions per second}) = \frac{1}{2.2 \times 10^6}\,\text{s}^{-1}$$

So

$$\omega_\text{n} = \frac{(I_\odot \omega_\odot)}{I_\text{n}} = \frac{6 \times 10^{46}}{2.2 \times 10^6 \times 10^{38}}\,\text{s}^{-1} = 270\,\text{s}^{-1}$$

Therefore the neutron star rotates on its axis in (1/270) s, or a few milliseconds.

In fact it is not the Sun, but a solar mass (or so) in the centre of the supergiant that collapses to become the neutron star, so the calculation is not strictly relevant. However, it is a good indication of the rapid spin expected for a newly formed neutron star.

So now we see that neutron stars are small objects, predominantly made of neutrons, with high density and large gravitational fields, which rotate extremely rapidly. Do they have yet more unusual features?

We have seen how the rotational properties of the star become concentrated and produce rapid spin as the star collapses. In an analogous manner, any magnetic field that there was in the core of the supergiant would become intensely concentrated in the collapse. Once again, let's suppose that it is the Sun that shrinks to form a neutron star, and ask what would happen to the Sun's magnetic field strength in that process.

We can represent fields like magnetic fields by lines – the direction of the lines gives the direction of the field, and the strength of the field is shown by how closely packed they are (that is, by the number of lines per unit area). Figure 4.7 shows how the magnetic field of a star changes as the star shrinks. The magnetic field strength, in SI units, is measured in tesla (T). At the Earth's surface the magnetic field strength of the Earth is about 4×10^{-3} T. The Sun has a general magnetic field strength at the solar surface of about 2×10^{-4} T, which we can think of as being through a cross-sectional area of $\pi R_\odot^2$. If the radius of the Sun were to decrease, the magnetic field would become compressed (or concentrated), and its strength would increase as the cross-sectional area decreased. So the magnetic field strength of the neutron star would be larger by the factor $R_\odot^2/R_\text{n}^2$, where R_n stands for the radius of the neutron star. This factor is equal to $(7 \times 10^5)^2/10^2$, or about 50×10^8. So the expected field of the neutron star is $2 \times 10^{-4} \times 50 \times 10^8$ T, or about 10^6 T. This is an enormous magnetic field! In fact it is an underestimate – for reasons that are beyond the scope of this Course we believe that the magnetic field of a neutron star can be 10^8 T or even 10^9 T.

So neutron stars are small dense objects, rich in neutrons, with huge gravity and enormous magnetic fields, and they carry all this round with them as they spin many times per second. Does that complete the list of bizarre properties that neutron stars possess? No, it does not, for neutron stars stretch physicists' understanding of material at high densities, test Einstein's general theory of relativity, and produce copious radiation in ways that are not yet understood. However, such extreme physical phenomena are beyond the scope of this Course (the magneto-electrodynamics are beyond the scope of most astrophysicists too!) and will not be discussed further here.

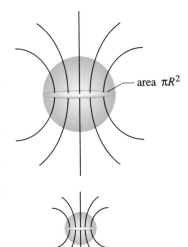

Figure 4.7 The magnetic field of a star through a cross-sectional area of πR^2, and how it becomes concentrated as the area shrinks.

4.4.2 Pulsars

Not surprisingly, most astrophysicists had never dreamt that such unlikely objects as neutron stars could exist. There were a few notable exceptions to this statement, but they were not taken too seriously! The unexpected discovery of neutron stars as pulsating radio stars in the late 1960s therefore produced some excitement and amazement. (An account of the discovery is in Subsection 4.4.3.)

The neutron star, swinging its immense magnetic field around each time it rotates, behaves like a combination of a huge dynamo and a huge lighthouse. It generates a beam of radio waves which is in a direction determined by the magnetic field, and which is swept around by the neutron star as it spins. The essential ingredients in producing the radio signal are the intense magnetic field and the rapid rotation; it is probably also important that the magnetic axis is at an angle to the axis of rotation as shown in Figure 4.8 (see also Plate 1.29b).

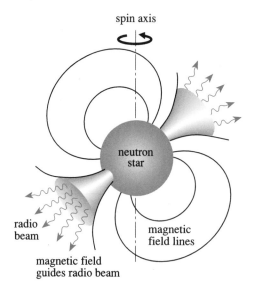

Figure 4.8   How the beam of radio waves is produced in a rapidly spinning neutron star.

At this point it may help you envisage what is happening if you do an experiment with a pair of scissors (preferably straight-bladed ones with rounded ends) as shown in Figure 4.9. Fix the blades open with Blu-Tack and twirl them about one shaft, which is held upright. With a bit of experimenting, you should be able to find a position for the scissors and an appropriate opening angle for the blades so that as you twirl the scissors there will be one point in each revolution where the slanted blade is point-on to you and you see right along its length (Figure 4.9). (Don't get so engrossed with the experiment that you stab yourself with the scissors!)

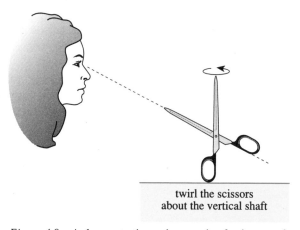

Figure 4.9   A demonstration using a pair of scissors, of the visibility of the beam of radio waves from the neutron star. (Take care not to wound yourself with the scissors.)

Similarly with the neutron star; if the relative orientation of the Earth and the neutron star is correct then, once in every revolution of the star, the Earth will look along the beam of radio waves.

☐   What happens if the orientation of the Earth and the neutron star is not right?

■   The radio beam misses the Earth.

☐   If a neutron star rotating at four times a second is orientated so that its beam sweeps across the Earth, how many flashes of radio waves per second are received at Earth from this beaming star?

■   The beam sweeps across the Earth every time the star rotates. So if the star rotates four times a second then the observer on Earth with a suitable receiver will detect four pulses per second of radio emission.

An observer on Earth with the appropriate radio-receiving equipment can detect the signal produced by a suitably aligned neutron star. The signal received is a string of regular pulses, a set of equally spaced bursts of radio emission as illustrated in Figure 4.10. These neutron stars are called **pulsars** – the name is an abbreviated form of pulsating radio star.

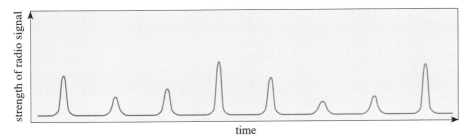

Figure 4.10   The radio signal received from a pulsar.

ITQ 4.12   It is believed that the time-averaged radio luminosity of a pulsar is about 10^{20} W. Compare the signal picked up from a pulsar at a distance of 10 kpc with that detected from a 100 kW radio transmitter 100 km away.

The accidental discovery of radio pulses from one of these objects caused considerable surprise. First, the repetition rate of the pulses (typically several per second) was much greater than anything previously known in astronomy. An object cannot change its brightness in a time less than the time it takes a light wave to travel across the object. If something is producing (say) four pulses per second then it must be less than a quarter of a light second across.

☐   How far is a quarter of a light second? How does that distance compare with the size of the Sun?

■   A quarter of a light second $= \frac{1}{4}(3 \times 10^8)$ m $= 75\,000$ km. This is about a tenth of the solar radius.

The only objects of that sort of size or smaller that were known at the time were not normally radio emitters, and certainly not rapidly pulsed radio emitters.

The second cause for surprise was that the pulsation rate was accurately maintained. This meant that, whatever the source was, it had large reserves of energy so that it could radiate pulse after pulse after pulse without showing any sign of slowing. If an object has large energy reserves, that usually means it is big.

So the object producing these radio pulsations was big, and yet it was small!

This is a good demonstration of the need for precision in scientific language. Our use here has been a little loose and resulted in a conundrum. Let's sharpen up the terminology a little.

☐   In what respect is the source of the radio pulses small? (Small in temperament, in outlook, in stature, in mass, in diameter?) And in what respect is it big?

■ It is small in size, in overall dimension. Our deductions about it being big came from noting that it must have considerable energy reserves. Most likely therefore it is big in the sense of being massive.

With hindsight (our best developed faculty!), we can see that neutron stars fit the bill exactly – they are very dense so are both small in size and massive.

There are now over 600 pulsars known; they lie far outside the Solar System but within the bounds of the Milky Way. If their positions in the galaxy are plotted it is seen that they tend to lie in the nearer half. This distribution is apparent, not real; there are pulsars throughout the galaxy, we believe, but they are sufficiently weak that we can only detect the nearer ones.

All the pulsars *emit* a beamed signal continuously at radio wavelengths which we *receive* as a stream of regular pulses. The pulse period is unique to each pulsar. The fastest known pulse hundreds of times per second, the slowest once every four seconds. All are believed to have been formed in Type II supernova explosions, although curiously only a handful have unambiguous association with a supernova remnant, so their origins are still under investigation.

Pulsars are very good time-keepers. The pulse repetition rate is maintained to an accuracy better than that of most of our clocks and watches! A quartz watch is accurate to 1 part in 10^5, and an atomic clock to 1 part in 10^{14}. Pulsars are also typically accurate to 1 part in 10^{14}, with some of them being as good as 1 part in 10^{19}. The discovery of several apparently 'smooth running' pulsars has led to the suggestion that a combination of such pulsars should be used to establish a new time standard against which the caesium clocks would be checked.

ITQ 4.13   An accuracy of 1 part in 10^{14} corresponds to how many seconds per century?

When we remember that the pulse period is (presumably) the rotation period of the neutron star, then these accuracies are not so surprising, for it takes a lot to change the rotation of a star. However, the energy radiated comes ultimately from the rotational kinetic energy of the neutron star (although we do not yet understand exactly how). We can, through studying changes in the pulse period of the neutron star, monitor its loss of rotational energy as the pulsar ages.

Putting together all the available information, the picture we have is of a neutron star formed in a supernova explosion, initially rotating tens of times per second, but slowing as the star loses energy. After about a million years it will be a middle-aged, typical pulsar, with a pulse period of around 0.5 second. It continues to slow as it ages, until the mechanism for generating radio waves ceases to be effective when the star is rotating only once every few seconds, and the radio emission stops. The pulsar then becomes invisible, some 10^7 or 10^8 years after the supernova exploded.

☐   What sort of object is left when the pulsar has stopped pulsing?

■   We are left with a slowly rotating neutron star which is invisible – a black star. It still has mass, and gravity.

Considering that the supernova explosion was almost totally devastating, it is amazing that there should have been this lively object left. What is even more amazing is that, for some pulsars, the run-down just described is not the end – for some there is a rejuvenating mechanism that stirs them into life yet again!

Later in this chapter we shall discuss briefly interacting binary systems – examples of stars that are paired with a companion, and so closely paired that they affect each other's evolution. If a pulsar is paired in this manner then it is possible for its companion to transfer matter on to the pulsar, and transfer it in such a way that that the pulsar is made to rotate faster. This way, we believe, the rapidly rotating pulsars that have periods of milliseconds and tens of milliseconds have been produced.

While the pulsar's gravitational field is drawing material off the companion and spinning up, several other things are happening. First, any radio radiation that might be produced at this stage is blanketed by the material streaming between the companions and so no radio pulses are seen. Secondly, the transferred material is compressed as it approaches the compact neutron star and is heated. Often it is heated sufficiently so that there is copious emission of X-rays. Most of the strongest X-ray sources in our galaxy are of this kind, and such is their strength that examples in other galaxies, external to our own, can also be seen by X-ray telescopes.

4.4.3   The discovery of pulsars

In the mid-1960s Tony Hewish, a radio astronomer at the University of Cambridge (UK), was awarded a grant to build a special radio telescope to map the quasars in the sky visible from Cambridge and to determine their angular diameters. Quasars will be a subject of Block 3, but briefly they are powerful radio sources that are believed to be in the distant reaches of the Universe; studying them gives valuable information on the Universe at an earlier age.

Quasars apparently have very small angular diameters, but Tony Hewish was exploiting a newly discovered technique which allowed these diameters to be determined. It had been noticed that the signal from some radio sources tended to fluctuate rapidly – they 'twinkled', or scintillated – and these were all quasars. The larger angular diameter radio galaxies did not show this fluctuation. The scintillation is produced by turbulence in the solar wind; detailed study of the scintillation gives the angular diameter of the quasar.

The first purpose of the experiment was to scan the sky for objects that scintillated – they were presumed to be quasars. The scintillation is a rapid flickering and so the telescope had to be able to follow rapid variations in the radio signal. If the signal were to be detectable the radio telescope had to have a large collecting area. The telescope Tony Hewish designed covered 4.5 acres (which is an area that could accommodate 57 tennis courts). I joined Tony Hewish as a research student just as construction of this telescope was about to start. We put up over a thousand posts and strung more than 2 000 antennae like TV aerials between them. The whole thing was connected by 120 miles of wire and cable. It took five of us two years to build; when finished it looked like a hop field, but it worked beautifully (Figure 4.11).

The construction was finished in mid-1967 and the construction crew melted away, leaving me to operate the telescope as it surveyed the sky for scintillating quasars. Computing power was very limited so the telescope output was on pen chart, 96 feet of it every day. As a mere research student the job of analysing these charts fell to me. As the telescope repeatedly scanned the sky it detected the quasars, but also, inevitably, it picked up interference from local sources, and one of the skills quickly acquired was the ability to distinguish between them on the charts.

However, after a few weeks' operation I realized that there was, very occasionally, a third type of signal. When present it occupied about a quarter-inch in the four hundred feet it took for a complete sky scan, and it wasn't always present. After a few sightings it clicked that this curious signal (nicknamed a piece of 'scruff') had been seen before *from the same part of the sky*. Curiosity raised, we decided to explore further, but at that point the 'scruff' faded and for a month could not be detected! Finally, perseverance paid off and a signal like that in Figure 4.10 with a pulse period of 1.33 seconds was traced out by the chart recorder pen.

Discoveries are rarely straightforward, and this is where our problems began. As described in the previous subsection, the pulses were too fast and too

Figure 4.11 The radio telescope used in the discovery of pulsars (the upright posts are about 2.5 m high).

accurately maintained to be any known type of star; it seemed logical to search for their origin within our equipment. No fault could be found, and when a colleague and his research student using their own telescope and receiver also picked it up this suggested its origin was beyond the observatory. It was suspiciously like a man-made signal, but when we found that it kept a fixed place among the stars that seemed to rule that out. We dubbed it LGM, for Little Green Men, and argued that if it were another civilization signalling to us they would probably be on a planet orbiting their star. Through studying accurately the pulse arrival times, we should be able to detect the Doppler effect as their planet went round their star. This experiment did indeed find a Doppler effect, but it was that due to the Earth orbiting the Sun. (Remember the Doppler effect works for movement of the observer as well as for movement of the source.) Using a technique called radio dispersion, we estimated the distance of the source as 65 parsecs – well beyond the Solar System, but well inside the Milky Way.

Several months had elapsed by this time (and several thousand feet of survey chart paper accumulated) and we had reached the point where we didn't really believe it was a signal from little green men, but we didn't have a sound physical explanation to put forward instead. We were wondering what to do next, when routine scanning of the charts surveying a totally different part of the sky suggested that there might be a second source of scruff-like signals. Difficult observations at the dead of night just before Christmas confirmed the pulsing signal – this time with a period of 1.25 seconds and of course from a different direction in space.

This discovery was much more exciting because it looked as if we really had found a new kind of star; it was highly unlikely that two lots of little green men would both choose to signal at the same time to an inconspicuous planet, both using a non-ideal method of communicating. When the third and fourth examples were found just after Christmas 1967 it became clear that these had to be stars, but it was probably another six months before the astronomical community agreed that these objects had to be neutron stars.

4.4.4 Black holes

Case Study 1

Imagine a neutron star, a massive one as neutron stars go, close to the maximum mass that can be supported by neutron degeneracy pressure. The star's gravity pulls down onto it some of the gas and dust that are in the vicinity. The extra material takes the mass of the star over the limit, so that the gravitational contraction force now overwhelms the neutron degeneracy pressure. The neutron star collapses.

Case Study 2

Imagine now the core of SN 1987A. A burst of neutrinos gave a clear indication that a neutron star had been formed, but there has been no subsequent sign of such a star's existence. Suppose the neutron star did exist, briefly, and that it was a massive neutron star, close to the maximum mass that could be supported by neutron degeneracy pressure. The supernova explosion has expelled a lot of the surrounding material, but it has been estimated that the neutron star's gravity could cause about $0.1M_\odot$ of the material to fall back onto the star in the first few hours after the explosion. If this added material caused the gravitational force to exceed the neutron degeneracy pressure then the neutron star would collapse under its own gravity.

Case Study 3

Picture now a particularly massive supergiant with a large iron core near the end of its evolution. As described earlier (Section 4.3) when the core contraction starts the iron nuclei break up, electrons merge with protons to form neutrons and in a matter of seconds the inner core has collapsed to neutron star densities. Suppose, however, that the collapsing inner core is more massive than in the case considered in Section 4.3, so massive that the neutron degeneracy pressure cannot withstand the gravitational force. The collapse will not halt at nuclear densities but will continue beyond.

These three case studies all point to the same question: what happens when the gravitational force is greater than the force provided by the neutron degeneracy pressure? Reviewing the story so far, we see that in stars too massive to be white dwarfs, where the electron degeneracy pressure was insufficient to support the star, collapse to another form of matter (the neutron-rich material) ensued. The existence of this other stable form of matter at higher densities allowed the collapse to halt and produced an unusual kind of star.

Will something similar happen in this case, in stars too massive to be neutron stars? Is there another kind of particle and another kind of pressure that will come into play and halt the contraction? Theoretical studies suggest there *might* be a denser form of matter, made up of the fundamental particles called quarks. (Quarks are the particles that make up neutrons and protons.) It *may* be possible to halt the collapse and form quark stars. However, there is as yet no observational evidence for the existence of these stars, so we shall not consider this concept further in this Course.

Quarks apart, there has been no mechanism suggested that would halt the collapse of a star too massive to be a neutron star. It seems that there is no force that can resist the gravitational contraction. There is nothing to stop the star shrinking under gravity.

As shown in Subsection 1.4.1 of *Preparatory science*, the strength of the gravitational force on a object of mass m at the surface of a star of mass M_* and radius R_* is

$$F_g = \frac{GM_*m}{R_*{}^2}$$

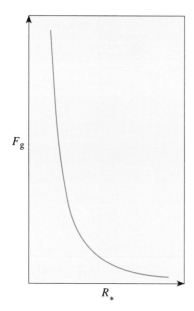

Figure 4.12 How the strength of the gravitational force at the surface of a star depends on the radius of the star.

☐ What happens to the gravitational force at the surface of the star if the radius of the star decreases?

■ As the radius of the star (R_*) diminishes, the gravitational force at its surface, F_g, increases, as shown in Figure 4.12.

The increase in F_g makes it less likely that there can be a force that can effectively resist this gravitational force. More importantly, the increase in F_g produces yet more contraction…which of course increases F_g, which produces more contraction! (Strictly speaking, as the force increases there comes a point where this formula ceases to apply. However, it still serves as an indication of what will happen.)

So the collapse continues relentlessly, apparently until the star has been squashed into an infinitely small space, that is, until it has become a point mass.

☐ If the volume of the star has become infinitely small, what has happened to its density?

■ The density has become infinitely high; the star has zero volume but finite mass!

This is called a singularity; it is a concept that is mathematically and physically difficult to handle (and perhaps you feel that in other ways too it is difficult to handle!) so there is discussion about whether quantum effects or some other effects come into play when the density is extremely high, but not quite infinite, so as to avoid the formation of a singularity. The details need not concern us here – the star collapses down to something not far short of a point, if not an actual point.

During the collapse the gravitational effects increase enormously and we now turn to consider these effects. We shall work with a quantity called the **escape velocity**, which was shown in Section 1.5 of *Preparatory science* to have a magnitude (escape speed) given by:

$$v_{esc} = \sqrt{\frac{2GM}{R}}$$

where M is the mass of the (spherical) body from which escape is desired, and R is its radius. Note that the speed of escape does not depend on the mass of the escaping object – it is the same for a ball or a rocket. For escape from the Earth it is $11\,\mathrm{km\,s^{-1}}$.

☐ As a star of mass M shrinks, how does its escape speed change?

■ The escape speed increases (apparently without limit as the star's radius shrinks to approximately zero).

A full treatment of black holes requires an understanding of Einstein's Theory of General Relativity, which will not be taught in S281. However, you may be aware of one of the conclusions of Relativity Theory, which is that nothing can travel faster than c, the speed of light.

☐ Can you guess what will happen when the star shrinks sufficiently that the escape speed reaches the speed of light?

■ It looks as if for radii smaller than this, things will not be able to escape from the collapsing star, because to do so would require speeds greater than c, which are not possible.

The radius where the escape speed equals the speed of light is a critical radius in the collapse of a star, called the **Schwarzschild radius** (pronounced Sh-<u>vartz</u>-child). At radii smaller than this no material can escape from the collapsing star. It also represents a point-of-no-return for the collapsing star itself – once this radius has been passed the collapse of the star cannot be halted. Furthermore, no light waves (or radio, or X-ray, or infrared, or any other electromagnetic radiation) can directly escape either. The collapsing star as it crosses the Schwarzschild radius becomes a **black hole**; black because no radiation gets out, and a hole because the material of the star cannot get out of it!

ITQ 4.14   Derive an expression for the Schwarzschild radius (R_S) in terms of G, M and c.

ITQ 4.15   Calculate the size of the Schwarzschild radius for a star of $1.0M_\odot$.

Although black holes are not luminous their gravitational fields still exist. Anything that comes too close to a black hole is pulled towards it by the gravity. Anything that is pulled closer than the Schwarzschild radius cannot escape; it is sucked in and squashed to (near) infinite density.

When something falls down a black hole do we see any change in the black hole? If we can ascertain the mass of the black hole (perhaps through measuring the strength of its gravitational field) then we would see that its mass has increased. The only other quantities that can be measured for a black hole are its electric charge and its angular momentum. All other information about what went down a black hole is lost. One cannot tell whether it was a one pound bag of feathers or a one pound bag of lead that has just been swallowed by the hole.

Disembodied gravity is difficult to detect, so is there any observational evidence for the existence of black holes or are they a theoretician's dream (or nightmare)? Isolated black holes would be hard to see, but many stars are in binary systems; if one of the stars in a close binary had evolved into a black hole, then it would be possible to infer its presence from observations of the binary. Figure 4.13 is a representation of how such a binary system might look.

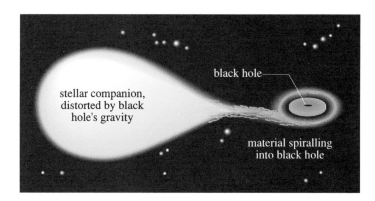

Figure 4.13   Artist's impression of a binary star system in which one star has evolved into a black hole. The black hole, of course, is not visible, but it is located at the centre of the 'doughnut ring' shape.

Imagine a binary system in which a pair of stars of very different masses once orbited close together. The more massive star (star A) evolved faster and has become a black hole, while its companion (star B) is still on (or close to) the main sequence. The gravitational attraction of the black hole distorts star B and drags some of the material off star B towards the black hole. The material has angular momentum around the black hole, so does not immediately cross the Schwarzschild radius, but gradually spirals inwards towards this critical radius. All the time it is being compressed and heated; indeed, it is heated to such high temperatures that it becomes a strong emitter of X-rays. This emission can escape because it is from outside the Schwarzschild radius. Material is continually disappearing from the inner part of the spiral into the black hole, but fresh material is continually arriving from star B on to the outer part of the spiral. However, the flow of material through the spiral is lumpy rather than smooth, and so the X-ray emission is not perfectly steady but rapidly flickers a little in brightness.

X-ray astronomers have discovered several X-ray sources with these properties; the most famous is in the constellation of Cygnus and is known as Cyg X-1. Optical astronomers have confirmed that the X-ray emission is from (some part of) a binary star system. One component of the binary is clearly visible and has been identified as an O9 or B0 supergiant; the other component is not directly visible and is assumed to be compact. Through study of the orbit (as in Subsection 2.5.1) and estimation of the mass of the supergiant, the mass of the invisible companion has been obtained. It is most probably about $12M_\odot$ and certainly greater than $3.3M_\odot$. It is too heavy to be a neutron star; the consensus is that it is a black hole.

So far we have discussed black holes that are roughly the mass of a star. The theoretical basis of black holes, however, does not restrict the mass to this range and at least two other sizes of black hole are under consideration by astrophysicists. Quasars, and some galaxies (see Block 3), have particularly active centres, which are responsible for the production of enormous amounts of energy; it has been suggested that there are black holes of $10^7M_\odot$ to $10^9M_\odot$ in the centres of these objects. At the other end of the scale, there is interest in the possible existence of mini black holes, of mass about 10^{11} kg. Conditions in which these latter could form no longer exist, but were thought to exist in the very early stages of the Universe.

Summary of Section 4.4 and SAQs

1   Neutron degeneracy pressure allows the existence of another stable form of stellar matter, more dense than the white dwarf and rich in neutrons. This type of star is known as a neutron star.

2   Such a star is formed when the core of a supergiant collapses in a supernova explosion.

3   Angular momentum is conserved in the collapse of the core of the supergiant, and so the neutron star will be rotating very rapidly on its axis.

4   If magnetic field lines are trapped as the core collapses then the neutron star will have a very strong magnetic field.

5   Pulsars are rapidly rotating, highly magnetized neutron stars, which produce beamed radio emission. As the star rotates, the beam is swept around the sky. If the orientation is such that the beam sweeps across the Earth, regular pulses of radio emission can be observed repeating at the pulsar rotation period.

6   Pulsars were discovered accidentally when a radio telescope designed to study rapid fluctuations in the signal received from quasars was brought into operation.

7   A black hole is believed to be the end-point of the evolution of a star too massive to become a neutron star.

8   The Schwarzschild radius of a black hole of mass M is given by

$$R_S = \frac{2GM}{c^2}$$

9   When an object collapses to a radius smaller than its Schwarzschild radius then its collapse cannot be halted, and nothing can escape from it.

10   A black hole in a binary star system may be detectable through the emission of rapidly flickering X-rays. The X-ray source Cygnus X-1 is probably one such system. Estimates of the mass of the non-luminous companion can help to confirm the existence of a black hole.

SAQ 4.6 (Objective 4.1)   A malfunctioning satellite of moment of inertia $2\,500\,\mathrm{kg\,m^2}$, spinning at 20.0 revolutions per minute, is to be repaired by a visiting astronaut. The satellite is cylindrical in shape with radius $1\,\mathrm{m}$. The astronaut, who has a mass of $100\,\mathrm{kg}$, latches on to the curved surface of the satellite. The astronaut's moment of inertia is given by the product of the astronaut's mass and the square of their distance from the spin axis. At how many revolutions per minute will the satellite-astronaut combination rotate?

SAQ 4.7 (Objective 4.5)   If $10^{-19}\,\mathrm{W\,m^{-2}}$ are received at Earth from a pulsar and you have a radio telescope of collecting area $5\,000\,\mathrm{m^2}$, compare the power received by the telescope from the pulsar with the power you would use lifting an OU mailing of $5\,\mathrm{kg}$ through a height of $1\,\mathrm{m}$ in 1 second.

SAQ 4.8 (Objective 4.6)   If the core of a supergiant is so massive that its collapse cannot be halted at nuclear densities, what happens to the core? Is there an explosion of the star as the core passes through nuclear densities? Will any of the processes that build heavier elements operate in this instance?

4.5   Bangs in binaries

Most stars in the Milky Way, unlike our Sun, are to be found in binary systems or bigger groupings. In many multiple star systems the stars are sufficiently far apart (more than $100\,\mathrm{AU}$) that the presence of the companion(s) does not affect the evolution of a star. However, there are systems in which the two stars orbit each other sufficiently closely that their interaction alters their evolution. Such binary systems are the subject of this Section.

4.5.1   Interacting binaries

A star's evolution may be affected when material is transferred either *to* the star *from* a companion, or *from* the star *to* a companion. Such a pair of stars is called an **interacting binary**. For there to be a significant amount of material transferred the two stars must be close together and, as shown in Subsection 2.5.1, this means we are concerned with binary systems with short orbital periods.

In previous Sections of this chapter, we have mentioned several instances of stars (or stellar remnants) paired in binary systems in which there is a transfer of material between the two stars.

☐   How many of these examples can you recall?

■   Mention was made of neutron stars in binary systems with more normal stars. The neutron stars accreted material from their companions and produced X-rays. At the same time the neutron star could be made to rotate faster and rejuvenated as a pulsar. Black holes in binary systems accrete in a similar manner and also emit X-rays. This was seen to be one of the few ways of detecting a black hole of stellar mass.

How did these interacting binaries get to their present form, and what will they become next? We assume that both stars were formed at the same time, but that they did not necessarily have the same mass.

☐   How does the mass of a star affect its rate of evolution?

■   The more massive stars take a shorter time to go through their life cycle.

Suppose we have a binary system in which the more massive star has reached the red giant stage while its less massive companion is still on the main sequence. As it expands, the envelope of the red giant is held less tightly by the giant's gravity.

Meanwhile, part of the envelope is coming closer to the giant's companion and more under the influence of the companion's gravity. Could the situation arise where (some of) the material of the envelope is pulled off the giant and accreted by the companion?

ITQ 4.16   A blob of gas is between the two stars of a binary system and is influenced by the gravitational attraction of both stars. One star has mass $10M_\odot$ and the other $1M_\odot$. Their centres are separated by $130R_\odot$. The blob of gas marks the limit to which the $10M_\odot$ star will expand when it becomes a red giant with a radius of $100R_\odot$. Compare the gravitational forces due to the two stars on the blob in this position. Which is the larger?

This ITQ indicates that, because at the surface of the $10M_\odot$ red giant the $1M_\odot$ star exerts the stronger force, it is quite possible to have material transferred from a giant (or a supergiant) envelope onto a companion star. There will be a number of points in the vicinity of the two stars where the blob of gas experiences equal gravitational pull towards the two stars; we did the calculation for a point on the line joining the stars, but there are, for example, points either side of this line where this is also true. In practice, the stars are rotating about each other and this complicates the picture, adding centrifugal forces, but it is still true that there are positions where a blob of gas experiences no net force. If we join up the points marking all these positions around the two stars we define a surface. Figure 4.14 shows a cut through the two stars and this surface.

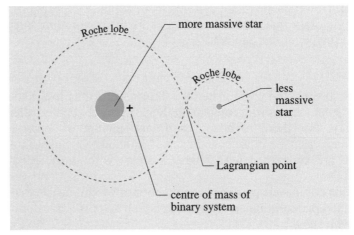

Figure 4.14   A cross-section through a close binary system; the dashed line shows where there is no net force on a blob of gas.

The slightly pear-shaped surfaces surrounding the stars are called **Roche lobes**, and the place where the two lobes touch, the cross-over point, is called a **Lagrangian point**. If, when a star becomes a giant, it swells sufficiently to fill its Roche lobe, then material at the outer edge of the lobe is so lightly bound to the giant that it can be pulled down on to the companion. This happens particularly near the pointed end of the pear shape – material leaks through the Lagrangian point there and funnels on to the companion. Figure 4.15 shows how this might look. As can be seen, there is a strong similarity between this system and the accreting black hole illustrated in Figure 4.13.

Material approaching the companion star tends to have angular momentum about the (centre of the) companion – in other words, the material is heading close past the companion rather than directly towards it, and it preferentially heads to one side of the companion. The material is then caught in the gravitational field of the companion and spirals down towards its surface, interacting with other infalling material as it does so. The spiralling system of

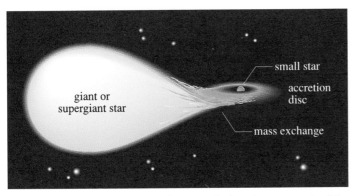

Figure 4.15 Transfer of mass from a red giant (or a supergiant) by Roche lobe overflow on to a smaller companion.

infalling material thus forms a disc around the star, called an **accretion disc.** (In some interacting binaries an accretion disc does not form. Instead, the material drawn from the giant crashes on to the outer layers of the companion. One such binary is Algol (β Per), as shown in Plate 1.25a).

As the giant star loses mass its Roche lobe shrinks, but its radius changes very little; this enhances the mass transfer. The temperature and luminosity of the giant drop and those of its companion increase.

Following the evolution further, we find that the former giant (we shall call this star 1 from now on) can lose all its outer layers, leaving a naked helium or carbon star. The second star is now the more massive and is a bright main sequence star. Nuclear reactions will cease in star 1 and it will become a white dwarf, or perhaps a neutron star. We shall then have a system like Sirius, with an old white dwarf and an *apparently* younger, more massive main sequence star.

What happens next? The system remains in this configuration for quite some time, but eventually star 2 will reach the end of its main sequence lifetime; depending on how massive it is there can be various outcomes. During its red giant or supergiant phase it may fill its Roche lobe and lose mass to star 1 (the white dwarf or neutron star). A number of the known X-ray stars are binary systems at this stage of evolution. So too may be the variable stars called novae.

If star 2 does not lose too much mass this way, then it may continue its evolution and become a supernova (or even a black hole) so that we can find binary systems that contain a white dwarf and a black hole. Figure 4.16 illustrates this sequence. Note that there can be variants on this – the origins of many kinds of unusual system can be explained through the evolution of interacting binaries.

This seems a plausible picture but, as with so many aspects of stellar evolution, our understanding is shaky. The picture may have to change – markedly! The same can be said for much of the material presented in this chapter. It presents our best understanding of the evolution of massive stars, but it is a subject where we have an incomplete (and therefore insecure) picture of what is happening, and our understanding is fast evolving!

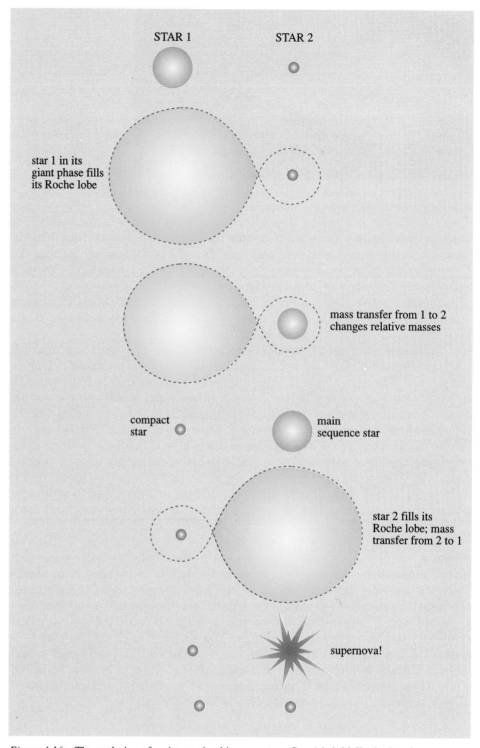

STAR 1

STAR 2

star 1 in its
giant phase fills
its Roche lobe

mass transfer from 1 to 2
changes relative masses

compact
star

main
sequence star

star 2 fills its
Roche lobe; mass
transfer from 2 to 1

supernova!

Figure 4.16 The evolution of an interacting binary system. Star 1 is initially the heavier.

1   If a star is one of a close binary system, its evolution will be significantly modified because of the transfer of material between the two stars in the system.

2   Roche lobe overflow is the most likely method for the transfer of material in a close binary system.

3   Many unusual binary systems, such as those containing two compact objects, or a compact object and a more normal star, can be accounted for by the evolution of interacting binary systems.

SAQ 4.9 (Objective 4.8)   A supergiant, spectral class B, mass $15\,M_\odot$, is in a binary system with a pulsar. The B star has emission lines; describe how the spectrum seen by an optical astronomer changes during one orbital period. What changes does a radio astronomer see during one orbital period? Outline the history and future evolution of the binary system.

4.6   *Conclusions from Chapters 3 and 4*

How are stars made? What powers them? What is their ultimate fate? These were the questions raised at the beginning of Chapter 3. What answers are we able to give, and how secure are those answers?

Undoubtedly there are gaps in our knowledge, areas where we think we know what must be happening but we lack convincing theory or convincing proof. As we have worked through the life histories of stars in these chapters these more uncertain areas have been identified. They include: some aspects of protostars; details of the post main sequence behaviour of stars, especially massive stars; mass loss from stars; and some of the phenomena associated with supernovae.

However, we have a broad understanding of the birth, life and death of stars, and we know what is required to make a star in the first place. Figure 4.17 summarizes the material presented in these two chapters and shows the stages occupied by stars of different masses at different times in their lives. To illustrate the use of this figure, we shall follow the tracks of a $1\,M_\odot$ star and a $20\,M_\odot$ star as they evolve.

The $1\,M_\odot$ star spends about 3×10^7 years in the protostar stage before appearing on the main sequence when nuclear fusion reactions start in its core. It stays on the main sequence for about 10^{10} years, all the while converting hydrogen into helium by the pp nuclear fusion processes. It then spends about 10^9 years as a giant before losing some of its mass and becoming a white dwarf. (Note the logarithmic scale – the width of the giant band for the $1\,M_\odot$ star is 10^9 years!)

The $20\,M_\odot$ star reaches the main sequence after only 10^5 years, and once there it fuses hydrogen rather more rapidly by the CNO process. In spite of its greater mass, after only 10 million years it is moving off the main sequence to become a supergiant. It may lose a significant amount of mass during this next stage, but on the assumption that it still retains about $8\,M_\odot$ it can be expected to undergo a supernova explosion after a million years or so in the supergiant stage. It loses yet more material to the interstellar medium through the supernova explosion, material that is enriched in the heavy elements. If the core that remains is under about $2\,M_\odot$ it will become a neutron star; if it is more massive it is expected to become a black hole.

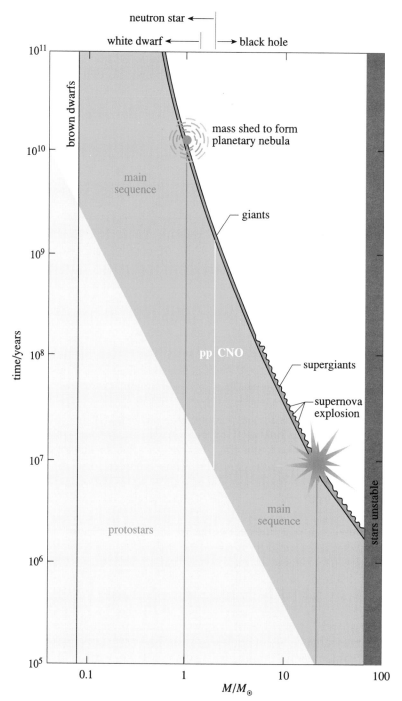

Figure 4.17 How stars of various masses change with time.

There is a cyclic nature to all this; stars are created from the interstellar material, live their lives, shed material back to the interstellar medium and die. Have there been any net changes? Yes! There are long-term changes in the interstellar medium, which will be discussed in Chapter 5. Also, as the galaxy ages, more and more material is locked up in white dwarfs, neutron stars and black holes. Ultimately there will not be enough hydrogen and helium in the interstellar medium to create new stars.

Objectives for Chapter 4

After studying Chapter 4 (and any associated audio, video or TV material) you should be able to:

4.1   Give brief definitions of the terms, concepts and principles listed at the end of the Objectives.

4.2   Describe in general terms the nuclear processes taking place in stars of higher mass, how they depend on temperature, and where they are located in the star.

4.3   Describe the main features of a Type II supernova in terms of the external appearance, the reason for the onset of collapse, the formation of a neutron core, the ejection of a shell, the formation of chemical elements, the time-scale on which all this happens, and the frequency with which supernovae occur.

4.4   Give details of the observation of supernova 1987A, including the detection of emitted neutrinos.

4.5   Describe the nature of pulsars, and explain why they are thought to be neutron stars.

4.6   Explain how some stars are expected to collapse to a black hole and describe the consequences, including the main properties of a black hole.

4.7   Describe how black holes might be detected.

4.8   Explain some of the consequences of mass transfer in an interacting binary.

Term	Page	Term	Page	Term	Page
accretion disc	161	interacting binary	159	r-process reactions	141
angular momentum	148	Lagrangian point	160	Roche lobes	160
angular speed	148	light curve	142	Schwarzschild radius	156
black hole	157	moment of inertia	148	SN 1987A	144
conservation of angular momentum	148	neutron degeneracy pressure	139	supergiant	134
escape velocity	156	neutron star	147	supernova	140
half-life	142	pulsar	151	supernova remnant	146

Chapter 5
The interstellar medium

Prepared for the Course Team by Barrie W. Jones

Contents

5.1 Introduction

On a number of occasions in this Course, you have met the idea that the vast spaces between the stars in a galaxy are not empty, but contain gas and dust. Thus, in Chapter 2 you saw that interstellar matter attenuates the light from the stars, in Chapter 3 you saw that stars are born from dense clouds, and in Chapters 3 and 4 you learned that stars return matter to interstellar space in a variety of ways. Interstellar matter constitutes the **interstellar medium**, or ISM for short.

The ISM is richly varied, and highly photogenic as many of the colour plates show, and on these grounds alone it is worth spending time on. It is also intimately associated with stellar evolution, and this will be further explored in this chapter, though in the main we shall focus on the ISM itself. In particular, we shall answer the questions

- What are the main features of the ISM in our galaxy today?
- Why is the ISM as it is?
- How does the ISM evolve?

We shall also consider, briefly, how the ISM is studied, mainly in the two TV programmes *A cosmic cycle* and *Mapping the Milky Way*.

5.2 The interstellar medium today

5.2.1 Some history

Until as recently as the 1920s, most astronomers believed that interstellar matter was confined to a handful of isolated clouds, some glowing brightly, as in Plates 1.16 and 1.21, and some, through their obscuration of stars, appearing dark, as in Plate 1.14. The truth began to emerge from long-exposure photographs, which showed that such clouds are far more common than had previously been thought. Furthermore, by 1930 it had become clear that interstellar matter is not confined to such clouds, but is widespread in the spaces between them. There were two pieces of evidence for this.

First, a characteristic type of attenuation of starlight had been observed in many directions in space, and it had been shown that this is caused by dust particles with sizes of the order of the wavelength of visible light, about 10^{-6} m. This dust attenuates starlight, partly by absorbing it and partly by **scattering** it. You can picture scattering as a process in which photons bounce off particles in random directions, and so some of the photons that were travelling towards us from the star do not reach us. Scattering plus absorption is called **extinction**.

Second, it had also been observed that, in many directions in space, there are absorption lines in stellar spectra that, for various reasons, could not have originated in the stellar atmospheres, but must have originated in cool gas between us and the star. For example, the lines are very narrow, suggesting that they originate in a medium far cooler than a stellar atmosphere. In a stellar atmosphere the random thermal speeds are so rapid that the absorption lines would have been far more broadened through the Doppler effect (Subsection 2.2.1) – at any instant, the atoms moving towards us would have had their lines much more blue-shifted, and those travelling away, much more red-shifted. By contrast, in a cool gas the Doppler effect is weaker and the lines are narrower. By 1941, such interstellar absorption lines had led to the identification of atoms and ions such as Na and Ca^+, and the molecules CH, CN and CH^+.

The next major advance came in 1951, when the new science of radioastronomy led to the discovery of interstellar atomic hydrogen (H), through its spectral emission line at a wavelength (in vacuum) of 21 cm. The origin of this line is in the spin of the proton that constitutes the nucleus of the hydrogen atom, relative to the spin of the orbiting electron. These spins are illustrated in Figure 5.1: the proton and the electron can be regarded as small spheres, each spinning at a fixed rate around axes through their centres. In the hydrogen atom, though the electron rapidly changes its position with respect to the proton, the spin is always either parallel to that of the proton, as in Figure 5.1a, or opposed to it, as in Figure 5.1b. There is a small energy difference between the two states in Figure 5.1, and it is the transition from the higher energy level (a) to the lower (b) that gives rise to the 21 cm line.

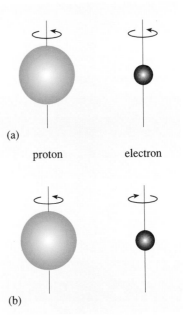

(a)

proton   electron

□   What is the energy difference between these two levels?

■   From Equations 1.3 and 1.2, the energy difference ε is given by

$$\varepsilon = hf = hc/\lambda \qquad (5.1)$$

Thus, with $\lambda = 0.21$ m, and the values of c and h given on the back cover of the *Introduction and Guide*, we get $\varepsilon = 9.5 \times 10^{-25}$ J.

For us to observe this emission line, the hydrogen atoms must be exposed to sufficient energy to raise them into the upper energy level at a reasonable rate compared with the rate at which they are reverting to the lower energy level by emitting radiation. One energy source is provided by the collisions between hydrogen atoms as a result of their random thermal motion – this is an example of **collisional excitation**. For a reasonable proportion of such collisions to be sufficiently energetic, the average translational kinetic energy of an atom e_k (*Preparatory science*, Section 2.4) must be such that $e_k \gtrsim \varepsilon$. Now, for thermal motion, e_k is related to the temperature T of the hydrogen via Equation 2.3 in *Preparatory science*, i.e.

(b)

Figure 5.1 The hydrogen atom, in which the proton and electron spins are (a) parallel or (b) opposed.

$$e_k = 3kT/2 \qquad (5.2)$$

where k is Boltzmann's constant. Thus, with $e_k \gtrsim \varepsilon$, we get

$$T \gtrsim 2\varepsilon/(3k) \qquad (5.3)$$

Putting in the above value of ε, we get the requirement $T \gtrsim 0.05$ K, which is met everywhere in the ISM!

You might be wondering why the studies, in the 1920s, of absorption lines in stellar spectra at *visible* wavelengths did not reveal the presence of interstellar atomic hydrogen through its visible wavelength absorption lines – the Balmer lines (Figure 2.10). Given that, to observe an absorption line, we initially need appreciable numbers of atoms in the lower energy level of the line, part of the answer lies in the fact that the regions of the ISM studied were cool.

ITQ 5.1   So, why were the Balmer lines not seen?

The low temperatures are only part of the answer. Had the cool regions been exposed to much ultraviolet (UV) radiation, then UV photons would have raised appreciable numbers of hydrogen atoms into the $n = 2$ level, thus allowing Balmer absorption lines to appear in the spectra of background stars. Therefore, the low UV fluxes in such regions complete the answer.

Given that the hydrogen atoms are in the lowest ($n = 1$) energy level, it should be possible to detect interstellar hydrogen through the absorption lines it would produce in stellar spectra when the radiation from the background star excites the electrons (even in small numbers) to any of the higher energy levels. However, these lines are at UV wavelengths, to which the Earth's atmosphere is opaque. Thus, it was only in the 1970s, when observations from rockets and satellites were made from above the Earth's atmosphere, that atomic hydrogen was detected via its UV absorption lines.

Today, the ISM is studied at a great variety of wavelengths. From such studies we obtain the composition of the gas, and we can infer the composition of the dust. Such studies also give us temperatures, densities, motions, and magnetic fields. Few of the details of how these studies are conducted will concern us in this text: we shall be more concerned with what the studies reveal.

5.2.2 Overview

Various types of region can be distinguished in the ISM. In certain respects they are very different; in other respects they are rather similar. Let's look at the similarities first.

With few exceptions, the various types of region share the following features.

1   The chemical elements are present in relative abundances that are not very different from the cosmic relative abundances, introduced in Subsection 2.3.5. Thus, the relative percentages of atomic nuclei of hydrogen, helium and heavy elements ($Z > 2$), are approximately 92%: 7.8%: 0.2%, though the proportion of an element present as ions, atoms, or combined in molecules or dust, does vary from one type of region to another.

2   Dust accounts for roughly 1% of the mass of most types of region. The particles are very small – about 10^{-7} m to 10^{-6} m in diameter – and consist of some fraction of each of the less volatile substances found in the ISM, such as metals and their compounds. In the cooler regions of the ISM, substances with greater volatility also condense, so there are regional differences in the composition of the dust. The gas is always dominated by hydrogen and helium, which are abundant and very volatile.

3   The various types of region are far from quiescent, being racked by internal motions, and by physical and chemical transformations, often rapid compared with many astronomical changes. Each type of region is also highly structured, and far from uniform.

Let's turn now to the main differences, starting with temperature and number density. These are important physical parameters that have a wide range of values in the ISM, and they provide the basis on which the different types of region are defined. The number density n is the number of atoms per unit volume in a region, so has SI units of m^{-3}. The atoms can be neutral, ionized, or combined in molecules or in dust. Because of the predominance of hydrogen, to a sufficient approximation we can take n to be the number of hydrogen atoms per cubic metre.

In Chapter 3, it made sense to define n as the number of *particles* per unit volume.

Even when we ignore the other elements, n is not the same as the number of separate *particles* per cubic metre. For example, if all the hydrogen is present in the molecular form, H_2, then the number of separate particles per cubic metre is about $n/2$.

☐   What is the particle number density if all the hydrogen is ionized?

■   About $2n$ (the electron is a separate particle when the hydrogen is ionized!).

Only if hydrogen is present mainly as un-ionized atoms will the particle number density be about the same as the number density n. However, n always gives us a good measure of the mass density ρ, because $\rho \sim nm_H$, where m_H is the mass of the hydrogen atom, little changed by ionization, and unchanged by combination in molecules.

Figure 5.2 shows the number densities and temperatures found in the ISM. First, note the enormous range of number densities, from a miniscule value of about $100\,m^{-3}$, to the much greater value of about $10^{17}\,m^{-3}$. Second, note that the temperature range is also enormous, from a frigid $10\,K$ or so, to temperatures comparable with those found in stellar interiors. However, within these wide ranges, the various temperatures and number densities are not equally represented. Thus, the names given in Figure 5.2 are not of arbitrary subdivisions, but correspond to where the measured temperature and number density values tend to concentrate. It is because there are such concentrations that temperature and number density provide a useful basis on which the different types of region are defined.

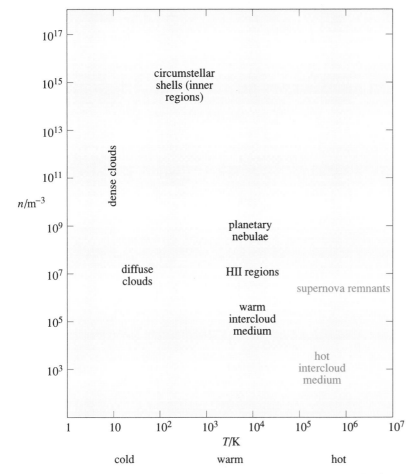

Figure 5.2 Various types of region in the ISM, distinguished on the basis of the number density n of atoms, and the temperature T. The atoms can be neutral, or ionized, or combined in chemical compounds. To a sufficient approximation in the ISM, we need only count hydrogen atoms.

ITQ 5.2 At the surface of the Earth, the Earth's atmosphere, mainly N_2 and O_2, has a temperature of about 300 K, and a density of about $1\,\mathrm{kg\,m^{-3}}$. Where, in Figure 5.2, do these atmospheric conditions lie? You can ignore the relatively small difference in mass between the oxygen and nitrogen atoms.

The type definitions in Figure 5.2 are reinforced when we examine some other properties of the regions, as in Table 5.1. Clearly, between the various types there are yet further striking differences. First, note the overall abundance of each type, expressed as a volume fraction of the whole ISM. The **intercloud media** (hot and warm) account for most of the volume, and together form a low-density, optically transparent, widespread matrix in which the other types of region are embedded. Each of these other types is present not as a single piece, threading the ISM, but instead consists of a large number of separate objects: typical sizes are given in the table. For comparison, note that the distance across the spiral arms of our galaxy is about 30 000 pc, and that the diameter of the orbit of Neptune, the outermost of the large planets, is 3×10^{-4} pc. Thus, each object is much smaller than our galaxy, but much larger than the domain of the planets in our Solar System.

Second, note the mass fractions of each type. Here, it is not the intercloud media, but the dense and diffuse clouds that dominate, their comparatively small volumes being more than offset by their comparatively high densities (Figure 5.2).

Finally, note the striking differences in the predominant form of hydrogen present, and in the abundance of molecules. A bit more detail on these chemical features is provided in the next subsection, but an explanation of these chemical differences, and of the various other differences and similarities, is deferred to Section 5.3.

Table 5.1 Some features of the various types of region in the ISM

Type of region	Fraction of the ISM/%[a]		Typical size/pc[c]	Predominant form of hydrogen	Abundance of molecules
	By volume[b]	By mass			
hot intercloud medium	~60	≤0.1	–	H^+	very low
warm intercloud medium	~30	~20	–	H^+ or H	very low
diffuse clouds	~3	~30	~3 to ~100	H or H_2	diatomic molecules common
dense clouds	≤1	~45	~0.1 to ~20	H_2	molecules common, even large ones
HII regions	~10	~1	~1 to ~20	H^+	very low
circumstellar shells	negligible	negligible	≤1	H or H_2	diatomic common
planetary nebulae	negligible	negligible	≤2	H^+	very low
supernova remnants	d	negligible	≤1 000	H^+ or H	very low

[a] These percentages are only rough estimates, so do not sum to 100%.

[b] The total volume of the ISM is taken to be a disc with a diameter roughly that of the spiral arms of the Milky Way, i.e. 30 000 pc, and a thickness of 300 pc.

[c] These are typical distances across a region, such that the volume $V \sim \frac{4}{3}\pi(\text{size}/2)^3$. For roughly spherical regions the size is roughly the diameter.

[d] The volume is included in the hot intercloud medium (see text).

5.2.3 Thumbnail sketches

The **hot intercloud medium** is one of the hottest types of region (Figure 5.2), and it is also very widespread (Table 5.1). You might therefore be wondering why it doesn't blaze down on us from the night sky. The reason is its extremely low density, coupled with its highly ionized state. Ionized media are very inefficient radiators, and the low density means that in any case there is little material to radiate. The low density also means that it is highly transparent, and so the medium does not obscure anything lying in or beyond it. For much the same reasons the **warm intercloud medium** is also not very apparent.

By contrast, the other types of region are much more readily detected, often at a variety of wavelengths, and so are well represented in *Images of the Cosmos*. These other types of region can be subdivided into those that are associated with particular stars, and those that are not. The latter are the diffuse and dense clouds. The former are the planetary nebulae and the supernova remnants that you met in Chapters 3 and 4, respectively, and the circumstellar shells and the HII (h-two) regions.

An **HII region** is associated with starbirth, being a low-density cavity created inside a dense cloud by the formation there of one or more hot, bright stars (spectral class O or B). They get their name from the predominant form of hydrogen that they contain, namely ionized hydrogen: for historical reasons, HII indicates hydrogen in its ionized form. (An alternative name for this type of region is 'diffuse nebula', but this is easily confused with the very different diffuse clouds, so we won't use it.) Many HII regions are visible to the unaided eye, and easily visible in binoculars. A particularly easy one to find is in Orion, in the 'sword' below the 'belt', as described in the *Project file*. This is the Orion Nebula, which you should have seen in the project *In and around Orion*; it is shown in Plate 1.16 – rather better than the view through binoculars! Further beautiful examples are shown in other plates. In all cases, note the irregular shapes, and, in the visible images, the red coloration due to emission by the hydrogen Balmer line Hα. In many of these plates, the HII region has burst through the surface of the dense cloud, and so is seen at visible wavelengths, a configuration shown in Figure 5.3. HII regions that are completely shrouded in dense clouds can sometimes be detected at infrared, microwave and radio wavelengths, at which the dense clouds are fairly transparent. These longer wavelengths are emitted by the cavity star(s) at the long wavelength tail in the stellar spectrum, and by dust and molecules at the cool boundary of the HII region. Plate 1.17b shows some such buried stars.

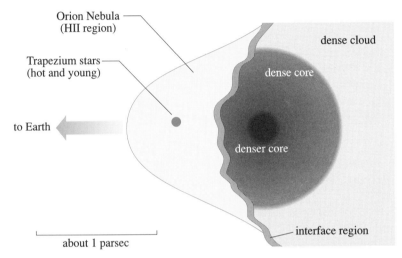

Figure 5.3   A section through the Orion Nebula (simplified).

Circumstellar shells, planetary nebulae and supernova remnants are all associated with stars near or at the ends of their lives. They are all too faint to be seen with the unaided eye, though some examples of the latter two types have angular diameters exceeding that of the Moon. **Circumstellar shells** are formed from matter ejected by cool giants/supergiants, and are rich in molecules and in dust. They are by far the densest parts of the ISM (Figure 5.2). Plate 1.26 shows a rather spectacular circumstellar shell.

A **planetary nebula** is a shell of material shed by a star of modest mass – less than about $8M_\odot$ (Chapter 3). Plate 1.27 shows two such shells, in these particular cases somewhat spherical. They appear ring-like only because of the change in projected thickness across the shell, as illustrated in Figure 5.4. The red coloration is partly due to Hα emission, but other spectral colours are also present.

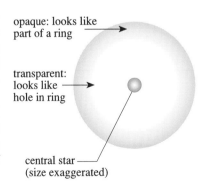

Figure 5.4   A planetary nebula appears like a ring.

Stars with masses greater than about $8M_\odot$ end their lives as Type II supernovae (Chapter 4). In these explosions all, or nearly all, of the star's mass is violently ejected. The ejected material sweeps up interstellar matter, to form a **supernova remnant**. Such remnants emit radiation across a wide range of wavelengths, as shown in Plates 1.29–1.31.

Let's turn now to the final two types of region, the diffuse and dense clouds. These clouds are usually irregularly shaped, and are often more sheet-like than spherical. **Diffuse clouds** are cold regions, of moderate density (Figure 5.2) such that stars can be seen through them at visible wavelengths, and consequently they are not apparent to the unaided eye. Hydrogen is present in both atomic (H) and molecular (H_2) forms, and a number of other simple molecules are also found. The clouds are often mapped, and otherwise investigated, via the 21 cm line emitted by collisionally excited atomic hydrogen (Subsection 5.2.1), and by spectral lines emitted at microwave frequencies by the molecule CO, again after collisional excitation. The mechanisms of molecular emission will be outlined in Subsection 5.2.5.

Dense clouds are as cold, or colder than diffuse clouds, and, unsurprisingly, are denser! Unless it is very thin in the direction of our line of sight, a dense cloud is opaque at visible and UV wavelengths, because of extinction by the dust in it. It is then seen by its obscuration of the stars beyond, and is then often called a dark cloud. Such obscuration is apparent in Plate 1.14, which shows The Coal Sack, near the Southern Cross, readily seen with the unaided eye from any latitude south of about 25° N. Dense clouds are also visible near the HII regions in Plate 1.16: remember that HII regions result from star formation in dense clouds.

The gas in dense clouds consists largely of molecules, of which there are a great variety. Moreover, extinction by dust is far less severe at longer wavelengths, and so mapping, and other investigations, often rely on the collisionally excited microwave emissions from molecules such as HCN, OH, CS and CO. Plate 1.15c shows a map of CO emission in and around Orion: the more copious the emission the greater the amount of material. Roughly speaking, the regions in this map are dense clouds, and, though unseen here, they are fringed in most places by diffuse clouds. Typically, the two types of region are closely associated.

ITQ 5.3   Why do you think dense clouds are not mapped using the hydrogen 21 cm line? (Note that the 21 cm line is not emitted by hydrogen *molecules*.)

Any region in which hydrogen is predominantly in the molecular form is called a **molecular cloud**. Thus, *all* dense clouds are molecular clouds, and so too are some diffuse clouds (some circumstellar shells could be included, though the name is not normally extended to cover them). No other type of region in the ISM qualifies.

Many diffuse clouds have dense clouds moving around inside them (Plate 1.15c). Moreover, within a dense cloud, whether inside a diffuse cloud or not, there are often even denser regions called cores and clumps, with masses in the range from $\sim 0.3 M_\odot$ to $\sim 10^3 M_\odot$, and it is in such cores and clumps that stars tend to form. The largest of such hierarchical clouds are called **giant molecular cloud complexes**, or GMC complexes for short. They have dimensions up to ~ 100 pc and masses up to $\sim 10^6 M_\odot$. They are being increasingly recognized as the fundamental cloud structure in the ISM, rather than the individual diffuse or dense clouds. Figure 5.5 illustrates the hierarchical structure of a GMC complex, and Plate 1.15 shows the local example, in and around Orion, the Orion Nebula (Plate 1.16) being just one small part of the whole. It is indeed a pity that we can see so little of the ISM with the unaided eye.

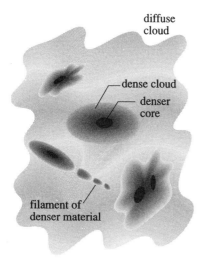

Figure 5.5   The hierarchical structure of a giant molecular cloud complex.

5.2.4   The distribution of the ISM in our galaxy

Our galaxy was described briefly in the *Introduction and Guide*, and it will be described further in Block 3. Here we need know only enough of its structure to outline the distribution of the ISM in it, and Figure 5.6 is sufficient for this purpose. This shows our galaxy schematically, with the main zones labelled, and Plate 3.2 shows an artist's impression.

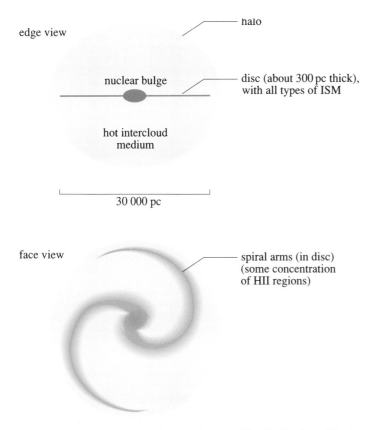

edge view

halo

nuclear bulge

disc (about 300 pc thick),
with all types of ISM

hot intercloud
medium

30 000 pc

face view

spiral arms (in disc)
(some concentration
of HII regions)

Figure 5.6   The main zones in our galaxy, and the distribution of the interstellar medium.

In the halo, the ISM consists almost entirely of the hot intercloud medium (Figure 5.6). This hot medium is also present in the disc (which includes the nuclear bulge), where it probably accounts for over half of the disc volume (Table 5.1). The *warm* intercloud medium is largely confined to the disc, and this is also the case for all the other types of region. Indeed, the concentration of the HII regions and the associated bright O and B stars goes a long way towards delineating the spiral arms at visible wavelengths, as in Plate 3.2.

In the nuclear bulge the ISM is somewhat depleted, though this bulge does contain some of the more massive GMC complexes. By contrast, the stars are *more* densely packed in the bulge, though the average interstellar distance remains vastly greater than the size of the stars themselves. In our own neck of the woods, in a spiral arm about two-thirds of the way out from the centre, the Sun lies in an irregularly shaped bubble a few hundred parsecs across (Plate 1.13), with densities and temperatures in most of this volume like those of the hot intercloud medium. The bubble is bounded by warm intercloud medium.

Overall, the total mass of the ISM is equal to about 10% of the total mass of the stars in our galaxy.

So, that's the cast of characters – the various types of region that make up the ISM – and how they lie on the stage that is our galaxy. We must soon turn to explanations of why the ISM is the way it is. But first we must pause briefly, and consider a few radiative processes that are important in the ISM.

5.2.5   Radiative processes in the ISM

You have seen that the ISM has been studied through the radiation that the gas and dust absorb, emit and scatter. Figure 5.7 summarizes the differences between these three phenomena.

Let's first consider the three phenomena in relation to the *gas*. Scattering by the gas is far weaker than by the dust, and so we need consider only absorption

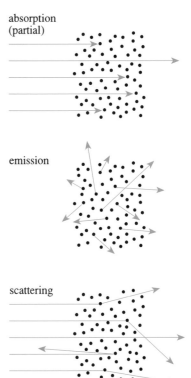

absorption
(partial)

emission

scattering

Figure 5.7   Absorption, emission and scattering of radiation.

175

and emission of radiation. You have already met absorption and emission of photons by *atoms* (which we shall call **photoexcitation** and **photoemission**, respectively), and the possibility of atomic excitation through collisions (collisional excitation). The new feature here is with these processes as they operate in *molecules*, which are found in many parts of the ISM. The CO molecule, which is common in the ISM, is a simple case that serves to introduce the important ideas.

Figure 5.8 shows the *electronic* energy levels of the CO molecule. The levels above the lowest one correspond to the various excited states of just one of the 14 electrons that this molecule contains, in particular one of the outermost electrons, which are the least tightly bound and thus require less energy to excite them than the inner, more tightly bound electrons. For comparison, the electronic energy levels for atomic hydrogen are also shown. The excitation of a CO molecule from a lower electronic energy level to a higher one can happen through photoexcitation or through collisional excitation.

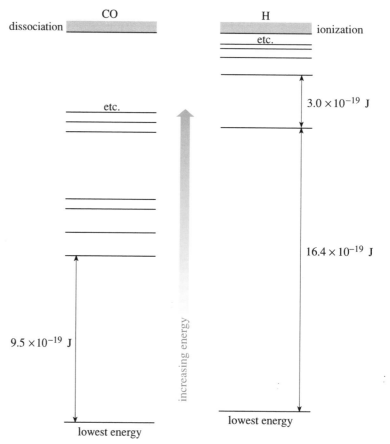

Figure 5.8 Electronic energy levels in CO and in H.

ITQ 5.4 For the excitation of CO from its lowest electronic energy level to the one above it, calculate (a) the maximum photon wavelength for photoexcitation and (b) the minimum gas temperature for appreciable collisional excitation.

Thus, CO remains in its lowest electronic energy level unless it is exposed to photons at least as energetic as those in the near-UV region, or is at a temperature of order 10^5 K, or greater. These are the same sorts of criterion obtained for many atoms, and for many other molecules too, though in some atoms and molecules the lower electronic levels are not quite so widely spread.

Not all electronic excitations require such large energies. Thus, the higher electronic energy levels (Figure 5.8) are much more closely spaced, and excitations among them can be achieved by longer wavelength photons, and at lower temperatures. The energy levels of atomic hydrogen in Figure 5.1, which give rise to the 21 cm line, are a further example of closely spaced electronic levels.

As well as electronic transitions, a molecule can also undergo vibrational and rotational transitions. A **vibrational transition** of CO is illustrated schematically in Figure 5.9, along with the lowest few vibrational energy levels for the case in which the molecule remains in the *electronic* state corresponding to the lowest electronic energy level. Note how much smaller are the gaps between the energy levels than is the case for the electronic transitions in Figure 5.8. This means that photoexcitation can take place at infrared (IR) wavelengths, and collisional excitation at temperatures down to the order of 10^3 K. These criteria are typical for vibrational transitions in molecules.

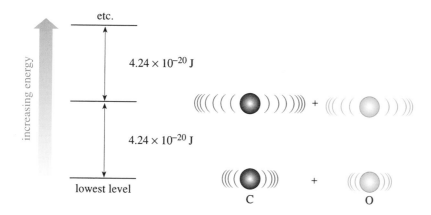

Figure 5.9 Vibrational transitions and vibrational energy levels in CO. To the right are the vibrational states corresponding to the lowest two energy levels.

A **rotational transition** of CO is illustrated schematically in Figure 5.10, along with the lowest few rotational energy levels corresponding to the lowest energy electronic and vibrational states. The energy gaps are yet smaller, and photoexcitation can now be caused by microwaves, and collisional excitation occurs at temperatures down to the order of a frigid 10 K. Again, these criteria are typical, though many molecules have even smaller rotational energy gaps, and a few have much larger gaps.

A transition from a lower to a higher energy level can also involve some combination of electronic, vibrational and rotational energy changes, necessarily so in some cases.

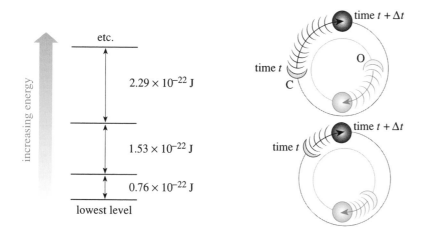

Figure 5.10 Rotational transitions, and rotational energy levels in CO. To the right are the rotational states corresponding to the lowest two energy levels.

177

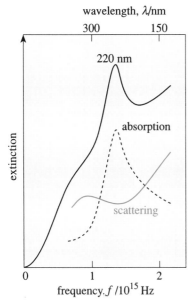

wavelength, λ/nm

Figure 5.11 Extinction by interstellar dust: the top curve is the sum of the other two.

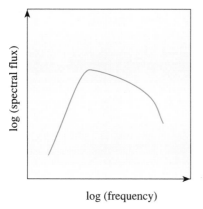

Figure 5.12 A typical spectrum of synchrotron radiation.

Photoemission is the reverse process of photoexcitation, and so yields photons at wavelengths equal to those that would have caused photoexcitation between the two levels concerned.

Not all transitions involving photoexcitation and photoemission are equally probable, and so some spectral absorption and emission lines tend to be far weaker than others, and some are completely absent. Molecules consisting of two identical atoms, such as H_2, have particularly weak vibrational and rotational lines.

Let's now consider the dust. Photoexcitation and collisional excitation occur in the atoms and molecules that constitute the surface of a dust grain. Much of this energy is shared throughout the grain, raising its temperature until thermal radiation from the grain balances the energy absorbed. An alternative fate for an incident photon is to be scattered (Figure 5.7), a fate that the grains administer very efficiently at certain wavelengths. A typical outcome for the combined effects of absorption and scattering (extinction) by interstellar dust is shown in Figure 5.11. Note how the extinction increases strongly through visible wavelengths, and on into the UV. Note also how broad the spectral features are, which makes it difficult to determine the composition of the dust from such spectral studies. Not much more about composition is revealed by the *emission* spectrum of the dust, which is a broad smooth thermal spectrum, depending on the dust temperature, the particle size, and only weakly on its composition. At 20 K, the dust emission lies right across the far-IR and microwave parts of the spectrum.

Thermal emission from the dust is only one of several types of emission from the ISM that have a broad, smooth spectrum, devoid of narrow lines. We will outline just one other type, **synchrotron radiation**. This is emitted by electrically charged particles when they pass through magnetic fields, though the amounts of radiation are very small unless the particles have very high energy. In the ISM, electrons can be copious sources of synchrotron radiation, provided that they are travelling close to the speed of light. Figure 5.12 shows a typical broad spectrum of synchrotron radiation. The peak wavelength depends on the energy of the electrons, and on the strength of the magnetic field. The radiation has been observed in the ISM at wavelengths ranging from X-rays to radio. For example, supernova remnants are copious emitters at radio wavelengths.

This concludes our brief look at some important radiative processes in the ISM. We now turn to explaining why the ISM is as it is.

Summary of Section 5.2 and SAQs

1   Evidence of a widespread interstellar medium (ISM) was established by 1930 from the extinction of starlight by interstellar dust, and from absorption lines produced in starlight by cool gas between us and the star. The ISM today is studied over a wide range of wavelengths, through emission, absorption and scattering.

2   Most of the ISM has cosmic composition. Dust consists of the less volatile substances, and almost everywhere accounts for about 1% of the ISM by mass. The ISM is far from quiescent.

3   The main types of region in the ISM, and some of their major properties, are shown in Figure 5.2 and Table 5.1. The intercloud media are a matrix in which the other types of region are embedded. These other types each consist of a large number of objects, each object being much smaller than our galaxy, but much bigger than the planetary region of the Solar System. The HII regions, and the clouds (particularly the dense clouds) are associated with starbirth. The circumstellar shells, planetary nebulae and supernova remnants are associated with stars at, or near, the ends of their lives.

4   The fundamental cloud structure seems to be the giant molecular cloud (GMC) complex, with sizes up to ~100 pc, and masses up to ~$10^6 M_\odot$.

5   The distribution of the ISM in our galaxy is summarized in Figure 5.6.

6   The main radiative processes in the ISM are summarized in Table 5.2.

Table 5.2   The main radiative processes in the ISM

Source	Main wavelength range	Temperature[a]/K
Spectral lines		
H electron spin	21 cm	$\geqslant 0.1$
electronic I[b]	X-ray, UV, visible, near-IR	$\geqslant 10^4$
electronic II[c]	IR, microwave, radio	$\geqslant 10$
vibrational	IR	$\geqslant 10^3$
rotational	microwave, radio	$\geqslant 10$
Broad, smooth spectra		
dust extinction	UV, visible	–
dust emission	IR, microwave, radio	–
synchrotron radiation	X-ray to radio	–

[a] For collisional excitation.

[b] Involving a lower energy level.

[c] Between higher energy levels.

SAQ 5.1 (Objective 5.3)   Calculate *rough* values for the typical mass of a diffuse cloud, a dense cloud and an HII region, expressing your answers in solar masses. Lay out your answer in tabular form, under the following headings, and state any simplifying assumptions that you make.

Type of region	Size/pc	Volume/m^3	n/m^{-3}	Mass/$M_\odot$

Which of these three types of region are common in the disc of the Milky Way?

SAQ 5.2 (Objectives 5.2–5.4)   A diffuse cloud is at a temperature near the upper end of the observed range for such clouds. The radiative flux on the cloud is slight. The gas in the cloud contains significant amounts of the molecule CN, which has energy levels comparable with those of CO.

(a)   Discuss what sort of absorption and emission lines from CN are likely to be observable for the study of this cloud.

(b)   Comment briefly on whether H_2 absorption and emission lines are likely to be observed.

(c)   Discuss whether extinction by the dust is likely to obscure the stars beyond the cloud in each of the following wavelength ranges: IR, visible, UV.

(d)   Estimate the wavelength range over which thermal emission from the dust is likely to occur, assuming that the spectral form is not very different from that of a black body.

5.3 Why is the interstellar medium as it is?

In answering the question posed by the title of this Section, we shall follow two themes: first, the *matter theme*, which is about the dispersal of matter from stars to the ISM, followed by the formation of clouds from dispersed matter; second, the *composition theme*, which is about the elements, ions, molecules and dust found in the ISM.

5.3.1 The matter theme I: from the stars to the intercloud media

The dispersal of matter from stars involves the return to the ISM of some of the matter from which the stars formed. You have seen that this dispersal occurs in several different ways: via stellar winds, the shedding of planetary nebulae, and Type II supernovae.

Stellar winds and circumstellar shells

Stellar winds are a relatively gentle form of dispersal. All stars lose some matter in this way, but in our galaxy the overall amount of matter returned by stellar winds to the ISM is dominated by the copious winds from hot (class O and B) stars, and by strong winds from cool red giants. These latter winds give rise to circumstellar shells of the sort shown in Plate 1.26. In their inner regions, circumstellar shells are kept moderately warm by the star's luminosity, with temperatures around 1 000 K, not much less than that of the star's photosphere.

☐ Of what order are the photospheric temperatures of cool red giants?

■ From Subsection 2.4.1, about 2 000 to 3 000 K.

Circumstellar shells are, as you might expect, less dense than the photospheres of red giants, but are enormously dense by ISM standards, with $n \sim 10^{17} \, \text{m}^{-3}$ in their inner regions. However, as the matter in such shells moves outwards it becomes less dense, and also cools, and the next we see of it might be widespread but thin **interstellar cirrus**, so called because of its resemblance to the terrestrial cloud type called cirrus. An example of the interstellar variety is shown in Plate 1.32 – what we are seeing is thermal radiation from dust at about 20 K. Interstellar cirrus was discovered in 1983 by the infrared space telescope IRAS.

Ultimately, all matter from stellar winds becomes thinly dispersed.

Shedding of planetary nebulae

More violent than mass loss via stellar winds is the shedding of a planetary nebula (Plate 1.27). In Chapter 3 you saw that this is the fate of a giant, which becomes unstable and throws off a significant fraction of its mass. All but the lowest and highest mass stars become giants, and so planetary nebulae are an important source of matter for the ISM. The remnant star is very hot, and also emits a powerful wind. As a result, planetary nebulae are hotter than circumstellar shells, with temperatures of order 10 000 K. They are also fairly dense, with $n \sim 10^9 \, \text{m}^{-3}$. As in the case of stellar winds, the matter in planetary nebulae moves away from the star, at speeds of the order of several kilometres per second, cooling and thinning as it proceeds. It takes about 30 000 years for a planetary nebula to disperse: not long on the cosmic time-scale.

Supernovae, and their effects

Yet more violent is a supernova: Plate 1.28 shows part of the Large Magellanic Cloud, before and after the Type II supernova 1987A, discussed in Chapter 4. A

Type II supernova is a cataclysmic stellar explosion, involving massive stars, in which most of the star's mass is flung into space. This might lead you to think that supernovae are major sources of interstellar matter, but this is not really the case.

☐ Why not?

■ Supernovae are rare.

However, though supernovae are not major sources of *mass* for the ISM, they are important sources of heavy elements, a point to which we return later.

Supernovae are also important in two other ways. First, they provide important amounts of very energetic particles, mainly H^+, called **cosmic rays**. Many of these tiny particles have individual energies in excess of 10^{-9} J, and they are thus able to pervade all regions of the ISM, and in some types of region they have significant effects, as you will see.

Second, supernovae release huge amounts of energy into the ISM, about 10^{46} J per explosion. Most of this is radiated in the form of neutrinos, which have little effect on the ISM, but there is still a prodigious 10^{44} J carried off as kinetic energy in a radially expanding gas shell and about 10^{42} J in the form of electromagnetic radiation. The kinetic energy of the shell means that the expelled material does not simply cool and vanish into the general ISM in the manner of stellar winds and planetary nebulae, but wreaks far-ranging and profound changes. Some indication of this can be seen in the supernova remnants in Plates 1.29 to 1.31.

To explore the effects of Type II supernovae further, consider the speed at which the shell is initially expelled, given that

- Of the ~5 to ~10 solar masses of material returned to the ISM, only about $0.25 M_{\odot}$ carries most of this kinetic energy

- The kinetic energy is almost entirely in the radial motion of the shell, rather than in the random thermal motions within it.

ITQ 5.5   Calculate the initial radial speed of such a shell.

Thus, a shell can have a radial speed that is a few percent of the speed of light.

These high speeds mean that the kinetic energy of an atom in the shell is *far* higher than the thermal kinetic energy of a typical atom or molecule in the surrounding ISM. Because of this we get the following effects, which are summarized in Figure 5.13.

1   The shell sweeps up much of the gas that it encounters, the swept-up gas being greatly compressed, greatly heated, and trapped within the shell, of which it becomes a part. The shell, which started hot and highly ionized, thus remains in this condition. It also remains thin compared with its radius.

2   A small amount of gas finds its way into the volume of space enclosed by the shell. This gas has also been greatly heated, and expands to fill the volume, giving rise to a roughly spherical cavity pervaded by hot, low-density gas.

3   The gas ahead of the shell gets no warning of the shell's approach, and thus its transition from a peaceful life to the tortured conditions in the shell is abrupt. The very thin transition zone is called a **shock front**, and the swept-up gas is said to have suffered a **strong shock**.

The shell constitutes the supernova remnant. The temperatures within it range from 10^5 K to 10^7 K.

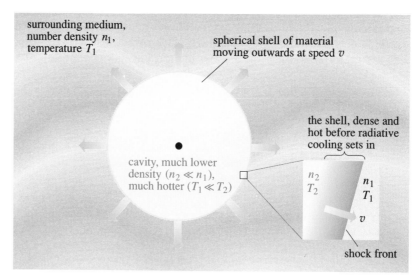

Figure 5.13   Conditions produced by the shell expelled by a supernova.

☐   From Wien's displacement law (Equation 1.4), calculate the peak wavelength emitted by a supernova remnant at 10^6 K.

■ $\lambda_{peak} = 2.9 \times 10^{-3}$ m K$/10^6$ K $= 2.9 \times 10^{-9}$ m.

Thus, from Figure 1.23 we see that much of the thermal radiation from supernova remnants comes out as X-rays. X-ray images of two remnants are shown in Plates 1.30b and 1.31b. Supernova remnants also emit copious amounts of radio waves, in the form of synchrotron radiation from electrons speeding among the magnetic fields in the shell. Plates 1.30c and 1.31c show the outcome in two cases. Radio waves are not appreciably absorbed by the ISM, and so most remnants have been discovered through the radio waves they emit.

As the shock front spreads out, the high kinetic energy per atom in the shell gradually falls, because the total kinetic energy in the shell is shared among more and more atoms as its mass grows. This leads to a major change when the kinetic energy of the front has fallen sufficiently for its heating effect to be reduced to the point at which ionization in the shell is far less complete. Radiative cooling is then strong – in a medium of comparatively low density, electron transitions in neutral atoms provide a far more efficient radiative process than interactions between electrons and ions. Therefore, the temperature of the shell falls, and consequently its pressure falls, allowing it to be squeezed by its surroundings to yet higher densities until a pressure balance is again achieved. At this higher density, collisional excitation is more frequent, which further enhances radiative cooling. The temperature fall can be quite dramatic. In this cool, high density form, the shell's effectiveness in sweeping up material is increased, though the shock it causes is no longer strong.

As the temperature falls, X-ray emission also diminishes, whereas the synchrotron radio emission persists. Indeed, it persists for much of the 10^5 or so years before the shock front grinds to a halt, whereupon the supernova remnant dissolves into the general ISM.

Let's now briefly consider the growing cavity contained by the shell. The high temperatures, 10^5 K to 10^6 K, ensure a high degree of ionization. This, coupled with the low densities, 10^2 m^{-3} to 10^4 m^{-3}, means that radiative cooling is inefficient, and so the cavity gas remains very hot as the shell expands. The low radiative efficiency and the low densities result in such a slight amount of radiation from the cavity that there is little to see. However, if a pulsar is present then this can energize the cavity near to it, to give a much more impressive display. In a young and hence small supernova remnant, the remnant can be mingled with this relatively small energized region. This is the case in the Crab Nebula, in Plate 1.29.

A single cavity can grow to ~300 pc across, and cavities can overlap. Moreover, because the material in the cavity cannot cool very readily, it can outlast the supernova remnant. Therefore, we might expect to find in the ISM large regions of hot, low density material, not necessarily bounded by supernova remnants. We do indeed find such regions.

☐ What do these regions constitute?

■ They constitute the hot intercloud medium.

Thus, it seems fairly certain that the hot, intercloud medium is supernova cavity material. It is believed that this medium first forms mainly in the disc of the Milky Way (Figure 5.6), which is where most supernovae occur, and that leakage to the halo gives rise to most of the hot intercloud medium there. Eventually, the halo material cools, and probably returns in fragments to the disc. It has been estimated that material equivalent to roughly $10M_\odot$ per year passes around this cycle.

The warm intercloud medium

☐ Could warm intercloud matter be obtained by cooling hot intercloud matter?

■ In principle it could: Figure 5.2 shows that it is not only cooler but denser than hot intercloud matter, and if a medium cools then it is compressed by its surroundings to higher density.

However, though we cannot rule out a significant contribution by this mechanism, it is believed that the major source of the warm intercloud medium is gas 'evaporated' from interstellar clouds. This evaporation can be caused in many ways, for example through collisions between clouds, and through stellar radiation.

We have thus reached the point where we can account for the low density, hotter regions in the ISM, namely the intercloud media, but as yet we have not accounted for the clouds themselves, the essential precursors to the formation of new stars. So we must now ask how the various types of cloud are formed.

5.3.2 The matter theme II: from the intercloud media to clouds

To form clouds from more dispersed matter, compression is clearly required: even diffuse clouds are at least an order of magnitude denser than the warm intercloud medium, and several orders of magnitude denser than the hot intercloud medium (Figure 5.2). Moreover, clouds are cooler than the intercloud media, and so cooling is also required.

You have already met one process that compresses interstellar matter, yet can leave it in a cool state.

☐ What is this process?

■ It is the shock produced by a supernova, when the shock is no longer strong enough to ionize the matter it sweeps up.

Moreover, the sweeping-up action of the shock means that a lot of matter is processed into this denser, yet cool form.

Any shock will process interstellar matter in this way: it does not have to be from a supernova. Another source of shock, though over a smaller volume of space than that from a supernova, is from regions where several O and B stars form – such groups of stars are called **OB associations**. Young O and B stars are well up the main sequence, so are massive, and highly luminous. It is therefore not surprising that the formation of several of them causes shock in the surrounding ISM.

Shock fronts alone are probably not sufficient to produce clouds. But they do make the matter they gather up susceptible to various instabilities that can lead to further increases in density. One such instability you have already met in Chapter 3 – the gravitational instability that was described there by the Jeans criterion. In discussing the formation of clouds from at least partially ionized matter, we have to include magnetic forces, which, on the whole, resist contraction, but the general idea is the same: if enough mass is gathered together with sufficient density, and if it is not too hot, then gravity 'wins' over the random thermal motions, and contraction ensues. Thus, because shock fronts can gather matter *and* increase its density, and can also leave it in a cool state, they are particularly effective at making matter susceptible to Jeans contraction.

There are a few other instabilities that can also aid cloud formation by promoting contraction and cooling. Under the action of one or more instabilities, plus the various effects of shock fronts, we have a plausible mechanism for forming, from the warm intercloud medium, the fundamental cloud structure – the GMC complex. Indeed, it is thought that the instabilities alone, without the aid of a shock front, could suffice in some cases.

Clouds of lower mass (less than about $10^4 M_\odot$) can probably be formed by the same variety of means, though additional mechanisms seem possible too, such as fragmentation of supernova remnants, and the disruption of more massive clouds as a result of high-speed collisions between clouds of comparable mass.

As soon as we have clouds of any sort, then *low* speed collisions, or almost any sort of collision between clouds of dissimilar mass, can lead to cloud *building*. Such collisions are promoted by the sweeping-up action of shocks, but can also occur elsewhere in the ISM. Collisions presumably play a role in building the complex architecture of GMC complexes, though on the whole the origin of the architectural details is very poorly understood.

However, even though such details are beyond us at present, we have made considerable progress in understanding how clouds are formed. Let's now consider, briefly, how clouds evolve.

Cloud evolution

Much of cloud evolution is as poorly understood as the origins of the initial cloud architecture, though there can be little doubt that the most catastrophic event is star formation. Left alone, clouds and GMC complexes might be stable, but if externally perturbed, for example by shocks (acting now on *clouds*), or if their internal motions cause sufficiently violent collisions between the denser regions, then the denser regions can contract and fragment to form clusters of stars, as outlined in Chapter 3. Once the contraction is initiated, it takes only the order of 10^7 years for stars to form. If the young star is hot – if it is an O or B star – then it will lie in the midst of an HII region of its own creation. It will have created this region around itself by forming a cavity in the dense cloud, and then by energizing the remnant matter in the cavity through the action of its own radiation and its winds.

The winds, shocks, and UV radiation from young stars, particularly from O and B stars, are the main cause of disruption of dense clouds, and of any complexes of which they may be a part, and this disruption ends the process of star formation. Only a small fraction of dense cloud mass is transformed into stars. The remnants of the dense cloud, and of any associated complex, can survive as independent clouds, perhaps to play a role in the build up of new, more massive clouds, and new GMC complexes.

Clearly there is a cycle operating in the ISM, and we shall return to it after we have addressed our second theme: the composition theme.

5.3.3 The composition theme

There are four aspects to this theme: chemical elements, ions, molecules, and dust. We shall discuss each of these in turn.

Chemical elements

You have seen (Subsection 5.2.2) that in most of the ISM the chemical elements have relative abundances that are not very different from the cosmic relative abundances presented in Chapter 2. There are, of course, regional variations, particularly near to where stars have ended their lives. This is because of the enrichment in heavy elements resulting from stellar nucleosynthesis: stars with masses up to around $3M_\odot$ produce elements up to about oxygen; stars with masses greater than this additionally produce elements up to around iron, plus small amounts of a few of the heavier elements; supernovae produce, during the explosion, elements predominantly in and beyond the iron group. However, with the exception of supernovae, and the more massive giants, most of the material enriched in heavy elements remains locked up in the remnant cores of the stars, and so there are not many places in the ISM where large departures from the cosmic relative abundances occur.

Ions

The degree of ionization in the various types of region in the ISM is broadly indicated by the ionization state of hydrogen in Table 5.1. To account for the differences, we must look at the competition between factors that produce ions, and those that destroy them.

Ions are produced at a low rate everywhere in the ISM by cosmic rays, which are so energetic that they can reach even to the heart of the densest cloud. Ions are destroyed through recombination with electrons, to yield neutral atoms or molecules. The recombination rate increases with density, because the denser the medium the smaller the average distances between ions and electrons, and the more frequently they meet. Indeed, in all but the least dense regions, the recombination rate is so high that the degree of ionization produced by cosmic rays is very small.

A higher degree of ionization requires production of ions by a means other than cosmic rays. Ultraviolet radiation from stars provides one such means: the hotter the star, the greater the UV flux.

☐ Why is this?

■ The hotter the star, the greater the amount of radiation at all wavelengths, and the greater the proportion at short wavelengths (see Figure 2.8).

This explains the high degree of ionization in HII regions (Plates 1.16 and 1.21), and in planetary nebulae (Plate 1.27): in the former case there is a hot, young star, and in the latter case a hot stellar remnant.

The degree of ionization in a diffuse cloud also depends on its proximity to stars, though it can't be too close or the cloud will be destroyed. Thus, the degree of ionization observed in diffuse clouds has to be low. In dense clouds it is even less, and this is because the dust is also dense, and dust is a very effective absorber of short wavelength radiation (Figure 5.11). The small degree of ionization is produced largely by cosmic rays.

Another factor that determines the degree of ionization is temperature. As temperature increases, the particles move faster and hence meet more often, thus promoting recombination. But their collisions are also becoming more energetic, and at *very* high temperatures this favours production.

ITQ 5.6 Show that a typical supernova remnant is at a sufficiently high temperature to produce a high degree of ionization in any of the chemical elements, given that the largest first ionization energy, that for helium, is 4.0×10^{-18} J. (The first ionization energy is the energy required to remove the first electron from an atom.)

In Subsection 5.3.1 you saw that, as a supernova remnant spreads out, it loses its heating effect, and hence its temperature and the degree of ionization in it fall. The cavity, when small, is as hot as the remnant, and so is also highly ionized. However, this ionization is not lost as the cavity expands, and so the hot intercloud medium is highly ionized too. It retains its ionization partly because it does not cool very much, and partly because of its extremely low density. Moreover, there is always some UV and cosmic radiation to create fresh ions.

Molecules

Table 5.1 shows not only differences in ionization between the different types of region in the ISM, but also differences in the molecular content, including whether hydrogen is found predominantly in atomic form (H), or in molecular form (H_2). What determines the molecular content?

☐ Could the relative abundances of the chemical elements be the main factor?

■ Given the uniformity of these relative abundances across the ISM, this cannot be the main factor.

The molecular content, like the ionic content, is determined by the competition between factors that favour the production of molecules, and factors that favour their destruction.

Without going into much detail, a high molecular content is to be expected in regions where the density is high (which promotes the meeting of atoms), the temperatures are not high (to avoid collisional disruption of molecules), and the UV flux is also not high (to avoid photodissociation of molecules). In accord with these expectations, high molecular content is a feature of circumstellar shells, diffuse clouds, and particularly dense clouds (Table 5.1).

In dense clouds, not only is the hydrogen present mainly as H_2, but all of the chemically reactive elements are predominantly combined into molecules. Only unreactive elements, such as He and Ne, remain predominantly as atoms. There are not only small molecules, such as H_2 and CO, but some quite large ones, such as ethanol CH_3CH_2OH, more often known as 'alcohol': even in a modest dense cloud, with a volume of about a cubic parsec, there is *far* more alcohol than there is water in the Earth's oceans. To date (late 1993) about 100 different molecules have been detected in dense clouds.

☐ Most of these molecules consist of compounds of H, C, N and O. Why?

■ This is because, except for the unreactive elements He and Ne, these four elements are the most abundant in the ISM (Appendix, Chapter 2).

Note that because over 90% of nuclei are hydrogen, most of it is present in dense clouds as H_2 (plus some H), rather than combined with other elements.

In dense and diffuse clouds, all but one of the various types of molecule are formed through reactions between atoms and molecules in the gas itself. The exception in H_2, which is formed on the surfaces of dust grains, and then escapes.

In diffuse clouds, the ratio of H_2 to H can be lower than in dense clouds, because the UV penetration can be greater, and in turn this is because of the lower density of the diffuse clouds. The greater UV penetration also reduces the molecular content in general.

Heating and cooling in clouds

The temperature of a region depends on the competition between heating and cooling. Cooling in dense and diffuse clouds is mainly through the efficient process in which molecules are excited by collisions into higher rotational energy levels (Figure 5.10), and then emit radiation on de-excitation, the radiation subsequently escaping from the cloud.

The degree of heating depends crucially on the extent to which UV radiation penetrates to the cloud interior. This is crucial because energy absorbed by dust is an important means of heating the region as a whole, and, as Figure 5.11 shows, dust is particularly effective at absorbing UV radiation. Indeed, it is so effective that, in dense clouds, the UV radiation does not penetrate beyond the surface regions, and so the UV heating of the cloud as a whole is slight – there is a small amount of heating by cosmic rays. By contrast, in diffuse clouds, UV radiation does get to the whole cloud volume, and so diffuse clouds exposed to UV radiation will be warmer than dense clouds.

At IR and longer wavelengths, both types of cloud are fairly transparent, and consequently these wavelengths cause little heating effect.

Dust

It is clear that dust, which accounts for only about 1% of the mass of the ISM, plays an important role in determining the temperature, ion content, and molecule content of a region. It also acts as a tracer of interstellar matter, through its own thermal emission (Plate 1.32), and through its obscuration of visible wavelengths (Plates 1.16 and 1.14). This obscuration also hides much of our galaxy from view. Dust might also play an important role in star formation, and, as you will see in Block 2, it could be a significant factor in the formation of planetary systems. So, how is the dust itself formed?

It is formed by the condensation of atoms and molecules from the gas in the ISM, the condensation being directly from the gas to the solid: liquids do not form. Condensation is favoured by high densities and low temperatures. The lower the temperature, the greater the range of materials that will condense: at the higher temperatures, only the least volatile materials condense, particularly carbon, metal oxides (compounds of metal and oxygen), certain metals, and silicates (compounds of metals, silicon and oxygen, common in Earth rocks).

Conditions suitable for the condensation of the least volatile materials are well met in circumstellar shells (Figure 5.2), and so these shells are dust factories as well as being molecule factories: such dust is well seen in Plate 1.26.

You might think that dense clouds, being so much colder than circumstellar shells, would also be copious producers of dust, even extending to the more volatile materials. However, there is a further factor to bear in mind.

☐ What is this factor?

■ It is the density: dense clouds are about 100 times less dense than circumstellar shells (Figure 5.2).

The consequence of this is that new dust grains appear far too slowly in dense clouds to account for many of the grains we observe in them. However, when a dense cloud forms, it will already contain the grains condensed elsewhere. These act as condensation nuclei, and so considerable grain *growth* occurs in dense clouds. At the low temperatures in dense clouds, this growth embraces not only more of the least volatile materials, but some of the more volatile materials too, such as water (H_2O), ammonia (NH_3), carbon monoxide (CO), and so on. These volatile materials are abundant, and though only a small fraction condenses, the grains nevertheless can acquire substantial icy mantles, increasing the grain diameter from about 10^{-7} m to around 10^{-6} m. Hydrogen and helium do not condense at all: they are *too* volatile.

Chemical reactions in the grain mantle surfaces are thought to produce a variety of molecules that, unlike H_2, remain there. These could include complex carbon compounds, sometimes called 'glue', and some astronomers have even speculated that amongst this glue there might be traces of molecules very similar to large biological molecules. If, in the formation of the Solar System (Block 2), any such molecules survived, then this raises the interesting possibility that the Earth's biosphere owes a good deal to this direct interstellar inheritance.

1   Some of the matter removed from the ISM to form stars is returned to the ISM by stellar winds, the shedding of planetary nebulae, and supernovae. Overall, this matter has been enriched in heavy elements by stellar nucleosynthesis, but remains dominated by hydrogen and helium.

2   Supernovae are important sources of cosmic rays, and also release huge amounts of energy into the ISM. Some of this energy is in the form of strong shocks, induced in the ISM by the expanding supernova remnant. Such shocks create hot intercloud medium in the cavity bounded by the remnant, and sweep interstellar matter into the remnant. The swept-up material becomes compressed and heated; subsequently, the remnant cools. The cavities seem to be the hot interstellar medium.

3   The ISM is susceptible to various instabilities, including a Jeans-type gravitational instability. These instabilities, with or without the preceding action of a shock, can act on the warm intercloud medium and produce the fundamental cloud structure, the GMC complex. The major source of the warm intercloud medium is believed to be matter evaporated from earlier generations of clouds, though cooled, compressed hot intercloud medium might also be a significant source.

4   Star formation is the main cause of cloud dissipation. The formation can be triggered by the action of shocks on GMC complexes, and on individual dense clouds.

5   The temperature of a region depends on the balance between heating and cooling. Different processes are important in different types of region (Table 5.3).

Table 5.3   Summary of heating and cooling processes in the ISM

Process	Some of the types of region where important
Heating	
stellar radiation	circumstellar shells, planetary nebulae, HII regions
UV radiation (stellar)	diffuse clouds (absorption by dust)
strong shocks	the hot intercloud medium (during its formation)
cosmic rays	dense clouds
Cooling	
line emission from neutral atoms and molecules	all regions that contain significant concentrations of these particles: the hot intercloud medium is notably devoid of them

6   The degree of ionization in a region depends on the competition between the production and destruction of ions. The degree of ionization increases as the UV flux increases, and also, at *very* high temperatures, as the temperature increases. It decreases as density increases. The degree of ionization is particularly high in HII regions, planetary nebulae, hot supernova remnants, and the hot intercloud medium.

7   The abundance of molecules in a region also depends on the competition between their production and destruction. High abundances are favoured by high densities, and by temperatures and UV fluxes that are *not* high. Molecules in the gas are formed in the gas itself, except for H_2, which is formed on the surfaces of dust grains. Dense clouds and circumstellar shells are particularly rich in molecules.

8   Dust plays an important role in the ISM. It is produced in large amounts in the dense conditions in circumstellar shells, which are cool enough to allow the least volatile materials to condense. Dust grains grow in the cold conditions of dense clouds, by acting as condensation nuclei for a range of materials, including volatile materials that form icy mantles.

SAQ 5.3 (Objective 5.5)   A supernova occurs in a region of warm intercloud medium, consisting largely of un-ionized hydrogen atoms. Ultimately, it creates a cavity of hot intercloud medium 150 pc in radius, consisting largely of ionized hydrogen and the liberated electrons. For the purposes of this question you can ignore all other chemical species. Further data are as follows:

Intercloud medium	n/m^{-3}	T/K
warm	10^5	10^4
hot	10^3	10^6

(a) Calculate the total energy increase in the cavity, assuming that this consists of the increase in the thermal kinetic energy of the matter in the cavity (as reflected by the increase in temperature), plus the energy needed to ionize the hydrogen atoms (2.18×10^{-18} J per atom).

Hint: In the warm medium the electrons are in their lowest energy levels in the hydrogen atoms, and so (ignoring other chemical species) the only thermal kinetic energy is the translational kinetic energy of the hydrogen atoms as a whole. In the hot medium the situation is different: remember that Equation 5.2 applies to *any* type of separate particle in a medium!

(b) Decide whether the shell expelled by the supernova could have delivered the energy in part (a).

SAQ 5.4 (Objective 5.5)   Imagine a diffuse cloud a long way from any stars other than cool, dim ones. Suddenly, one of these nearby stars flares up, to become a lot hotter and a lot more luminous. Discuss the possible effects on the diffuse cloud.

SAQ 5.5 (Objective 5.5)   Discuss the main effects on the ISM had supernovae been far rarer in our galaxy than has actually been the case.

5.4   The evolution of the interstellar medium

Many features of the evolution of the ISM have been covered earlier in this chapter. Here we want to bring the broad features together, and fill in one or two missing gaps.

Figure 5.14 summarizes the ISM's *physical* evolution (see also TV programme 3). The first thing to note is the mass cycle: mass loss from stars is followed by cloud formation, which is followed by star formation, which is followed by mass loss from stars, and so on. However, there are also non-cyclic processes. Thus, there is loss of matter from the cycle to stellar remnants, such as white dwarfs, neutron stars, and black holes. Such matter is no longer available to the ISM. There is also *new* matter for the cycle, namely the infall of gas and dust from the *intergalactic* medium (Block 3). The question therefore arises of whether, over galactic history, the accumulated loss is ahead of the gain, and the answer seems to be that it is. We come to this conclusion by noting that the Milky Way probably started its life largely as interstellar matter (Block 3), yet today the ISM has a mass equal to only about 10% of the mass of the stars.

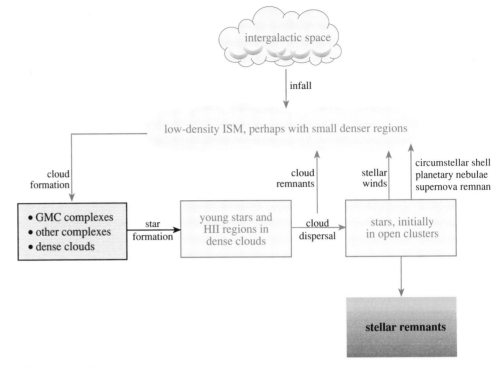

Figure 5.14 The evolution of the interstellar medium.

What are the rates of gain and loss today? The present rate at which matter is entering the ISM is probably somewhere between about $0.4M_\odot$ and $3M_\odot$ per year, of which no more than about $1.4M_\odot$ is infall from the intergalactic medium. The present rate at which mass is leaving the ISM, to form new stars, is probably somewhere between about $3M_\odot$ and $10M_\odot$ per year, and so it is likely that the rate of loss is still exceeding the rate of gain.

The ISM has evolved not only in the fraction of galactic mass that it contains, but also in its chemical composition. For example, a significant source of the rare elements lithium, beryllium and boron is from the break-up of interstellar carbon, nitrogen and oxygen, as a result of cosmic ray impacts in the ISM. However, the dominant cause of chemical evolution has been the enrichment of heavy elements through stellar nucleosynthesis. Given that the stars are about ten times as massive as the ISM, and that our galaxy is sufficiently old to have seen more than one generation of all but the least massive stars, you might therefore expect there to have been a substantial shift in the ISM from hydrogen to the heavy elements. (Helium is both created and destroyed in stellar nucleosynthesis, so our cursory expectations are less clear here.) In fact, this is not so: observational evidence, for example from stars of very low mass, which are therefore very old, suggests that, in the primeval ISM, the abundance ratio H : He : heavy, for the relative numbers of nuclei, was 93 : ~7 : ~0. This ratio is not very different from the present one, which is something like 92 : 7.8 : 0.2.

☐ Why is this shift in the ISM from light to heavy elements so slight?

■ This is because much of the material returned to the ISM is from the mantles of stars of low and medium mass, in which little enrichment of the heavy elements has occurred, the remnant cores being the repositories of much of the enriched material. Supernovae lose more of their mass, and are massive to start with, but are rare, and so return a relatively small amount of mass to the ISM (though they are responsible for nearly all of the small amounts of the elements beyond the iron group).

The ISM is thus still chemically young in that it still consists largely of hydrogen and helium. The future of the ISM, chemical and physical, is something for you to consider in the final SAQ.

Conclusion

You have now come to the end of Block 1, *The stars and the interstellar medium*, in which we have described our observations of the Sun and of the other stars, and outlined the evolution of the major stellar types. In this final chapter we have looked at the interstellar medium, including its relationship to the stars, and including also an outline of some of the major physical and chemical processes that mould it. Among the many topics that you have met there are several that link strongly to Block 2, *The Planets*: after all, not only the Sun but the whole Solar System formed from one and the same fragment of a dense cloud, and the whole system has been profoundly influenced by the way this material, and the Sun, subsequently evolved, as you will see.

SAQ 5.6 (Objectives 5.1 and 5.6)   In a couple of sentences, describe the amount and composition of the ISM that will exist in our galaxy a *long* time in the future.

Objectives for Chapter 5

After studying Chapter 5 (and any associated audio, video or TV material), you should be able to:

5.1   Give brief definitions of the terms, concepts and principles listed at the end of the Objectives.

5.2   Outline, briefly, how the interstellar medium (ISM) is studied.

5.3   Describe the main features of the various types of region in the ISM, and their distribution in our galaxy.

5.4   Outline the main radiative processes that are important in the ISM.

5.5   Describe some of the main physical and chemical processes occuring in the ISM, including how one type of region might be transformed into another.

5.6   Describe the long term evolution of the ISM.

List of scientific terms, concepts and principles used in Chapter 5

Term	Page	Term	Page	Term	Page
circumstellar shell	173	intercloud media	171	scattering	168
collisional excitation	169	interstellar cirrus	180	shock front	181
cosmic rays	181	interstellar medium	168	strong shock	181
dense cloud	174	molecular cloud	174	supernova remnant	173
diffuse cloud	174	OB association	183	synchrotron radiation	178
extinction	168	photoemission	176	vibrational transition	177
giant molecular cloud complex	174	photoexcitation	176	warm intercloud medium	172
HII region	172	planetary nebula	173		
hot intercloud medium	172	rotational transition	177		

ITQ answers and comments for Chapter 1

ITQ 1.1

Because $1\,\text{W} = 1\,\text{J}\,\text{s}^{-1}$, the value of $L_\odot$ in terms of watts is simply $L_\odot = 3.84 \times 10^{26}\,\text{W}$. Since $2\,500\,\text{MW} = 2.5 \times 10^9\,\text{W}$, it follows that the number of 'typical' power stations required to match the Sun's energy output is given by

$$\frac{3.8 \times 10^{26}\,\text{W}}{2.5 \times 10^9\,\text{W}} = 1.5 \times 10^{17}$$

[*Comment*: In part, this question was intended to emphasize the immensity of the Sun's energy output, but an equally important purpose was to draw your attention to the use of SI units (the joule (J), the watt (W), the megawatt (MW), etc.) and to the manipulation of powers of ten ($10^{26}/10^9 = 10^{17}$ etc.). Using SI units and manipulating powers of ten are vital skills that will be in constant demand throughout this Course; if you are unsure of either of them you should consult the appropriate sections of *Preparatory science*.]

ITQ 1.2

It was stated earlier that the diameter of the photosphere is about $1.4 \times 10^6\,\text{km}$. The size of the sunspot can be estimated by simply measuring the diameter of the spot's image in Figure 1.1 and comparing this with the size of the image of the photosphere:

$$\text{diameter of sunspot} = \frac{d_{si}}{d_{pi}} \times d_p$$

where d_{si} is the diameter of the sunspot's image, d_{pi} is the diameter of photosphere's image, and d_p is the diameter of the photosphere. However, in using this formula it is important to remember that the Sun is a spherical body, so the farther a spot is from the centre of the solar disc, the more it will be 'turned away' from the observer and the more its image will be foreshortened. Although it would be possible to make allowance for this foreshortening, it is much easier just to examine spot images near the centre of the disc, where the effect can be ignored. Such spot images seem to have a diameter that is about 1% of the diameter of the disc image. It follows that, for the large spots near the centre of Figure 1.1,

$$\text{spot diameter} \simeq \frac{1}{100} \times 1.4 \times 10^6\,\text{km} = 1.4 \times 10^4\,\text{km}$$

[*Comment*: It follows that large spots have diameters that are roughly comparable with the diameter of the Earth, which is $1.3 \times 10^4\,\text{km}$. Occasionally very large spots, tens of thousands of kilometres across, are seen, but none of these is visible in Figure 1.1.]

ITQ 1.3

No. In the case of Figure 1.14 all of the sources being measured were *of the same size* and *at the same distance* from the detector. If sources of different sizes had been used, or if the sources had been at different distances from the detector, the results might well have been different. A 3 000 K source of sufficient size or located sufficiently close to the detector could certainly provide more energy per second than a 6 000 K source that was small or distant.

ITQ 1.4

Assuming that the heated ball can be treated as a rough approximation to an ideal thermal source of light, it is to be expected that the ball would emit relatively more light with wavelengths towards the blue end of the spectrum (as opposed to the red end) as the temperature increases, as indicated by Figure 1.14. Thus, at relatively low temperatures red light will predominate and the ball will glow 'red-hot'. As the temperature rises the proportion of shorter wavelengths will gradually increase, making the colour progress from red to orange-white to yellowish-white to white – the last being a mix of all the colours.

ITQ 1.5

It follows from Equation 1.1 that the wavelength of the absorbed electromagnetic radiation must be

$$\lambda_{hi} = \frac{v}{f_{hi}}$$

$$\lambda_{hi} = \frac{vh}{E_h - E_i}$$

where v is the speed of light in the gas containing the atom. If the gas were very thin, then v would be approximately equal to the speed of light in a vacuum and we could write

$$\lambda_{hi} \simeq \frac{ch}{E_h - E_i}$$

[*Comment*: Any of these three equations constitutes an acceptable answer to the question.]

ITQ 1.6

On the whole, the chromosphere is very dim compared with the photosphere. Thus, we can expect to see chromospheric emissions at only those wavelengths where the photosphere is relatively dark. These will be the wavelengths at which the solar spectrum exhibits absorption lines, because most of the light at other wavelengths comes from the photosphere. In the case of the Hα line, for example, it is the chromosphere that is mainly responsible for the absorption of photospheric light at that wavelength, and it is also the chromosphere that is mainly responsible for the (weak) emitted light.

ITQ 1.7

It follows from Wien's displacement law that the wavelength at which the Planck curve attains its maximum is

$$\lambda_{peak} = \frac{2.90 \times 10^{-3}\,\text{m K}}{2 \times 10^6\,\text{K}} = 1.5 \times 10^{-9}\,\text{m} = 1.5\,\text{nm}$$

ITQ 1.8

Wavelength, λ/m	3×10^{-14}	6×10^{-10}	3×10^{-7}	1×10^{-5}	5×10^{-3}	10
Corresponding frequency, f/Hz	1×10^{22}	5×10^{17}	9×10^{14}	3×10^{13}	6×10^{10}	3×10^7
Corresponding photon energy, ε/J	7×10^{-12}	3×10^{-16}	6×10^{-19}	2×10^{-20}	4×10^{-23}	2×10^{-26}
Temperature T/K of black body that has a peak in its spectrum at this value of λ	1×10^{11}	5×10^6	1×10^4	3×10^2	1	3×10^{-4}
Corresponding part of the electromagnetic spectrum	γ-ray	X-ray	ultraviolet	infrared	microwave	radio wave

ITQ 1.9

$X + Y + Z = 1$ at any depth. This follows from the fact that we defined Z to be 'everything else' apart from hydrogen (X) and helium (Y).

ITQ 1.10

Since X departs significantly from a constant value only in the central 30% of the Sun (that is, where $R/R_\odot$ is less than 0.30) it seems pretty clear that the nuclear processes that convert hydrogen into helium must be confined to that inner region. Further, because X falls progressively as the fractional radius decreases in this inner region, it must have been the case that conversion of hydrogen into helium has been most common in the most central parts of the Sun.

ITQ 1.11

(a) The three distinct kinds of reaction are:

$$2\,{}_1^1\text{H} \longrightarrow {}_1^2\text{H} + e^+ + \nu \tag{1}$$

$$\,{}_1^2\text{H} + {}_1^1\text{H} \longrightarrow {}_2^3\text{He} + \gamma \tag{2}$$

$$2\,{}_2^3\text{He} \longrightarrow {}_2^4\text{He} + 2\,{}_1^1\text{H} \tag{3}$$

(b) The incoming electric charge in Reaction 1 is that of the two hydrogen nuclei. Since each ${}_1^1\text{H}$ nucleus is simply a proton its charge is e. Thus the total charge of the two incoming nuclei is $2e$. The outgoing hydrogen nucleus, ${}_1^2\text{H}$, carries charge e (as indicated by the subscript, the atomic number) and the positron carries charge e. Thus the total outgoing charge is $2e$.

For Reaction 2, the total incoming charge is $2e$ and so is the total outgoing charge.

For Reaction 3, the total incoming charge is that carried by the protons in *two* helium nuclei, so it is $4e$. The total outgoing charge is that carried by *one* helium nucleus and two hydrogen nuclei, $4e$.

Thus, in all three reactions, electric charge is conserved.

(c) For all three reactions the baryon number entering or leaving is equal to the total number of protons and neutrons entering or leaving, and this total is given by the superscript, the mass number. You can easily see that on both sides of Reaction 1 this is 2, in Reaction 2 it is 3, and in Reaction 3 it is 6. It is thus conserved in each case.

ITQ 1.12

(a) The radiant energy eventually resulting from each occurrence of the ppI chain is given by the expression

$c^2\{(4 \times \text{mass of } {}_1^1\text{H}) - (\text{mass of } {}_2^4\text{He}) - (2 \times \text{mass of } e^+)$
$\qquad + (2 \times \text{mass of } e^+) + (2 \times \text{mass of } e^-)\}$

$= 9.00 \times 10^{16}\{4 \times 1.673 - 6.645 + 2 \times 0.001\} \times 10^{-27}\,\text{J}$

$= 4.41 \times 10^{-12}\,\text{J}$

[*Comment*: The accurate value is about 5% lower than this estimate.]

(b) If we assume (somewhat incorrectly) that the solar luminosity is entirely provided by the ppI chain and its supplementary reactions, then the number of times per second that the chain is completed is given by

$$\frac{3.84 \times 10^{26}\,\text{J s}^{-1}}{4.41 \times 10^{-12}\,\text{J}} = 8.71 \times 10^{37}\,\text{s}^{-1}$$

[*Comment*: This is only an estimate, but it is not too bad.]

(c) Each time the chain is completed, four hydrogen nuclei are consumed (and one helium nucleus produced). Since the mass of a hydrogen nucleus is $1.673 \times 10^{-27}\,\text{kg}$, it follows that the rate of hydrogen consumption is roughly

$4 \times 8.71 \times 10^{37} \times 1.673 \times 10^{-27}\,\text{kg s}^{-1} = 5.83 \times 10^{11}\,\text{kg s}^{-1}$

Now, the number of seconds in a year is 3.16×10^7. So the annual consumption of hydrogen is

$3.16 \times 10^7 \times 5.83 \times 10^{11}\,\text{kg} = 1.84 \times 10^{19}\,\text{kg}$

[*Comment*: This is about three millionths of the Earth's mass per year, and about one part in 10^{11} of the Sun's mass per year.]

ITQ answers and comments for Chapter 2

ITQ 2.1

With a parallax of 0.31 arcsec, the distance to 61 Cygni in parsecs is given by Equation 2.5 as

$$d/\text{pc} = 1/0.31 = 3.2$$

Thus $d = 3.2$ pc. This is $3.2 \times 206\,265$ AU $= 6.6 \times 10^5$ AU, and $6.6 \times 10^5 \times 1.50 \times 10^{11}$ m $= 9.9 \times 10^{16}$ m. The distance to the Sun is 1 AU, so 61 Cygni is 660 000 times farther away.

ITQ 2.2

The angular diameter of Betelgeuse is given in Subsection 2.3.1 as 0.050 arcsec, which is 2.4×10^{-7} radians. Thus, from Equation 2.6, the radius of Betelgeuse is given by

$$
\begin{aligned}
R &= 1.2 \times 10^{-7} \times 160\,\text{pc} = 1.9 \times 10^{-5}\,\text{pc} \\
&= 5.9 \times 10^{11}\,\text{m} = 850 R_{\odot}
\end{aligned}
$$

ITQ 2.3

From Figure 2.12 we see that the Balmer lines are weak at temperatures above approximately 30 000 K and below about 5 000 K. The corresponding spectral classes (Table 2.2) are O, K and M (G is a marginal case).

ITQ 2.4

Stellar radius can be obtained from Equation 2.7, rearranged as follows

$$R \simeq [L/(4\pi\sigma T^4)]^{1/2}$$

If we are given L in solar units, and if we have to give R in solar units, then a convenient form of this equation is obtained by dividing the left-hand side by $R_{\odot}$, and the right-hand side by the equivalent quantity $[L_{\odot}/(4\pi\sigma T_{\odot}{}^4)]^{1/2}$. We thus get

$$R/R_{\odot} \simeq (L/L_{\odot})^{1/2} \times (T_{\odot}/T)^2$$

Thus, for Aldebaran B

$$R/R_{\odot} \simeq (0.06)^{1/2} \times (5\,770/3\,400)^2 \simeq 0.7$$

and so

$$R \simeq 0.7 R_{\odot}$$

ITQ 2.5

From Figure 1.25, the more transparent bands in the Earth's atmosphere are: the visible region; some bands in the near infrared region; most of the microwave and radio wave regions.

ITQ 2.6

From Equation 2.10

$$
\begin{aligned}
d &= (6.1 \times 10^{30}\,\text{W}/(4\pi \times 4.4 \times 10^{-10}\,\text{W m}^{-2}))^{1/2} \\
&= 3.3 \times 10^{19}\,\text{m} \\
&= 1\,070\,\text{pc}
\end{aligned}
$$

The value of L_V for ι^1 Scorpio is 1.4×10^5 times that of the Sun, so its intrinsic visual brightness is very high. It is thus its distance that makes it seem not very bright. [*Comment*: It is both hotter and bigger than the Sun.]

ITQ 2.7

In obtaining temperature, we compare the strengths of absorption lines from *different* elements, whereas in obtaining composition we compare the strengths of different absorption lines from a *single* element.

ITQ 2.8

From the Appendix, the ten most abundant elements in the material from which the Solar System was formed are as follows, in descending order of abundance:

Order	By number of nuclei	By mass
1	hydrogen	hydrogen
2	helium	helium
3	oxygen	oxygen
4	carbon	carbon
5	neon	neon
6	nitrogen	iron
7	silicon	silicon
8	iron	nitrogen
9	magnesium	magnesium
10	sulphur	sulphur

[*Comment*: Thus, the only difference in the two lists is that nitrogen and iron swop over.]

ITQ 2.9

The positions in the H–R diagram of these types of star are as follows:

hot, high luminosity stars	top left
hot, low luminosity stars	bottom left
cool, low luminosity stars	bottom right
cool, high luminosity stars	top right

ITQ 2.10

From Figure 2.23, we see that white dwarfs have radii of order $0.01 R_{\odot}$, which is about the radius of the Earth. Likewise, we see that red giants have radii of order $30 R_{\odot}$, which is about 3 000 times the Earth's radius, or about a tenth of the distance of the Earth from the Sun. [*Comment*: Note that the *ranges* of radii for white dwarfs, and particularly for red giants, are large.]

ITQ 2.11

Such stars would move diagonally to the right and downwards, the luminosity as well as the temperature decreasing. [*Comment*: You will see later that many stars do indeed end their lives in this way.]

ITQ 2.12

Squaring both sides of Equation 2.13 we get

$$\tau^2 = \frac{4\pi^2 r^3}{G(M+m)}$$

We then transfer τ^2 to the right-hand side, and $(M+m)$ to the left-hand side, to obtain the desired result:

$$M + m = \frac{4\pi^2 r^3}{G\tau^2}$$

ITQ 2.13

From the second equation in the question we can substitute $3m$ for M in the first equation, to obtain

$$(3m + m) = 12M_\odot$$

and thus

$$m = 3M_\odot$$

Therefore, with $M/m = 3$,

$$M = 9M_\odot$$

ITQ 2.14

This is very similar to the situation in Figure 2.7, to which Equation 2.6 applies. We only have to substitute the semimajor axis a for $2R$ in Equation 2.6. We thus obtain

$$a = (\alpha/\text{radians}) \times d$$

ITQ answers and comments for Chapter 3

ITQ 3.1

For an object that is emitting as an ideal thermal body at temperature T, the wavelength, λ_{peak}, at which the maximum energy is radiated is given by Wien's displacement law, namely:

$$\lambda_{\text{peak}} = \frac{2.90 \times 10^{-3}\,\text{m K}}{T}$$

For a dense cloud collapsing on its way to becoming a protostar, we expect the temperature to still be very low, probably still only a few hundred kelvins – let's assume 300 K. In this case

$$\lambda_{\text{peak}} = \frac{2.90 \times 10^{-3}}{300}\,\text{m} \approx 10^{-5}\,\text{m}$$

This is in the infrared part of the spectrum (see Figure 1.23).

[*Comment*: If we had assumed a temperature different by a factor of 10, larger or smaller, our answer would still have been in the infrared!]

ITQ 3.2

The smaller the Jeans mass, the more likely gravitational contraction is to occur. From Equation 3.1, we can see that a small value for the Jeans mass requires that n, the number density, be as large, and T, the temperature, be as low, as possible. [*Comment*: The same conclusion could be derived from Figure 3.2.]

ITQ 3.3

The number of stars observed in a given phase of evolution should be roughly proportional to the time an individual star spends in that phase. When evolution is rapid, the phase of evolution is soon over and the probability of our observing objects in that phase is low. [*Comment*: One exception to this is a supernova – but that will be discussed later.]

ITQ 3.4

Ways in which the composition of the core could change during the main sequence are through (i) convection and (ii) fusion reactions. Figure 3.10 shows that, in stars of low mass, convection is confined to a thin outer envelope, so convective mixing of core material with the material around it won't occur. Therefore the only way in which the composition of the core will change during the main sequence lifetime is through fusion reactions. [*Comment*: As in the Sun, these result in a progressive depletion of hydrogen and enrichment of helium in the core.]

ITQ 3.5

The time for which the Sun's present luminosity could be maintained is given by (energy available)/(rate of energy consumption), where the rate of energy consumption is the Sun's luminosity. The energy available from chemical energy is given by the Sun's mass multiplied by the energy available per unit mass:

$$(2 \times 10^{30}\,\text{kg}) \times (3.5 \times 10^7\,\text{J kg}^{-1}) = 7 \times 10^{37}\,\text{J}$$

Thus, the time for which Sun's present luminosity could be maintained is

$$(7 \times 10^{37}\,\text{J})/(4 \times 10^{26}\,\text{W}) = 2 \times 10^{11}\,\text{s} \approx 6\,000 \text{ years!!}$$

[*Comment*: Evidence shows that the Sun has been shining at (approximately) its present luminosity for about 5×10^9 years. Therefore the generation of energy by chemical means does not appear to be the likely explanation of the Sun's luminosity.]

ITQ 3.6

The loss of gravitational energy is given by

$$\frac{-GM_\odot^2}{R_\odot} - \left(\frac{-GM_\odot^2}{0.1 R_\odot} \right)$$

$$= \frac{GM_\odot^2}{R_\odot}\left(\frac{1}{0.1} - 1\right)$$

$$= \frac{9GM_\odot^2}{R_\odot}$$

$$= \frac{9 \times 6.67 \times 10^{-11} \times (2 \times 10^{30})^2}{7 \times 10^8}\,\text{J}$$

$$= 3 \times 10^{42}\,\text{J}$$

Assuming that this energy is all converted into power for the Sun, the time for which the Sun's present luminosity could be maintained is given by

$$\frac{3 \times 10^{42}\,\text{J}}{4 \times 10^{26}\,\text{W}} = 8 \times 10^{15}\,\text{s} = 3 \times 10^8 \text{ years}$$

[Comment: Although much more promising than chemical energy (see ITQ 3.5) as an energy source, gravitational energy still can't provide sufficient energy to power the Sun for its known lifetime.]

ITQ 3.7

The ratio of radiation pressure to gas pressure can be calculated from Equations 3.12 and 3.13 as

$$\frac{P_{\text{rad}}}{P_{\text{gas}}} = \frac{\alpha T^3}{3nk}$$

For the Sun, the average mass density is

$$\rho = \frac{1.99 \times 10^{30}\,\text{kg}}{\frac{4}{3}\pi(6.96 \times 10^8\,\text{m})^3} = 1.41 \times 10^3\,\text{kg m}^{-3}$$

The mean number density of hydrogen nuclei is

$$\frac{\text{mass density}}{\text{mass per particle}} = \frac{1.41 \times 10^3\,\text{kg m}^{-3}}{1.67 \times 10^{-27}\,\text{kg}}$$
$$= 8.44 \times 10^{29}\,\text{m}^{-3}$$

In the ionized solar interior, there are as many free electrons as there are hydrogen nuclei, so n is double this value. Thus, using $T = 1.5 \times 10^7$ K for the centre of the Sun,

$$\frac{P_{\text{rad}}}{P_{\text{gas}}} = \frac{(7.55 \times 10^{-16}) \times (1.5 \times 10^7)^3}{3 \times (2 \times 8.44 \times 10^{29}) \times (1.38 \times 10^{-23})} = 3.6 \times 10^{-2}$$

So, according to this calculation, at the centre of the Sun radiation pressure is not very significant, amounting to about 4% of that due to gas pressure.

In Figure 1.27, we see that the mass density at the centre of the Sun is predicted to be about 1.5×10^5 kg m^{-3} compared with our average value of 1.4×10^3 kg m^{-3}. So, we have underestimated the number density by about a factor of 100. This means that the contribution of radiation pressure is even less than calculated here (by a factor of 100).

ITQ 3.8

The spherical shell of space at a distance r from the Sun, occupied by the solar wind emitted over time interval Δt, has a volume $V = 4\pi r^2 v \Delta t$, where v is the wind speed. The mass emitted in the time interval Δt is $M = 4\pi r^2 v \Delta t\, nm$, where n is the number density and m is the mass of the proton. Therefore, the mass emitted by the Sun per year

$$= 4\pi(1.5 \times 10^{11})^2 \times (2.5 \times 10^5) \times (3.2 \times 10^7) \times$$
$$(5 \times 10^6) \times (1.7 \times 10^{-27})\,\text{kg}$$

$$= 2 \times 10^{16}\,\text{kg}$$

$$= 10^{-14}M_\odot$$

ITQ 3.9

The luminosity of a star is related to its radius, R, and surface temperature, T, by Equation 2.7, i.e.

$$L \simeq 4\pi R^2 \sigma T^4$$

where σ is Stefan's constant. For the star we are considering here, we know that the star has expanded (i.e. R has increased) whereas the luminosity hasn't changed significantly (L approximately constant). Thus, referring to Equation 2.7, it is required that T *decreases* – i.e. the surface of the star cools.

ITQ 3.10

Equation 2.7 gives the relation between luminosity and radius, namely $L \simeq 4\pi R^2 \sigma T^4$. Suppose that the radius of a star changes from R_* to $1.02R_*$ (i.e. an increase in radius of 2%). Then

$$L'_* \simeq 4\pi(1.02R_*)^2 \sigma T^4$$
$$\simeq 1.04 \times 4\pi R_*^2 \sigma T^4$$
$$\simeq 1.04 L_*$$

where $L_* \simeq 4\pi R_*^2 \sigma T^4$. In other words, the luminosity increases by about 4%. If we substitute $0.98R_*$ for the radius (i.e. a decrease in radius of 2%), we similarly find that the luminosity decreases by about 4%. [Comment: This is the amount of variability found in the luminosity of some regular variables.]

ITQ 3.11

The density ρ is calculated from ρ = mass/volume. For a spherical body, with mass M and radius R,

$$\rho = \frac{M}{\frac{4}{3}\pi R^3}$$

For a white dwarf with

$$M = 0.8M_\odot = 0.8 \times 1.99 \times 10^{30}\,\text{kg} = 1.59 \times 10^{30}\text{kg}$$

and $R = 2\,000$ km $= 2 \times 10^6$ m, the density ρ_{WD} is given by

$$\rho_{\text{WD}} = \frac{1.59 \times 10^{30}\,\text{kg}}{\frac{4}{3}\pi(2.0 \times 10^6\,\text{m})^3}$$
$$= 4.74 \times 10^{10}\,\text{kg m}^{-3}$$

For the Sun, the average density $\rho_\odot$ is given by

$$\rho_\odot = \frac{M_\odot}{\frac{4}{3}\pi R^3}$$
$$= \frac{1.99 \times 10^{30}\,\text{kg}}{\frac{4}{3}\pi(6.96 \times 10^8\,\text{m})^3}$$
$$= 1.41 \times 10^3\,\text{kg m}^{-3}$$

Thus, the white dwarf has a density that is about 3×10^7 times greater than that of the Sun.

ITQ 4.1

In going to the right in the H–R diagram the surface temperature drops (considerably). The luminosity will rise a little if the star's evolution lifts it a little higher in the H–R diagram.

ITQ 4.2

Since the luminosity L is constant, and so are 4, π and σ, we can rearrange Equation 2.7 to be

$$R = \frac{\text{constant}}{T^2}$$

Therefore

$$\begin{aligned} \frac{R_{\text{final}}}{R_{\text{initial}}} &= \frac{(T_{\text{initial}})^2}{(T_{\text{final}})^2} \\ &= \left(\frac{25\,000}{5\,000}\right)^2 = 5^2 \\ &= 25 \end{aligned}$$

Therefore

$$\begin{aligned} R_{\text{final}} &= 25R_{\text{initial}} \\ &= 25 \times 10R_\odot \\ &= 250R_\odot \end{aligned}$$

ITQ 4.3

One reason for there being so few stars in this area is that massive stars evolve very quickly from being upper main sequence stars to being supergiant stars, so the chances of catching a star in between are slender.

ITQ 4.4

The answer is shown in Figure 4.18.

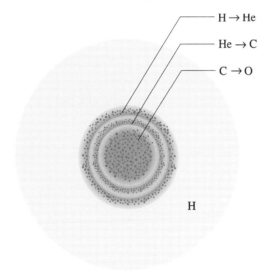

Figure 4.18 The structure of a star at the carbon-burning stage.

ITQ 4.5

Initially, the fusion of hydrogen to form helium takes place in the core of the star. When the amount of available hydrogen there is appreciably reduced the reaction stops in the core. With the rise in temperature it can continue where there is hydrogen available at the edge of the core. So we find next that hydrogen is being fused to helium in a thin shell around the core. Eventually there is a shortage of hydrogen here too, and when the temperature rises again the site of the reaction moves outwards again to a fresh supply. Then the reaction is found in the next layer out, i.e. in a shell of slightly larger radius surrounding both the previous shell and the core. This process is repeated over and over again, with the site of the hydrogen fusion reaction steadily moving outwards to shells of larger radius.

ITQ 4.6

The density is equal to the mass divided by the volume, and so

$$3 \times 10^{17} \, \text{kg m}^{-3} = \frac{6 \times 10^{24} \text{kg}}{\text{volume}}$$

Therefore

$$\text{volume} = \frac{6 \times 10^{24}}{3 \times 10^{17}} \text{m}^3 = 2 \times 10^7 \, \text{m}^3$$

But volume = $\frac{4}{3}\pi r^3$, therefore

$$\begin{aligned} r &= \left(\frac{3}{4\pi} \times 2 \times 10^7\right)^{1/3} \text{m} = (4.8 \times 10^6)^{1/3} \, \text{m} \\ &= 170 \, \text{m} \, (!) \end{aligned}$$

ITQ 4.7

A supergiant star might have a radius of 100 times the radius of the Sun, that is $100 \times 7 \times 10^5$ km, which is 7×10^7 km. Our expanding supernova is about 300 times bigger than the supergiant. Pluto, the outermost planet in our Solar System, is approximately 6×10^9 km from the Sun; taking this as the radius of the Solar System, we see that the supernova has expanded to about three times this size. The distance to the nearest star is 1.30 parsecs, which is roughly 4×10^{13} km; the supernova has (so far) expanded to only one two-thousandth of this.

ITQ 4.8

Neutrinos travel readily through the Earth, so it is not necessary for the source to be above the horizon. In this case one would suspect that some, if not all, of the neutrinos had travelled through some of the Earth before detection because (i) Japan and Ohio are approximately on opposite sides of the world, so it is unlikely that a source that they detect simultaneously would be above both their horizons at that time, and (ii) the Large Magellanic Cloud is in the southern sky and they are in the north, so it might well be below both their horizons. [*Comment*: In fact it is – about 20° below.]

ITQ 4.9

If there are two gamma rays of energy 1.3×10^{-13} J and 1.9×10^{-13} J, then the energy output per decay = 3.2×10^{-13} J. To provide a luminosity of 10^{33} W, i.e. 10^{33} J s^{-1}, the number of decays per second

$$= \frac{10^{33} \text{ J s}^{-1}}{3.2 \times 10^{-13} \text{ J}}$$
$$= 0.3 \times 10^{46} \text{ decays s}^{-1}$$

Each $^{56}_{27}$Co nucleus weighs about 56 times the mass of a neutron or proton, which is $56 \times 1.7 \times 10^{-27}$ kg. Therefore the mass decaying per second

$$\begin{aligned} &= 0.3 \times 56 \times 1.7 \times 10^{46} \times 10^{-27} \text{ kg s}^{-1} \\ &= 0.3 \times 56 \times 1.7 \times 10^{19} \text{ kg s}^{-1} \\ &= 3 \times 10^{20} \text{ kg s}^{-1} \\ &= 1.5 \times 10^{-10} M_\odot \text{ s}^{-1} \end{aligned}$$

[Comment: The cobalt gamma rays illuminate the remnant for hundreds of days, so clearly a large mass of nickel (which decayed into the cobalt) was created. It is estimated that, in SN 1987A, $0.07 M_\odot$ of nickel was formed.]

ITQ 4.10

It's best to express the star's mass in kilograms:

$$1.5 M_\odot = 3.0 \times 10^{30} \text{ kg}$$

and the radius in metres:

$$\text{radius } (r) = 10 \text{ km} = 10^4 \text{ m}$$

From the radius, we can get the volume:

$$\begin{aligned} \text{volume} &= \tfrac{4}{3}\pi r^3 \text{ (assuming the star is spherical)} \\ &= \tfrac{4}{3}\pi (10^4)^3 \text{ m}^3 \\ &= 4.0 \times 10^{12} \text{ m}^3 \end{aligned}$$

Therefore

$$\begin{aligned} \text{density} &= \text{mass/volume} \\ &= \frac{3.0 \times 10^{30}}{4.0 \times 10^{12}} \text{ kg m}^{-3} \\ &= 7.5 \times 10^{17} \text{ kg m}^{-3} \end{aligned}$$

We can take the volume of a thimble as $1 \text{ cm}^3 = 10^{-6} \text{ m}^3$, so the mass of a thimble-full, m_t, is

$$\begin{aligned} m_t &= 10^{-6} \times 7.5 \times 10^{17} \text{ kg} \\ &= 7.5 \times 10^{11} \text{ kg} \\ &\simeq 8 \times 10^8 \text{ tons} \end{aligned}$$

ITQ 4.11

In *Preparatory science* you saw that the acceleration due to gravity at the surface of the Earth is given by

$$g = \frac{GM_E}{R_E{}^2}$$

where M_E is the mass of the Earth and R_E its radius.

By analogy, the acceleration due to gravity at the surface of a neutron star is

$$g_n = \frac{GM_n}{R_n{}^2}$$

so, with $M_n = 3.0 \times 10^{30}$ kg and $R_n = 10 \text{ km} = 10^4$ m,

$$\begin{aligned} g_n &= \frac{6.67 \times 10^{-11} \times 3.0 \times 10^{30}}{(10^4)^2} \text{ m s}^{-2} \\ &= 2.0 \times 10^{12} \text{ m s}^{-2} \end{aligned}$$

[Comment: This is to be compared with 9.8 m s^{-2} on Earth!]

ITQ 4.12

This calculation is analogous to calculations about the brightness of stars at various distances discussed in SAQ 4.3; in both cases we have to remember that the flux density received diminishes as $1/d^2$, where d is the distance to the source. We need to compare the ratio of radio luminosity to d^2 for the transmitter and the pulsar.

$$\text{flux density from transmitter} = \frac{L_t}{4\pi d_t{}^2}$$

$$\text{flux density from pulsar} = \frac{L_p}{4\pi d_p{}^2}$$

Therefore

$$\begin{aligned} \frac{\text{flux density from transmitter}}{\text{flux density from pulsar}} &= \frac{L_t}{L_p}\left(\frac{d_p}{d_t}\right)^2 \\ &= \frac{10^5 \text{ W}}{10^{20} \text{ W}}\left(\frac{10^4 \times 3 \times 10^{16} \text{ m}}{10^5 \text{ m}}\right)^2 \\ &= 10^{-15} \times 9 \times 10^{30} \\ &= 9 \times 10^{15} \\ &\simeq 10^{16} \end{aligned}$$

Therefore the flux density from the radio transmitter is 10^{16} times stronger than that from the pulsar. [Comment: This highlights one of the problems of radio astronomy – the cosmic signals are weak and can easily be swamped by terrestrial radio signals if they stray onto the channels reserved for radio astronomy.]

ITQ 4.13

An accuracy of 1 part in 10^{14} means, for example, that the accuracy can be expressed as 1 second in 10^{14} seconds.

$$\begin{aligned} 1 \text{ century} &= 100 \text{ years} = 100 \times 3.2 \times 10^7 \text{ seconds} \\ &= 3.2 \times 10^9 \text{ s} \end{aligned}$$

Therefore the number of seconds accuracy per century

$$\begin{aligned} &= 3.2 \times 10^9 / 10^{14} \text{ s} \\ &= 3.2 \times 10^{-5} \text{ s} \\ &= 32 \text{ microseconds} \end{aligned}$$

ITQ 4.14

The magnitude of the escape velocity is given by

$$v_{esc} = \sqrt{2GM/R}$$

The escape velocity is equal to c at $R = R_S$, so

$$\begin{aligned} c &= \sqrt{2GM/R_S} \\ c^2 &= 2GM/R_S \end{aligned}$$

Therefore

$$R_S = \frac{2GM}{c^2}$$

[*Comment*: This is an important equation, which gives the Schwarzschild radius of a black hole of mass M. We have derived it without using relativity, so the derivation is somewhat artificial. However, it does give the right result, and it does illustrate some of the physical processes that we have to consider.]

ITQ 4.15

Using the relationship derived in ITQ 4.14,

$$
\begin{aligned}
R_S &= \frac{2 \times (6.7 \times 10^{-11}\,\text{N}\,\text{m}^2\text{kg}^{-2}) \times (2.0 \times 10^{30}\,\text{kg})}{(3.0 \times 10^8\,\text{m}\,\text{s}^{-1})^2} \\
&= 3.0 \times 10^3\,\text{N}\,\text{kg}^{-1}\,\text{s}^2 \\
&= 3.0 \times 10^3\,\text{kg}\,\text{m}\,\text{s}^{-2}\,\text{kg}^{-1}\,\text{s}^2 = 3 \times 10^3\,\text{m} \\
&= 3.0\,\text{km}
\end{aligned}
$$

ITQ 4.16

In comparing the magnitudes of the two gravitational forces we shall work with the masses of the objects in $M_\odot$ and distances in $R_\odot$:

$$
F_\text{g} = \frac{GMm}{R^2}
$$

Gravitational force due to $10M_\odot$ star:

$$
F_{10} = \frac{G(10M_\odot)m_\text{blob}}{(100R_\odot)^2}
$$

Gravitational force due to $1M_\odot$ star:

$$
F_1 = \frac{G(1M_\odot)m_\text{blob}}{(130R_\odot - 100R_\odot)^2}
$$

Therefore

$$
\frac{F_{10}}{F_1} = \frac{10 \times 30^2}{100^2} = \frac{9 \times 10^3}{10^4} = 0.9
$$

and F_1 is slightly larger.

ITQ answers and comments for Chapter 5

ITQ 5.1

For the Balmer absorption lines to be observed, appreciable numbers of hydrogen atoms would have to be in the $n = 2$ energy level (Figure 2.10) *before* they absorb the visible radiation from the background star. If the region is cool, then collisional excitation to the $n = 2$ level will rarely occur: nearly all collisions will be too feeble.

ITQ 5.2

If we ignore the relatively small difference in mass between the nitrogen and oxygen atom, then we can choose either to represent the *whole* of the Earth's atmosphere. We choose nitrogen. The common isotope of nitrogen, $^{14}_{7}\text{N}$, has an atomic mass of $14 \times (1.67 \times 10^{-27}\,\text{kg})$, and so the number n of *atoms* per cubic metre is given by

$$
n \sim 1\,\text{kg}\,\text{m}^{-3}/[14 \times (1.67 \times 10^{-27}\,\text{kg})] \sim 4 \times 10^{25}\,\text{m}^{-3}
$$

Comparison with Figure 5.2 shows that the atmosphere at the surface of the Earth is about 10^9 times more dense than the densest part of the ISM.

The surface temperature, about $300\,\text{K}$, is not much greater than that of the warmer diffuse clouds.

ITQ 5.3

The temperature is well above that required for collisional excitation of the 21 cm line, which only requires that $T \geqslant 0.05\,\text{K}$. However, this is an *atomic* hydrogen line, and in dense clouds the predominant form of hydrogen is H_2 (Table 5.1). Thus, the line is weak because there is little atomic hydrogen.

ITQ 5.4

From Figure 5.8 we see that, for CO, the difference in energy ε between the lowest electronic level and the one above it is $9.5 \times 10^{-19}\,\text{J}$.

(a) From Equation 5.1, ε corresponds to a photon wavelength given by

$$
\begin{aligned}
\lambda &= hc/\varepsilon \\
&= (6.63 \times 10^{-34}\,\text{J}\,\text{s}) \times (3.00 \times 10^8\,\text{m}\,\text{s}^{-1})/(9.5 \times 10^{-19}\,\text{J}) \\
&= 2.09 \times 10^{-7}\,\text{m} = 0.209\,\mu\text{m}
\end{aligned}
$$

This is the maximum photon wavelength (minimum energy) for this excitation.

(b) From Equation 5.3, the minimum temperature is given by

$$
\begin{aligned}
T &\sim 2\varepsilon/(3k) \\
&\sim 2 \times 9.5 \times 10^{-19}\,\text{J}/(3 \times 1.38 \times 10^{-23}\,\text{J}\,\text{K}^{-1}) \\
&\sim 5 \times 10^4\,\text{K}
\end{aligned}
$$

ITQ 5.5

The kinetic energy of the shell is given by Equation 1.7 in *Preparatory science*, namely

$$
E_\text{k} = Mv^2/2
$$

where M is the mass of the shell and v is the required speed. Thus

$$
v = (2E_\text{k}/M)^{1/2}
$$

With $E_\text{k} \sim 10^{44}\,\text{J}$, and $M \sim 0.25M_\odot \sim 5 \times 10^{29}\,\text{kg}$, we get

$$
v \sim (2 \times 10^{44}\,\text{J}/5 \times 10^{29}\,\text{kg})^{1/2}
$$

Replacing J by the equivalent units $\text{kg}\,\text{m}^2\,\text{s}^{-2}$ (back page of the *Introduction and Guide*), we get

$$
\begin{aligned}
v &\sim (2 \times 10^{44}\,\text{kg}\,\text{m}^2\,\text{s}^{-2}/5 \times 10^{29}\,\text{kg})^{1/2} \\
&\sim (4 \times 10^{14}\,\text{m}^2\text{s}^{-2})^{1/2} \\
&\sim 2 \times 10^7\,\text{m}\,\text{s}^{-1} \sim 0.07c
\end{aligned}
$$

ITQ 5.6

From Equation 5.3, the criterion for collisional ionization is given by

$$T \gtrsim 2\varepsilon_I/(3k)$$

where ε_I is the ionization energy. Thus, when ε_I has the value 4.0×10^{-18} J, we get

$$T \gtrsim 2 \times 4.0 \times 10^{-18}\,\text{J}/(3 \times 1.38 \times 10^{-23}\,\text{J K}^{-1})$$
$$= 2 \times 10^5\,\text{K}$$

A typical supernova remnant has a temperature of about 10^6 K (Figure 5.2), so will produce a high degree of ionization in all of the chemical elements.

SAQ answers and comments for Chapter 1

SAQ 1.1

The small-scale structure in Figure 1.3b is partly due to the solar granulation seen in the photosphere. (Sunspots may also contribute.) The granules are bright whereas the lanes that separate them are dark. This variation shows up in the graph.

SAQ 1.2

The frequencies are given by $f = c/\lambda$ (Equation 1.2, rearranged). So, for $\lambda = 400$ nm,

$$f = \frac{3.00 \times 10^8\,\text{m s}^{-1}}{400 \times 10^{-9}\,\text{m}} = 7.50 \times 10^{14}\,\text{Hz}$$

and, for $\lambda = 750$ nm,

$$f = \frac{3.00 \times 10^8\,\text{m s}^{-1}}{750 \times 10^{-9}\,\text{m}} = 4.00 \times 10^{14}\,\text{Hz}$$

Thus, the frequency range is from 4.00×10^{14} Hz to 7.50×10^{14} Hz.

[*Comment*: In air, the frequencies are the same but, the speed being slightly lower, the wavelengths are slightly longer.]

SAQ 1.3

The photon energies are given by $\varepsilon = hf$ (Equation 1.3). So, for $\lambda = 400$ nm,

$$\varepsilon = (6.63 \times 10^{-34}\,\text{J s}) \times (7.50 \times 10^{14}\,\text{s}^{-1})$$
$$= 4.97 \times 10^{-19}\,\text{J}$$

and, for $\lambda = 750$ nm,

$$\varepsilon = (6.63 \times 10^{-34}\,\text{J s}) \times (4.00 \times 10^{14}\,\text{s}^{-1})$$
$$= 2.65 \times 10^{-19}\,\text{J}$$

The energy range is from 2.65×10^{-19} J to 4.97×10^{-19} J.

SAQ 1.4

The only way to do this on the basis of the information given in this chapter is to compare the size of the plage in Figure 1.13 with the size of the solar disc. [*Comment*: This is similar to ITQ 1.2 and suffers from the same problem of foreshortening.] At a rough estimate, the longest dimension of the plage is about a quarter of the diameter of the Sun, which implies a (maximum) size of

$$\tfrac{1}{4} \times 1.4 \times 10^6\,\text{km} = 3.5 \times 10^5\,\text{km}$$

SAQ 1.5

This question can be answered with the aid of the relative spectral flux densities (R) given in Figure 1.14. At 6 000 K,

$$\frac{R_{6000}(400\,\text{nm})}{R_{6000}(750\,\text{nm})} = \frac{4.6}{3.5} = 1.3$$

At 5 000 K the ratio would have been

$$\frac{R_{5000}(400\,\text{nm})}{R_{5000}(750\,\text{nm})} = \frac{1.3}{1.8} = 0.7$$

[*Comment*: As you can see, the two ratios are very different. When treated properly, ratios of this kind are sufficient to determine the temperature of an ideal thermal source. There is no need to record the entire spectrum or even to determine the precise location of the peak.]

SAQ 1.6

The peak of the Sun's spectrum seems to be at a wavelength of about 470 nm. Substituting this value in Wien's displacement law gives

$$T = \frac{2.90 \times 10^{-3}\,\text{m K}}{470 \times 10^{-9}\,\text{m}} = 6\,170\,\text{K}$$

[*Comment*: This value is rather high, but we have taken an exceptionally crude approach. In fact, a Planck curve corresponding to an ideal thermal source with a lower temperature (5 800 K, say) provides a reasonable approximation to the data in Figure 1.18.]

SAQ 1.7

(a) It follows from Equation 1.5 that the frequency, f_{32}, of the radiation absorbed during a transition from E_2 to E_3 is $(1/h)(E_3 - E_2)$, which is

$$\frac{1}{6.63 \times 10^{-34}}\,[(-2.18 \times 10^{-18}/3^2) - (-2.18 \times 10^{-18}/2^2)]\ \text{Hz}$$
$$= 4.57 \times 10^{14}\,\text{Hz}$$

Now, the corresponding wavelength is given by

$$\lambda_{32} = \frac{c}{f_{32}} = \frac{3.00 \times 10^8}{4.57 \times 10^{14}}\,\text{m} = 656\,\text{nm}$$

which is close to the 656.3 nm measured for the Hα line.

[*Comment*: Since the numerical work in this question has been carried out to three significant figures, the third figure in the final answer is actually somewhat suspect and it would be best to conclude that the given transition will absorb photons of wavelength between 650 nm and 660 nm.

Clearly, such a conclusion makes it quite possible for the given transition to be responsible for Hα absorption, but it's hardly firm proof. What it does show is the need to work to much greater precision when dealing with spectroscopic quantities. In fact, more precise calculations *do* confirm that Hα absorption is due to the E_2 to E_3 transition.]

(b) Hβ absorption is caused by the E_2 to E_4 transition (which can be discovered by trial and error). Thus

$$\lambda_{42} = \frac{c}{f_{42}} = \frac{c}{(E_4 - E_2)/h} = \frac{ch}{(E_4 - E_2)}$$
$$= \frac{3.00 \times 10^8 \times 6.63 \times 10^{-34}}{(-\frac{1}{4^2} + \frac{1}{2^2}) \times 2.18 \times 10^{-18}} \text{ m}$$
$$= 487 \text{ nm}$$

This is to be compared with the wavelength of Hβ absorption, which is 486.1 nm.

(c) Hβ emission is due to the E_4 to E_2 transition (the reverse of the transition causing Hβ absorption).

(d) The transition from E_1 to E_2 produces a wavelength that is only one quarter of the Hβ wavelength. (Prove this!) Such a wavelength is so small that it is beyond the range covered by Figure 1.17.

SAQ 1.8

(a) Ca^{14+} and Fe^{9+}.

(b) The energy carried by the photons that contribute to the yellow and red lines must arise from appropriate transitions in the atoms concerned. For the yellow line the relevant energy is

$$\varepsilon = hf = h\frac{c}{\lambda} = \frac{6.63 \times 10^{-34} \times 3.00 \times 10^8}{5.69 \times 10^{-7}} \text{ J}$$
$$= 3.50 \times 10^{-19} \text{ J}$$

So this must represent the difference in energy between two of the energy levels of Ca^{14+}.

Similarly, in the case of the red line

$$\varepsilon = \frac{6.63 \times 10^{-34} \times 3.00 \times 10^8}{6.37 \times 10^{-7}} \text{ J}$$
$$= 3.12 \times 10^{-19} \text{ J}$$

So this must represent the difference between two of the energy levels of Fe^{9+}.

SAQ 1.9

It follows from Wien's displacement law that the wavelength of peak emission for a 100 000 K source will be

$$\lambda_{\text{peak}} = \frac{2.90 \times 10^{-3}}{100\,000} \text{ m}$$
$$= 2.9 \times 10^{-8} \text{ m}$$

On the basis of Figure 1.23 it is a little difficult to assign this to a particular part of the electromagnetic spectrum. On the one hand it certainly falls into the range covered by the ultraviolet. On the other hand it also just about fits into the low energy end of the X-ray range.

SAQ 1.10

At radio wavelengths, much of the Sun's emission comes from regions of the corona where temperature increases with height. Because (as argued in Subsection 1.2.2) observations made near the limb sample material that is, on average, at greater altitude than that sampled by observations made near the centre of the solar disc, it follows that at radio wavelengths limb observations will involve higher and hence hotter material than disc observations. Thus, at radio wavelengths the limb will be brighter than the disc centre.

[*Comment*: At visible wavelengths the corona is essentially transparent and its own emissions are very faint. Thus there is no chance of observing limb brightening in visible light produced by the corona.]

SAQ 1.11

The composition of the Sun is roughly 73% hydrogen and 25% helium, by mass. Thus, for every 73 kg of hydrogen in the Sun there are 25 kg of helium and 2 kg of everything else. Since the mass of a hydrogen nucleus, ^1_1H, is 1.673×10^{-27} kg and that of a helium nucleus, ^4_2He, is 6.645×10^{-27} kg (these figures were given in ITQ 1.12), it follows that 100 kg of typical solar material will contain roughly

$$\frac{73}{1.673 \times 10^{-27}} = 4.36 \times 10^{28} \text{ hydrogen nuclei}$$

and

$$\frac{25}{6.645 \times 10^{-27}} = 3.76 \times 10^{27} \text{ helium nuclei}$$

[*Comment*: This is a ratio by *number* of nuclei of roughly 100 : 8.6, hydrogen to helium.]

Now, the total mass of the Sun was given in Subsection 1.5.4 as 1.99×10^{30} kg. Thus, the total number of hydrogen nuclei in the Sun will be roughly

$$\frac{1.99 \times 10^{30}}{100} \times 4.36 \times 10^{28} = 8.68 \times 10^{56}$$

and the number of helium nuclei will be roughly

$$\frac{1.99 \times 10^{30}}{100} \times 3.76 \times 10^{27} = 7.48 \times 10^{55}$$

SAQ 1.12

According to ITQ 1.12c, the mass of hydrogen consumed every year is about 1.84×10^{19} kg. Since the total mass of the Sun is 1.99×10^{30} kg, and about 73% of this is hydrogen, it follows that the maximum duration of the conversion of hydrogen into helium at the present rate is

$$\frac{0.73 \times 1.99 \times 10^{30}}{1.84 \times 10^{19}} \text{ years} = 7.9 \times 10^{10} \text{ years}$$

[*Comment*: Of course, this is a crude estimate because it assumes that all of the hydrogen currently in the Sun will undergo conversion and it also makes use of a result (from ITQ 1.12) that is itself only an estimate. Nonetheless, the final answer is quite reasonable. More refined estimates of the Sun's hydrogen-fuelled lifetime provide figures of about 10^{10} years. Since the Sun is currently thought to be about 4.5×10^9 years old, it is usual to regard the Sun as a middle-aged star.]

SAQ 1.13

(a) The nucleus ^5_3He does not exist. Every helium nucleus *must* have an atomic number of 2, denoting two protons in the nucleus. The atomic number of 3 corresponds to lithium.

(b) This reaction does not conserve electric charge.

(c) This reaction also fails to conserve electric charge.

SAQ 1.14

The solar luminosity was given earlier as $3.84 \times 10^{26}\,\text{J s}^{-1}$. Since there are approximately 3.16×10^7 seconds in one year, it follows that the annual energy output of the Sun, E, is about $1.21 \times 10^{34}\,\text{J}$. Assuming that this energy is entirely supplied by the loss of mass from the Sun's core, it follows that the mass lost per year is

$$m = \frac{E}{c^2} = \frac{1.21 \times 10^{34}}{8.99 \times 10^{16}}\,\text{kg} = 1.35 \times 10^{17}\,\text{kg}$$

[*Comment*: It is worth emphasizing that this means the Sun is losing mass at the amazing rate of 4.27×10^9 kilograms per second, and will lose about 10^{27} kg in its hydrogen-burning lifetime, which is about 0.05% of its mass.]

SAQ 1.15

Two neutrinos are released each time the ppI chain is executed (Subsection 1.5.4). Assuming (somewhat unrealistically) that all nuclear reactions apart from those of the ppI chain can be ignored, we know (from ITQ 1.12b) that the ppI chain is completed about 8.71×10^{37} times per second. (This estimate involves various assumptions that are discussed in ITQ 1.12.) It follows that the rate at which neutrinos are produced in the core of the Sun is about $2 \times 8.71 \times 10^{37}\,\text{s}^{-1}$. Now, assuming (quite realistically) that all these neutrinos escape from the Sun and spread out evenly in all directions, the rate at which they pass through an area of $0.01\,\text{m}^2$ on a spherical surface of radius $1.50 \times 10^{11}\,\text{m}$, centred on the Sun, is

$$(2 \times 8.71 \times 10^{37}) \times \frac{0.01}{4\pi \times (1.50 \times 10^{11})^2}\,\text{s}^{-1}$$
$$= 6.16 \times 10^{12}\,\text{s}^{-1}$$

[*Comment*: Since $0.01\,\text{m}^2$ is roughly the cross-sectional area of a human brain, this calculation justifies the claim made earlier that more than a million million neutrinos pass through your head in the time it takes to read a sentence.]

SAQ answers and comments for Chapter 2

SAQ 2.1

(a) The angular diameter of the Moon (0.5°) is 1 800 arcsec. So, at the rate of 1.25 arcsec yr^{-1}, it will take Procyon A $1\,800/1.25 = 1\,440$ years to travel this angular distance.

(b) The transverse speed is obtained from the proper motion by means of Equation 2.1. Thus we must first obtain the distance d to Procyon. This is obtained using Equation 2.5:

$$d/\text{pc} = 1/0.285$$

Thus

$$d = 3.51\,\text{pc} = 1.08 \times 10^{14}\,\text{km}$$

Secondly, the proper motion is given as 1.25 arcsec yr^{-1}. There are 206 265 arcsec in a radian (Subsection 2.2.2), and 3.16×10^7 seconds in a year, so this proper motion corresponds to $(1.25/206\,265)(1/(3.16 \times 10^7))$ radians per second, that is 1.92×10^{-13} radians s^{-1}. Thus, from Equation 2.1,

$$\begin{aligned}v_t &= (p/\text{radians}) \times d \\&= (1.92 \times 10^{-13}\,\text{s}^{-1}) \times (1.08 \times 10^{14}\,\text{km}) \\&= 20.7\,\text{km s}^{-1}\end{aligned}$$

(c) Its spectral lines are blue-shifted, so its radial velocity is directed towards us.

(d) If we assume that transverse speeds are, on average, much the same at all stellar distances from the Sun, then, from Equation 2.1, we see that nearby stars will, on average, have large proper motions. From Equation 2.5 we see that nearby stars also have large parallaxes, which are therefore readily measurable.

SAQ 2.2

(a) From Table 2.2 we see that 13 000 K is a reasonable temperature for a B8 star. At 13 000 K, the Balmer lines are strong compared with the helium lines, and very much stronger than the lines of ionized helium and ionized calcium (Figure 2.12). [*Comment*: Remember that the actual procedure runs the other way: from the observed line strengths we establish the spectral class.]

(b) A far less luminous star of the same temperature would have broader spectral lines, and weaker lines from certain ionized atoms.

(c) Following the method in ITQ 2.4, we get

$$R/R_\odot \simeq (1.4 \times 10^5)^{1/2} \times (5\,770/13\,000)^2 \simeq 74$$

(d) From Figures 2.8 and 2.17, a rough estimate is that about 10% of its luminosity lies in the V waveband [*Comment*: Any value between about 5% and 15% is reasonable.]. Thus, with $L = 1.4 \times 10^5 L_\odot$, we get

$$L_V \sim 5 \times 10^{30}\,\text{W}$$

Thus, from Equation 2.10

$$\begin{aligned}d &\sim [5 \times 10^{30}\,\text{W}/(4\pi \times 3.0 \times 10^{-9}\,\text{W m}^{-2})]^{1/2} \\&\sim 1.2 \times 10^{19}\,\text{m} \sim 370\,\text{pc}\end{aligned}$$

[*Comment*: The actual distance to Rigel A is about 280 pc.]

(e) The angular diameter of Rigel A, from the Earth, is given by a straightforward rearrangement of Equation 2.6. Thus, using the values of radius R and distance d obtained earlier in this SAQ, we get

$$\alpha \sim (2 \times 74 \times 6.96 \times 10^8 \text{m})/(1.2 \times 10^{19} \text{m}) \text{ radians}$$
$$\sim 1.0 \times 10^{-8} \text{ radians}$$
$$\sim 0.002 \text{ arcsec}$$

This is measurable: at present the smallest measured values are about 0.000 4 arcsec (Subsection 2.3.1).

SAQ 2.3

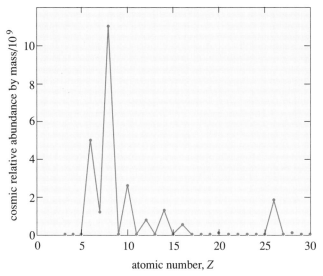

Figure 2.34 Cosmic relative abundances by mass, with respect to H = 10^{12}, for the elements $2 < Z < 31$.

From Table 2.3 we obtain Figure 2.34 for the heavy elements ($Z > 2$) as far as $Z = 30$. There is no simple trend with Z. Instead, there are some notably large values, as follows (values of Z in parentheses): carbon (6), nitrogen (7), oxygen (8), neon (10), magnesium (12), silicon (14), sulphur (16) and iron (26).

[*Comment*: The reasons for this relationship with Z will be made clear to you by the end of the Course.]

SAQ 2.4

The distance to a star does not influence its position on the H–R diagram: photospheric temperature and luminosity are intrinsic properties of a star. [*Comment*: We sometimes have to apply corrections to our observations in order to obtain intrinsic properties.]

SAQ 2.5

(a) Figure 2.35 shows the five stars plotted on an H–R diagram. By comparison with Figure 2.23, we can make the following assignments.

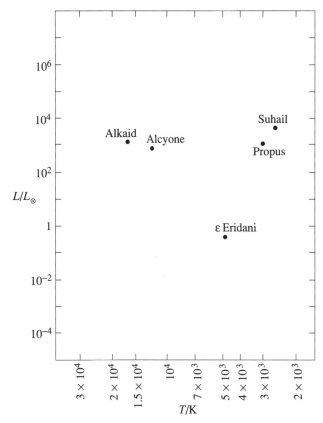

Figure 2.35 An H–R diagram with five stars, from SAQ 2.5.

Star	Main stellar class	Comment
Alkaid	main sequence	
Alcyone	giant	
ε Eridani	main sequence	a nearby (3.30 pc), solar-type star
Propus	red giant	
Suhail	red giant/supergiant	some stars fall between the four main classes

(b) Low luminosity stars can have a large apparent visual brightness only if they are particularly close to us. Thus, low luminosity stars will be under-represented in an H–R diagram that contains only the stars with the greatest apparent visual brightness. [*Comment*: There is always a likelihood that low luminosity stars will be under-represented, simply because any detection system will fail to detect stars that give too low a flux density at the detector. This is an example of a *selection effect*.]

SAQ 2.6

From Figure 2.23 we see that the Sun's photospheric temperature, $T_\odot$, luminosity, $L_\odot$, and radius, $R_\odot$, have the following relationships to the upper and lower ends of the ranges found for main sequence stars:

upper end: $\sim 6T_\odot$, $\sim 10^6 L_\odot$, $\sim 10 R_\odot$

lower end: $\sim 0.3 T_\odot$, $\sim 10^{-5} L_\odot$, $\sim 0.03 R_\odot$

Thus, the Sun is a very modest main sequence star.

SAQ 2.7

From Figure 2.23 you can see that an approach to the main sequence from just above it, where the T Tauri stars lie, with little change in temperature, results in a small reduction in stellar radius.

SAQ 2.8

From Equation 2.15. the sum $M + m$ is

$$4\pi^2 \frac{(20 \times 1.50 \times 10^{11}\,\mathrm{m})^3}{(6.67 \times 10^{-11}\mathrm{N}\,\mathrm{m}^2\,\mathrm{kg}^{-2}) \times (50 \times 3.16 \times 10^7\mathrm{s})^2}$$
$$= 6.4 \times 10^{30}\,\mathrm{kg}$$

From Figure 2.29

$$d_m/d_M = 2.3$$

This ratio is not influenced by our projected view of the orbit.

Thus, from Equation 2.16

$$M/m = 2.3$$

We thus have

$$(2.3m + m) = 6.4 \times 10^{30}\,\mathrm{kg}$$

and so

$$m = 1.9 \times 10^{30}\,\mathrm{kg} = 1.0 M_\odot$$

Thus

$$M = 2.3 \times 1.0 M_\odot = 2.3 M_\odot$$

[*Comment*: If we measure τ in years, and a in AU, then we can write Equation 2.15 as

$$(M + m)/M_\odot = (a/\mathrm{AU})^3/(\tau/\mathrm{yr})^2$$

Try it! This numerical simplification arises from the Earth–Sun system, for which $M = M_\odot$, $M_\odot \gg M_\mathrm{E}$ (Earth's mass), $\tau = 1$ year, and $a = 1$ AU.]

SAQ 2.9

To evolve into a supergiant, the red giant would have to acquire a lot of mass: see Figure 2.31. However, observations suggest that red giants *lose* mass (in the form of stellar winds), and so we can rule out the evolution of red giants to form supergiants.

SAQ 2.10

The H–R diagram of M67 in Figure 2.32b is dominated by the absence from the main sequence of all but the low mass stars (Figure 2.31), and the presence of considerable numbers of stars between the main sequence and the red giant region, which could represent the higher masses missing from the main sequence. This suggests that the more massive a star, the sooner it leaves the main sequence, and that most stars that have left the main sequence next become red giants. Supergiants are absent in M67, and this could be because massive main sequence stars, which are their precursors, are rare. Also, if, as it seems, massive stars evolve rapidly, then any small number of supergiants could have become Type II supernovae, and have thus vanished from the H–R diagram. The absence of white dwarfs is presumably because they are too faint to detect. Thus, the H–R diagram for M67 is consistent with the model of stellar evolution in Figure 2.33.

Assuming the model is right, we can conclude that M67 is older than The Pleiades, because in The Pleiades the main sequence is populated to higher stellar masses than the main sequence in M67 (Figure 2.32), and the more massive the star the sooner it leaves the main sequence. In M67 there has been enough time for all but the low mass stars to leave the main sequence, whereas The Pleiades is too young for this to have happened.

SAQ answers and comments for Chapter 3

SAQ 3.1

The mass of a hydrogen molecule is $2 \times 1.67 \times 10^{-27}\,\mathrm{kg}$.

Thus the total mass of the cloud is

$$\tfrac{4}{3}\pi \times (3 \times 3.09 \times 10^{16})^3 \times 10^9 \times (2 \times 1.67 \times 10^{-27})\,\mathrm{kg}$$
$$= 1.1 \times 10^{34}\mathrm{kg}$$

If we assume, for the present calculation, that all stars have a mass equal to that of the Sun ($2 \times 10^{30}\mathrm{kg}$), we can work out how many stars could be formed from the cloud.

$$\text{number of stars} = (1.1 \times 10^{34})/(2 \times 10^{30}) \approx 5\,500!$$

If we assume therefore that all the material in the original cloud goes into making stars, we find that there is plenty of material to make a large number of stars. In Chapter 2, we learnt that stars generally have masses in the range from about $0.08 M_\odot$ to about $50 M_\odot$, so our conclusion wouldn't change whatever mass we assumed for the stars that formed from this cloud.

SAQ 3.2

In bipolar outflow, the flow is highly directed. This means that observations of the Doppler shift will tend to show two distinct values corresponding to flow in two opposite directions. For a T Tauri star, outflow is in all directions, so a range of Doppler shifts can be observed. In addition, the outflow from T Tauri stars tends to have a higher velocity, leading to a larger Doppler shift. Furthermore, T Tauri stars sometimes show variable outflow.

SAQ 3.3

We calculate the Jeans mass in each case using Equation 3.1:

$$M_\mathrm{J} = \frac{9}{4} \times \left(\frac{1}{2\pi n}\right)^{1/2} \times \frac{1}{m^2} \times \left(\frac{kT}{G}\right)^{3/2}$$

Using the parameters for the two cases from the question and $m = 2 \times 1.67 \times 10^{-27}$ kg for the mass of the hydrogen molecule, we find, in the uncompressed case

$$M_J = \frac{9}{4}\left[\frac{1}{2\pi \times 5 \times 10^9\,\text{m}^{-3}}\right]^{1/2} \times \frac{1}{(3.34 \times 10^{-27}\,\text{kg})^2}$$

$$\times \left[\frac{1.38 \times 10^{-23}\,\text{J K}^{-1} \times 10\text{K}}{6.67 \times 10^{-11}\,\text{N m}^2\,\text{kg}^{-2}}\right]^{3/2}$$

$$= \frac{9}{4} \times (6 \times 10^{-6}) \times (9 \times 10^{52}) \times (3 \times 10^{-18})\,\text{kg}$$

$$= 4 \times 10^{30}\,\text{kg}$$

Thus, in solar masses ($M_\odot = 2 \times 10^{30}$kg)

$$M_J = 2M_\odot$$

Therefore, the core, mass $M_\odot$, has a mass *less* than its Jeans mass, so it is unlikely to contract, particularly if rotation or magnetic fields hinder contraction. In the compressed case, a similar calculation yields

$$M_J = 0.5M_\odot$$

Thus, the core mass is now *greater* than its Jeans mass, so it is likely to contract unless held up by rotation or magnetic fields.

SAQ 3.4

Centre to surface of the Sun: radiation in the deep interior, then convection in the outer regions. (Conduction doesn't play a significant part in energy transport in most stars.)

Surface of the Sun to the top of the Earth's atmosphere: radiation, because this region is occupied by a vacuum.

Top of the atmosphere to the surface of the Earth: radiation (the atmosphere is partially transparent to some of the Sun's radiation), conduction (through the atmosphere) and convection (of the atmosphere).

SAQ 3.5

(a) The reaction obeys the laws of conservation of electric charge and of baryon number. It will obey the law of conservation of energy provided that the sum of the rest energies and translational kinetic energies of the reactants, equals this sum for the product plus the energy of the gamma ray. The reaction is thus possible.

(b) Figure 3.11 shows that the rest energy *per nucleon* for $A = 12$ exceeds that for $A = 24$. Denoting these values by e_{12} and e_{24}, respectively, for the reactants we have a rest energy of $2 \times 12 \times e_{12}$, and for the product $24 \times e_{24}$. Thus, with $e_{12} > e_{24}$, the rest energy of the reactants exceeds that of the product, and so the reaction is exothermic. However, it is not an appreciable source of energy in main sequence stars because, compared with the pp and CNO cycles,

- with $Z = 6$ the electrical repulsion between the carbon nuclei results in a much lower reaction rate
- carbon is not nearly as abundant as hydrogen (or as helium).

SAQ 3.6

We see from Table 3.1 that upper main sequence stars have main sequence lifetimes much less than the present age of the Earth. We need to find the mass of a star that has a lifetime equal to the age of the Earth. This will represent the most massive star that existed on the main sequence both now and at the time of the Earth's formation. In the table, a lifetime of 4.5×10^9 years falls between the values for stars of mass $1M_\odot$ and $1.5M_\odot$, at a mass of approximately $1.3M_\odot$. It follows that any star more massive than this, and that is now on the main sequence, cannot have been on the main sequence when the Earth formed.

SAQ 3.7

(a) Using the data from Table 3.1, we can produce a graph as in Figure 3.24. We can draw a line that passes through the data points. Then, reading off a value of luminosity of $300L_\odot$, we find it corresponds to a mass of nearly $5M_\odot$.

(b) Using the data for lifetimes given in Table 3.1, a graph of lifetime against mass can be drawn, as in Figure 3.24. The graph shows a clear steepening of the slope as mass falls, thus showing that lower main sequence stars have a more sensitive dependence of lifetime on mass than do upper main sequence stars. [*Comment*: Equations 3.7 and 3.8 have gradients corresponding to the dashed lines in Figure 3.24, and are thus approximations to the curves for lower and upper main sequence stars.]

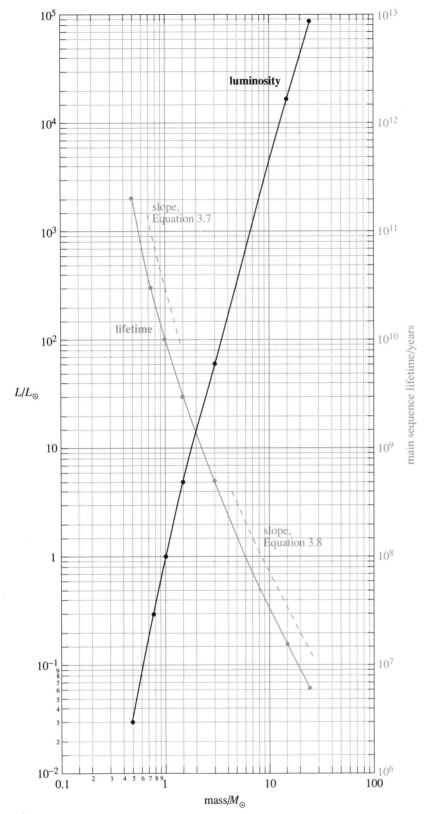

Figure 3.24   Answer to SAQ 3.7.

SAQ 3.8

1 When core hydrogen fusion finishes, there is no internal energy source to sustain a sufficient pressure gradient to counter the effect of gravity. Therefore, the core contracts.

2 As the core contracts the gravitational energy released increases the internal temperature to the point where hydrogen fusion takes place in a shell of unprocessed hydrogen. During this shell burning the star moves to the right, then upwards on the H–R diagram, much like the solar mass star in Figure 3.16. This movement corresponds to a considerable increase in radius, though the reasons for this are not fully understood.

3 As the core continues to contract and heat up, it reaches a temperature at which helium fusion starts, to form carbon, in the 3α process. Previous to this the electron gas in the core became degenerate, and so the helium burning starts violently, in a so-called helium flash. The rise in temperature removes the degeneracy, and the star becomes stable. The helium flash occurs at the top of the upward movement in the H–R diagram; the star then moves down and to the left (Figure 3.16).

4 During helium burning, fusion in the core also produces oxygen, via the reaction

$${}^{12}_{6}C + {}^{4}_{2}He \longrightarrow {}^{16}_{8}O + \gamma$$

5 When the helium in the core has been consumed, the core again contracts, and this leads to helium shell burning, and a rather complicated track on the H–R diagram. At some stage the star probably crosses the instability strip (Figure 3.21), perhaps to become an RR Lyrae variable.

6 Then, somehow, the star sheds a planetary nebula, and the hot remnant – consisting mainly of nuclei of carbon, oxygen and helium, in a sea of electrons – contracts. As it contracts its density rises until the electrons become degenerate, whereupon the contraction is halted by electron degeneracy pressure. The remnant is now a white dwarf, about Earth-sized, very dense, and with a surface temperature of about 10 000 K, though much hotter in the interior.

7 The white dwarf cools at approximately constant radius, moving down and to the right from the white dwarf region of the H–R diagram (Figure 3.23).

SAQ 3.9

The mechanisms are listed in Table 3.2.

Table 3.2 The main mechanisms of mass loss from stars

Mass loss mechanism	Comments
(i) T Tauri (and bipolar) outflow	Up to $0.5M_{\odot}$ may be lost in a T Tauri stellar wind
(ii) Main sequence star stellar wind	Despite the long time spent by most stars on the main sequence, the low rate of mass loss ($\simeq 10^{-14}M_{\odot}$ per year for a $1M_{\odot}$ star) means that the accumulated loss is not very significant
(iii) Red giant stellar wind	Although much more significant than the main sequence stellar wind, the relatively short duration of the red giant phase means that the accumulated mass loss is not a large fraction of the mass of the star.
(iv) Planetary nebulae	Mass loss is typically $0.1M_{\odot}$ to $0.2M_{\odot}$. This mechanism is therefore thought to be a significant contribution to the overall mass loss from stars
(v) Supernova explosion	A catastrophic explosion that ejects most of a star's mass into the interstellar medium. [*Comment*: You met such explosions in Chapter 2; supernovae will be dealt with in more detail in Chapter 4.]

Only the last two mechanisms appear to return a significant fraction of a star's mass into the interstellar medium. Mechanism (v), and possibly (iii) and (iv) if convection has brought it to the surface, will return 'processed' material (enriched in 'heavy' elements from fusion reactions).

SAQ 3.10

From Equation 2.7, we know that the luminosity of a star is given by

$$L \simeq 4\pi R^2 \sigma T^4$$

We can write, for the case of two different luminosities at constant radius

$$L_1 \simeq 4\pi R^2 \sigma T_1{}^4$$
$$L_2 \simeq 4\pi R^2 \sigma T_2{}^4$$

Therefore

$$\frac{L_1}{L_2} \simeq \left(\frac{T_1}{T_2}\right)^4$$

So, in this case, if $L_2 = 10^{-4}L_1$, then

$$10^4 \simeq \left(\frac{T_1}{T_2}\right)^4$$

and so

$$T_1/T_2 \simeq 10$$

In other words, the surface temperature has dropped by a factor of 10. We can check this by referring to Figure 3.23. If we follow the evolutionary track shown for a white dwarf, a drop in luminosity from, say, $L_\odot$ to $10^{-4}L_\odot$ (in other words, a reduction by a factor of 10^4), corresponds to a change in surface temperature from about 60 000 K to about 6 000 K. This confirms that a drop in luminosity by a factor of 10^4 corresponds to a drop in surface temperature by a factor of 10 (see also Figure 2.23).

SAQ answers and comments for Chapter 4

SAQ 4.1

The answer is a diagram – Figure 4.19.

SAQ 4.2

There are three reasons why a massive star goes through its life cycle at an ever-increasing pace:

- As the star evolves its central temperature rises; the nuclear reaction rates increase markedly as this happens;
- As the temperature rises there is an increase in the emission of neutrinos; the neutrinos carry away energy that is then lost to the star and has to be replaced by further nuclear reactions; the star must contract and heat up so that the reaction rate increases to compensate for this increasing energy loss;

- Heavier nuclei are produced as the star ages; the fusion of heavier nuclei produces less energy per kilogram than the fusion of lighter nuclei and so more of the heavy nuclei undergo fusion per second to maintain the necessary energy supply.

SAQ 4.3

The flux density F depends on luminosity L and distance d as given by Equation 2.8:

$$F = \frac{L}{4\pi d^2}$$

If the flux density from the supernova equals that from the Sun, then

$$\frac{L_\odot}{4\pi d_\odot^2} = \frac{L_{SN}}{4\pi d_{SN}^2}$$

where SN denotes the supernova. Thus

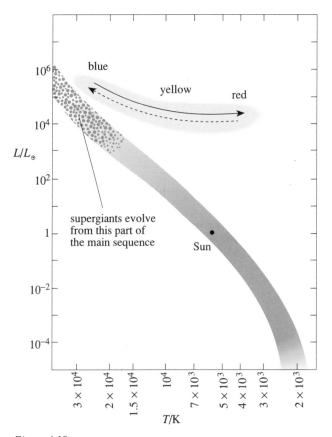

supergiants evolve from this part of the main sequence

Figure 4.19

$$d_{SN}^2 = \left(\frac{L_{SN}}{L_\odot}\right) d_\odot{}^2$$

Now, we are given that $(L_{SN}/L_\odot) = 5 \times 10^9$, and we know that $d_\odot = 1\,AU = 1.6 \times 10^{-5}\,ly = 4.9 \times 10^{-6}\,pc$. Therefore

$$
\begin{aligned}
d_{SN} &= (5 \times 10^9)^{1/2} \times 1\,AU \\
&\simeq 7 \times 10^4\,AU
\end{aligned}
$$

or
$$
\begin{aligned}
d_{SN} &= (5 \times 10^9)^{1/2} \times 1.6 \times 10^{-5}\,ly \\
&\simeq 1.1\,ly
\end{aligned}
$$

or
$$
\begin{aligned}
d_{SN} &= (5 \times 10^9)^{1/2} \times 4.9 \times 10^{-6}\,pc \\
&\simeq 0.3\,pc
\end{aligned}
$$

There are no supergiants that close! The nearest known star (of any sort) after the Sun is 1.3 parsecs aways (Subsection 2.2.2).

SAQ 4.4

Stellar winds and the diffusion of old planetary nebulae would be the main ways in which material was returned to the interstellar medium. Both these, however, are from the outermost layers of the star, and are predominantly hydrogen. Small amounts of graphite, silicates and ices would continue to diffuse into the interstellar medium from the dust shells found surrounding some stars. A few stars have deep convection currents that pull material up to the surface, but in most cases the elements created in stars would remain locked in the stars. Thus there would be a lower abundance of elements heavier then helium. Elements that can be created only by the r-process would not exist.

SAQ 4.5

The answer is a diagram – Figure 4.20.

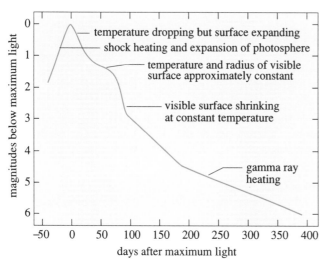

Figure 4.20

SAQ 4.6

If angular momentum is conserved, then $L_1 = L_2$, where the subscript 1 refers to the satellite before the astronaut arrives, and subscript 2 to the satellite–astronaut combination. Considering first the satellite alone:

$$L_1 = I_1 \omega_1$$

and $I_1 = 2\,500\,kg\,m^2$. The satellite spins at 20 revolutions per minute, therefore

$$
\begin{aligned}
L_1 &= (2\,500\,kg\,m^2) \times (20.0\,min^{-1}) \\
&= 5.00 \times 10^4\,kg\,m^2\,min^{-1}
\end{aligned}
$$

The astronaut has a moment of inertia about the spin axis of $100\,kg \times (1\,m)^2 = 100\,kg\,m^2$, so the satellite–astronaut combination has a moment of inertia of $2\,500 + 100\,kg\,m^2$; therefore

$$I_2 = 2\,600\,kg\,m^2$$

Now, since

$$
\begin{aligned}
L_2 &= I_2 \omega_2 \\
\omega_2 &= \frac{L_2}{I_2}
\end{aligned}
$$

But $L_2 = L_1$ so

$$
\begin{aligned}
\omega_2 &= \frac{L_1}{I_2} \\
&= \frac{5.00 \times 10^4\,kg\,m^2\,min^{-1}}{2\,600\,kg\,m^2} \\
&= 19.2\,min^{-1} = 19.2 \text{ revolutions per minute}
\end{aligned}
$$

SAQ 4.7

The power received from the pulsar is

$$10^{-19}\,W\,m^{-2} \times 5\,000\,m^2 = 5 \times 10^{-16}\,W$$

The change in gravitational potential energy (see Section 1.5 in *Preparatory science*) when lifting the mailing is

$$
\begin{aligned}
\Delta E_g &= mg\Delta h \\
&= 5\,kg \times 10\,m\,s^{-2} \times 1\,m \\
&= 50\,J
\end{aligned}
$$

Power used = ΔE_g/time taken = 50 J/1s = 50 W

Therefore

$$\frac{\text{power used lifting mailing}}{\text{power received from pulsar}} = \frac{50\,W}{5 \times 10^{-16}\,W} = 10^{17}$$

[*Comment*: Pulsar signals are weak!]

SAQ 4.8

As described in *Case Study 3*, the collapse continues to densities greater than nuclear densities. There has been a suggestion that the formation of quark material might halt the collapse. If this does not happen, then the core of the star forms a black hole. If the collapse is not halted at nuclear densities, then there will be no 'bounce' and no shock wave. However, neutrinos will be produced. The lifting off of the outer layers has to be effected by the neutrinos alone, and for this reason it may be less dramatic. There will still be floods of neutrons produced so the r-process can still take place, but the explosive nucleosynthesis that was triggered by shock-wave heating will not happen, or not happen so effectively.

SAQ 4.9

The B star and the pulsar will be moving around each other. The optical astronomer will therefore expect there to be changing Doppler shifts in the observed frequencies of the emission lines. The optical astronomer will not see the pulsar.

The radio astronomer will see similar changes in the pulsar period, owing to Doppler shifts the pulse period will be shorter than average for part of the orbit, and for part of the orbit it will be longer. The radio astronomer will not see the B star.

Assuming these two stars were formed as a binary pair, then the star that is now the pulsar (the neutron star) must originally have been the more massive and be more rapidly evolving. To become a neutron star it must have passed through its main sequence stage and its supergiant stage and then exploded as a supernova. Its core became the pulsar. Meanwhile its companion star was more slowly going through the main sequence stages, and is now presumably forming heavier elements in its core. There cannot at the moment be much transfer of material from the B star to the pulsar (because if there were this material would blanket the pulsar and prevent the radio emission).

We are not given any information about the size of the binary system. It may be that the stars are sufficiently far apart that they do not significantly affect each other. Or it could be that the B star received material from the companion when it was a supergiant. It could also be that the mass transfer from the B star to the neutron star has not yet begun because the B star has yet to swell sufficiently to fill its Roche lobe. If mass transfer does start, the radio emission will cease and X-ray emission begin. The rotation rate of the neutron star may be increased by the transferred material.

If there is a lot of mass transferred from the B star its evolution could be seriously affected – e.g. it might lose all its outer envelope and become a helium star or a carbon star. If the mass transfer is limited the B star will probably still pass through the supernova stage, perhaps with its core becoming a neutron star.

SAQ answers and comments for Chapter 5

SAQ 5.1

Taking sizes from Table 5.1 and values of n from Figure 5.2, we can fill in the table as shown in Table 5.4. [Comment: Don't worry if you chose somewhat different values.]

Table 5.4

Type of region	Size/pc	Volume/m³	n/m⁻³	Mass/$M_\odot$
diffuse cloud	~20	~10^{53}	~10^7	~10^3
dense cloud	~2	~10^{50}	~10^{11}	~10^4
HII region	~5	~2×10^{51}	~10^7	~20

The volumes are obtained from the size, as described in note c of Table 5.1, i.e.

$$V \sim \tfrac{4}{3}\pi(\text{size}/2)^3$$

though the region need not be spherical. To sufficient accuracy, we can take n to be the number density of *hydrogen* atoms (the form of the hydrogen, H^+, H, H_2, is immaterial), and so the mass M is given by

$$M/M_\odot \sim V n m_H / M_\odot$$

where m_H is the mass of the hydrogen atom, and $M_\odot$ is the mass of the Sun.

All three types of region are common in the disc of our galaxy.

[Comment: To get more accurate values, we could replace m_H with some average value for the mass of all the elements. However, given that only rough values are required, we have not made this correction. Note that the mass *range* for each type of region are quite wide.]

SAQ 5.2

The cloud temperature is about 100 K (Figure 5.2).

(a) At this temperature, collisional excitation is possible only for rotational transitions, and, given the weak radiative flux, photoexcitation of electronic and vibrational transitions will be rare. Therefore, in this cloud the only *emission* lines from the CN will be from rotational transitions, which will be at microwave and radio wavelengths.

Absorption lines in the spectra of stars beyond the cloud will be observed at UV, visible and IR wavelengths because of photoexcitation by the stars' radiation of electronic and vibrational transitions. Further excitation of the rotational transitions could give absorption lines at microwave and radio wavelengths.

(b) The difference from the case of CN is that the H_2 molecule consists of two identical atoms. Therefore, rotational and vibrational emission from, and absorption by, H_2, will be very weak.

(c) We know that whereas dense clouds can be seen at visible wavelengths through their obscuration of background stars, diffuse clouds are fairly transparent at such wavelengths. This is because their lower densities apply also to the dust, which almost everywhere accounts for about 1% of the mass of the ISM, and it is extinction by the dust that determines obscuration. The situation at other wavelengths can be gauged from Figure 5.11: we see that extinction by dust is less at IR wavelengths, but greater at UV wavelengths. Therefore it is conceivable that at UV wavelengths the dust in the diffuse cloud *does* obscure the stars beyond it.

(d) If the dust radiates rather like a black body, then the peak wavelength is given by Wien's displacement law (Equation 1.4), which at 100 K gives

$$\lambda_{peak} = 2.90 \times 10^{-3} \, \text{m K}/100 \, \text{K} = 29 \, \mu\text{m}$$

which is well into the IR (Figure 1.23). Thus, the dust radiates most strongly in the middle and far IR. [*Comment*: The dust particles are ~1 μm in size, much smaller than the emitted wavelengths, which makes them weak radiators. Also, the *shape* of the spectrum is only roughly that of a black-body spectrum.]

SAQ 5.3

(a) In the warm intercloud medium, the thermal kinetic energy is given by

$$E_{k, \, warm} = [\text{number of separate particles}] \times \\ [\text{average thermal kinetic energy per particle}]$$

Using Equation 5.2, we thus get

$$E_{k, \, warm} = [\tfrac{4}{3}\pi r^3 n_p] \times [3kT/2]$$

where r is the sphere radius (150 pc), n_p is the number of separate particles per unit volume, and T is the temperature. In the warm medium, nearly all the separate particles are hydrogen atoms, and so we can replace n_p by n, the number of atoms per unit volume. Thus,

$$\begin{aligned} E_{k, \, warm} \sim \; & [\tfrac{4}{3}\pi(150 \times 3.09 \times 10^{16}\text{m})^3 \times 10^5] \times \\ & [3 \times (1.38 \times 10^{-23}\text{J K}^{-1}) \times 10^4 \text{K}/2] \\ \sim \; & 9 \times 10^{42} \text{J} \end{aligned}$$

The total kinetic energy in the hot cavity is approximately given by

$$\begin{aligned} E_{k, \, hot} \sim \; & [\tfrac{4}{3}\pi(150 \times 3.09 \times 10^{16}\text{m})^3 \times 2 \times 10^3] \times \\ & [3 \times (1.38 \times 10^{-23}\text{J K}^{-1}) \times 10^6 \text{K}/2] \\ \sim \; & 2 \times 10^{43} \text{J} \end{aligned}$$

where we have remembered that, when the hydrogen is largely ionized, the number of separate particles per unit volume is ~$2n$ (Subsection 5.2.2).

If i_H is the energy required to ionize one hydrogen atom, then the energy required to ionize all of the hydrogen atoms in the hot cavity is given by

$$\begin{aligned} I_H \sim \; & (\tfrac{4}{3}\pi r^3)ni_H \\ \sim \; & \tfrac{4}{3}\pi(150 \times 3.09 \times 10^{16}\text{m})^3 \times 10^3 \times (2.18 \times 10^{-18}\text{J}) \\ \sim \; & 9 \times 10^{41} \text{J} \end{aligned}$$

Thus, the total energy increase in the cavity is

$$\sim [(2 \times 10^{43} - 9 \times 10^{42}) + 9 \times 10^{41}]\,\text{J}$$

which is about 10^{43} J.

(b) This is less than the radial kinetic energy in the shell given in Subsection 5.3.1, and so the shell expelled by the supernova could have delivered this energy.

[*Comment*: The energy accounting here is rather approximate, but it gives a clear indication that a supernova *can* easily create a large region of hot intercloud medium.]

SAQ 5.4

Greater stellar temperature and greater luminosity together lead to greater UV flux. The increased UV flux in the diffuse cloud would break up most of the molecules present, and also increase the degree of ionization.

For example, much of the H_2 would be converted into H, and much of the H would be converted into H^+. The dust would warm up as it absorbed some of the extra radiation, UV again being particularly important (Figure 5.11). This would cause partial evaporation of the dust grains, perhaps even total evaporation. The heated dust would also be an important source of heat for the diffuse cloud as a whole, and the subsequent rise in temperature would increase the pressure, thus tending to cause expansion and hence a reduction in density. Overall, the diffuse cloud could come to resemble an HII region, or warm intercloud medium.

SAQ 5.5

1 Supernovae are probably essential to the formation of the hot intercloud medium. Some of the warm intercloud medium might be derived from the hot medium. Thus, fewer supernovae would probably make the intercloud media less prevalent in our galaxy.

2 The shocks from supernovae are probably a significant agent in cloud formation, and in star formation in pre-existing clouds. We would therefore probably have fewer clouds and a lower rate of star formation, and thus fewer stars 'alive' at any one time.

3 Following on from 1 and 2, more of the ISM would be likely to be in the form of cool regions.

4 Cosmic rays would be less abundant, thus leading to cooler dense clouds, and to fewer ions in them. [*Comment*: Fewer ions also means fewer molecules, because ions are important in the production of molecules in the ISM.]

5 Supernovae are thought to generate nearly all of the elements beyond iron. Thus, there would be a far lower abundance of such elements in the ISM, and in our galaxy as a whole.

SAQ 5.6

Assuming that the rate of mass loss from the ISM continues to exceed the rate of gain, the ISM will become extremely rarified, consisting largely of any fresh infall from the intergalactic medium. Its chemical composition will then be dominated by that of this medium. [*Comment*: Before it is dominated by the intergalactic medium, the chemical composition of the ISM will become increasingly enriched in heavy elements from the stars. Later, it is quite likely that, as pointed out at the end of Chapter 4, hydrogen and helium will become too rarified for any more stars to form.]

Acknowledgements

Grateful acknowledgement is made to the following sources for permission to reproduce material in this book:

Chapter 1

Figures 1.1, 1.3a Ondrejov Observatory, Czech Republic; *Figure 1.3b* P. Foukal (1990), *Solar Astrophysics*, © Copyright John Wiley & Sons Inc., reprinted by permission of John Wiley & Sons Inc.; *Figures 1.5 and 1.17* Kitt Peak National Observatory; *Figures 1.7, 1.24 and 1.25* I. Nicolson (1982), *The Sun*, Mitchell Beazley; *Figures 1.8 and 1.13* National Optical Astronomy Observatories; *Figures 1.9 and 1.10* National Solar Observatory/Sacramento Peak; *Figure 1.18* M.V. Zombeck (1990), *Handbook of Space, Astronomy and Astrophysics*, Cambridge University Press; *Figure 1.20* The National Centre for Atmospheric Research; *Figure 1.21* Lick Observatory; *Figure 1.22* A. Gabriel (1976), Philosophical Transactions of the Royal Society of London, vol. 281, p. 339; *Figure 1.26* Solar Physics Group, American Science and Engineering Inc.; *Figure 1.33* Courtesy of Tersch, USA; *Figure 1.34* Brookhaven National Observatory.

Chapter 2

Figure 2.13 G. Walker (1987), *Astronomical Observations*, Cambridge University Press; *Figure 2.14b* Abt et al. (1968), *An Atlas of Low Dispersion Grating Stellar Spectra* and from a collection at The Royal Astronomical Society; *Figure 2.16* courtesy of Graseby Infrared Ltd; *Figure 2.23* M. A. Seeds (1984), *Foundations of Astronomy*, Wadsworth Publishing Co; *Figure 2.26* K. A. A. Strand (1937), 'Photographic measurements of the 6 double stars', *Annalen Van De Sterrewacht Te Leiden, Deel XVIII, Tweede Stuk*; *Figure 2.29* prepared with the assistance of M. A. Seeds.

Chapter 3

Figure 3.5 M. Zeilik (1988), *Astronomy – The Evolving Universe*, © 1988, 1991 by Michael Zeilik, reprinted by permission of John Wiley and Sons Inc.; *Figure 3.22* S. Mitton (editor) (1977), *The Cambridge Encyclopaedia of Astronomy*, Jonathan Cape Ltd, © Trewin Copplestone Publishing Ltd 1977.

Chapter 4

Figure 4.11 Courtesy of Prof. Jocelyn Bell Burnell.

Chapter 5

Figure 5.11 D. Whittet (1981), 'The composition of interstellar grains', *Quarterly Journal of the Royal Astronomical Society*, vol. 22, pp. 3–21, Blackwell Scientific Publications Ltd.

Index